Macmillan
Caribbean
Certificate Atlas

Second Edition

Editorial Consultant

Gitfah Niles

MACMILLAN
CARIBBEAN

Contents

Acknowledgements

Special acknowledgement is made for the information and assistance provided by the following: American Embassy Information Department, UK; Cabinet for the Netherlands Antilles, Netherlands; Canadian High Commission, UK; Caribbean Development Bank, Barbados; Caribbean Tourism Organisation, Barbados; Central Bank of Barbados; Consulate of the Dominican Republic, UK; Food and Agriculture Organisation of the United Nations; Institut National de la Statistique et des Etudes Economiques, France; Institute of Commonwealth Studies, University of London, UK; Lands and Survey Department, Grenada; Lands and Survey Department, Trinidad and Tobago; Ordnance Survey International, UK; Swiss Embassy, UK; The Meteorological Office, UK .

The publishers wish to acknowledge, with thanks, the following photographic sources: Worldsat International Inc./Science Photo Library.
Front cover photograph of Castries Harbour, St. Lucia courtesy of Chris Huxley.

Cartography by Lovell Johns Ltd

The publishers have made every effort to trace the copyright holders, but if they have inadvertently overlooked any, they will be pleased to make the necessary arrangements at the first opportunity.

First edition 1979
Reprinted twice
Revised edition 1985
Reprinted eleven times
Second edition 1996
Reprinted once
Paperback edition 1998

Published by MACMILLAN EDUCATION LTD
London and Basingstoke
Companies and representatives throughout the world

ISBN 0–333–73545–5

10	9	8	7	6	5	4	3	2	1
07	06	05	04	03	02	01	00	99	98

This book is printed on paper suitable for recycling and made from fully managed and sustained forest sources.

Printed in Hong Kong

A catalogue record for this book is available from the British Library.

Addendum
Hong Kong is now a Special Administrative Region of the People's Republic of China.
Zaïre has been renamed the Democratic Republic of the Congo.

STRUCTURE OF THE EARTH

The Structure of the Earth

The earth is an oblate spheroid in shape, slightly flattened at the poles and bulging at the equator. Its circumference around the equator is approximately 40 000 kilometres and its diameter through the north and south poles is about 12 700 kilometres.

The Earth's Interior

The earth consists of a series of uniform concentric shells. Its internal structure can be divided into three parts: the crust, a relatively thin surface layer; the mantle, extending down to 2 900 kilometres; and the core, which makes up its centre.

The Crust

The crust is the earth's outer layer, consisting of comparatively low density material. There is a fundamental difference between the composition of the continental crust and the crust found beneath the oceans.

A Section through the Earth's Crust

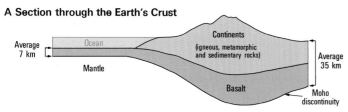

The ocean crust averages about 7 kilometres in thickness. The upper layer is made up of sediments and volcanic lava and is approximately 2 kilometres thick. The principal layer beneath this is made up of basalt and is about 5 kilometres thick. The main constituents of the oceanic crust rocks are silica and magnesium, thus this heavier part of the earth's crust is known as the 'sima' layer.

The continental crust is thicker, averaging about 35 kilometres and its structure is more complex. In most places it can be divided into an upper and lower part; the lower part being similar to the basaltic layer under the oceans. The upper part is composed of a complicated mixture of igneous, metamorphic and sedimentary rocks – all comparatively light rocks. The most abundant elements of these rocks are silicon and aluminium; hence the continental crust is known as the 'sial'.

The base of these crustal rocks is marked by a sharp change in rock density to that of the mantle rocks which are much heavier. This junction is called the Mohorovičić discontinuity (Moho for short) after the Yugoslav scientist who detected it in 1909.

The Mantle

The mantle differs from the crust in chemical composition. Its principal rock is peridotite which consists mainly of iron and magnesium. The upper, rigid part of the mantle can extend to about 100 kilometres below the Moho, and together with the earth's crust, forms the lithosphere.

The lower mantle, extending to 2 900 metres below the earth's surface, is less rigid and hotter. Known as the asthenosphere, this section of the mantle is capable of being deformed over long periods of time. Thus the concept of plate tectonics (see page 115) or the movements of the earth's crust, result from movement of the lithosphere over the asthenosphere.

At a depth of 2 900 kilometres below the earth's surface lies another important boundary where the rock density almost doubles. Discovered in 1914, this is known as the Gutenberg discontinuity, and below this level lies the earth's core.

A Cross-section through the Earth

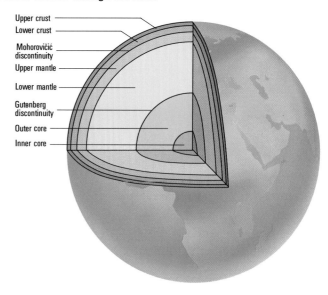

The Core

The core has a radius of about 3 500 kilometres and forms about 33% of the earth's mass. Seismic evidence suggests that the outer core is liquid whilst the inner core, with a radius of 1 220 kilometres is believed to be a solid nickel-iron alloy.

Temperature

There has been much speculation about the temperature of the earth's interior. It is known that temperatures increase with depth, probably at between 20°C-40°C per kilometre to begin with, but this rate is not believed to continue for long. The diagram below shows the estimated temperature at various levels.

The Main Subdivisions of the Earth

	Approximate depth in kilometres	State	Estimated temperature in °C
Upper crust / Lower crust	50	Solid	400
Upper mantle	100		1 000
Lower mantle		Semi-solid	
	2 900		3 500
Outer core		Liquid	
	5 180		3 700
Inner core	6 400	Solid	4 000–4 500

A Section through the Atmosphere

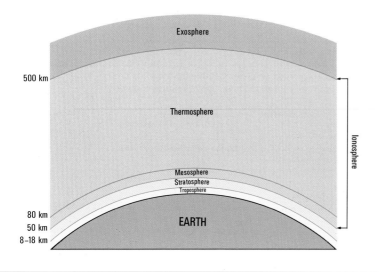

The Atmosphere

The earth is surrounded by a thin layer of gases which form the atmosphere. The atmosphere protects the earth from temperatures which would otherwise reach such extremes between day and night that life on earth would be destroyed.

The lowest part of the atmosphere, known as the troposphere, extends to about 8 kilometres over the poles and to about 18 kilometres over the equator. The temperature falls by 6°C for every kilometre in height until it stabilises at the tropopause, or the top of the troposphere.

The next section of the atmosphere is the stratosphere, which extends to about 50 kilometres. Within the stratosphere temperatures rise again from -55°C to 10°C until the ozone layer is reached, which filters out the sun's harmful ultra-violet rays.

Above the stratosphere is the mesosphere where cooling takes place again. Temperatures of about -100°C are reached at the top of the mesosphere at a height of 80 to 100 kilometres.

Beyond the mesosphere are the thermosphere and exosphere, where temperatures increase again. The exosphere eventually merges into space.

The region of the atmosphere between 50 and 500 kilometres is known as the ionosphere. It contains layers of ions, or electrically charged particles, which reflect radio waves around the earth, making long distance communications possible.

Latitude and Longitude

Features on the earth's surface can be located by using a geographical grid consisting of a network of imaginary intersecting lines. The lines run from east to west and north to south.

Lines running from east to west are lines of latitude. The line around the centre of the earth is the equator, and is numbered 0°. All lines of latitude run parallel to the equator, and are numbered in degrees north or south of the equator. The north pole is 90°N and the south pole is 90°S. Lines of latitude are also referred to as parallels.

Lines running from north to south connecting the poles are called lines of longitude or meridians. The prime meridian, numbered 0°, passes through Greenwich, London. All lines of longitude are numbered in degrees east or west of the Greenwich meridian. The line directly opposite the Greenwich meridian is numbered 180°.

Any place can therefore be accurately located by referring to the point where its line of latitude intersects its line of longitude.

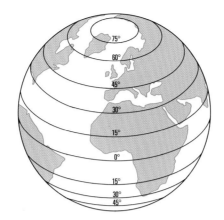
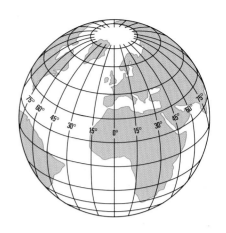

Map Projections

The most accurate method of representing the spherical shape of the earth is by using a scale model called a globe. However it often becomes necessary to represent this three dimensional shape on a flat two dimensional surface such as a piece of paper. To do this a map projection must be used.

The parallels of latitude and the meridians of longitude are projected from the globe onto a flat surface as a network, or graticule, of intersecting lines. To achieve a perfect map we should expect a representation which gives correct shape and direction to features on the earth's surface whilst keeping areas in proportion. However, because features are being transferred from a spherical surface to a flat surface there will always be some distortion of these properties. The choice of map projection will therefore depend largely on which of the three properties of correct shape, direction or area is the most important, bearing in mind the subject of the map and the geographical region to be covered.

Map projections can be classified into three major groups – cylindrical, conical and azimuthal, but many different forms of projection are derived from these major groups.

Conical Projection

Azimuthal Projection

Cylindrical Projection

Bonne's Projection

Lambert Equal Area Projection

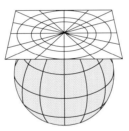

Mercator Projection

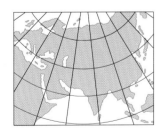

Conical Projections

Conical projections are produced by transferring lines of latitude and longitude (parallels and meridians) from a globe onto a cone. The cone is then developed into a flat map.

Scale is correct at the point where the cone touches the globe – the standard parallel. All other parallels are concentric circles; all meridians are straight lines which converge at either the north or south pole. Exaggeration of scale along both meridians and parallels increases with the distance from the standard parallel.

Bonne's projection, above, is a simple conic projection which has been modified to remove exaggeration of scale by spacing all meridians to their true distance along each parallel.

Azimuthal Projections

Azimuthal projections are constructed by projecting part of the globe onto a flat surface, or plane, placed directly on a particular point of the globe, such as a pole or the equator.

All meridians radiate as straight lines from the central point, and the parallels of latitude are concentric circles. Direction is true outwards from the centre of the projection, but distortion of scale and shape occurs uniformly away from the centre. The above diagram illustrates how an azimuthal projection depicts the globe as a flattened disc, in this case with the north pole as its central point. Azimuthal projections are most frequently used for mapping polar regions.

Cylindrical Projections

Cylindrical projections are constructed by projecting lines of latitude and longitude onto a cylinder wrapped around the globe. The cylinder is then cut along a convenient line and spread out. The cylinder may touch the globe at the equator, in which case the equator is the only line true to scale. Meridians are equally spaced vertical lines and are at right angles to the parallels. Cylindrical projections are essentially rectangular in shape and the whole globe can be shown.

One of the best cylindrical projections is Mercator's. In this case distortion of shape is avoided by increasing scale along the parallels, but consequently area is greatly distorted away from the equator.

TIME ZONES

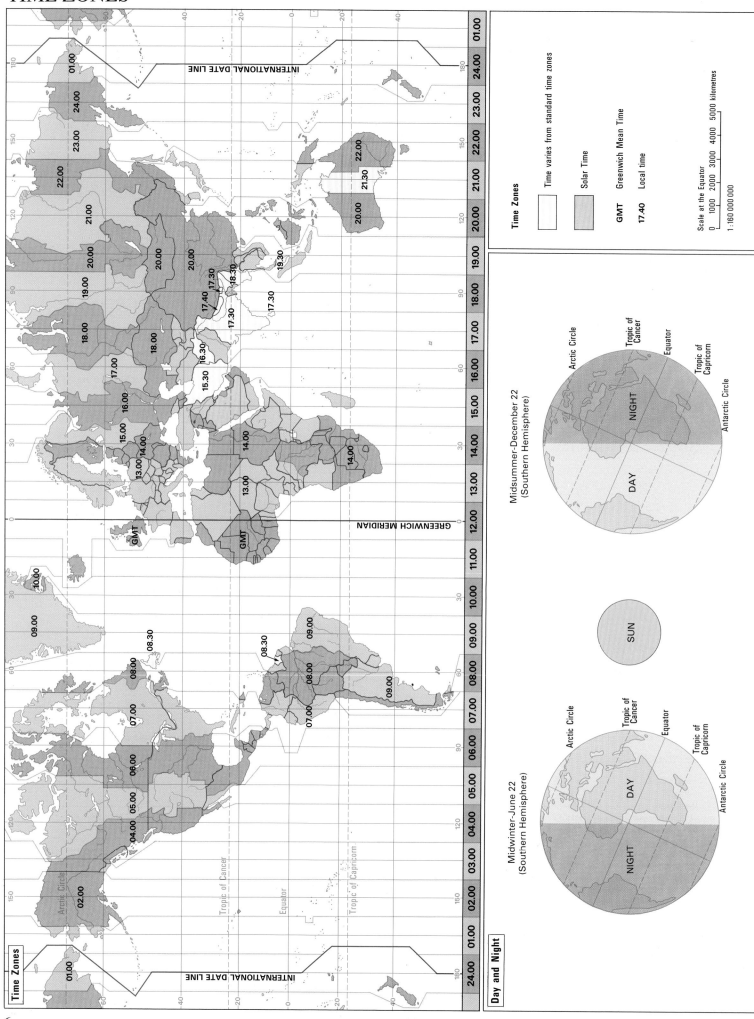

Time Zones

	Time varies from standard time zones
	Solar Time

GMT Greenwich Mean Time

17.40 Local time

Scale at the Equator

0   1000   2000   3000   4000   5000 kilometres

1 : 160 000 000

Day and Night

Midsummer–December 22
(Southern Hemisphere)

Midwinter–June 22
(Southern Hemisphere)

SUN

INTERNATIONAL DATE LINE

GREENWICH MERIDIAN

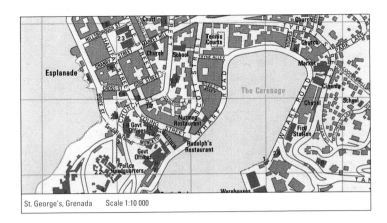

St. George's, Grenada   Scale 1:10 000

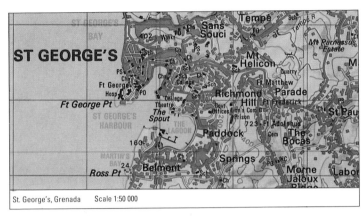

St. George's, Grenada   Scale 1:50 000

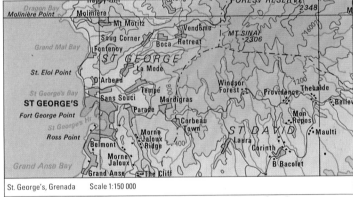

St. George's, Grenada   Scale 1:150 000

Map extracts reproduced with the permission of the Director of Lands and Surveys, Grenada

Map Scales

To draw a map of any area it is necessary to reduce, or scale down, the area in question so that it can be represented on a map sheet or atlas page.

Scale is defined as the ratio between a distance on the map and the corresponding true distance on the ground. Scale can be expressed in three ways:

1. As a representative fraction (R.F.) which itself can be given as a fraction, e.g. $\frac{1}{50000}$ or as a ratio, e.g. 1:50 000. Any unit can be used in an R.F. provided the same unit is used for both the numerator and the denominator. In the above example one unit on the map represents 50 000 units on the ground. As illustrated by the map extracts on this page, the larger the denominator the smaller the scale of the map.

2. By a statement of scale, e.g. 1cm to 1km. This means that 1 centimetre on the map represents 1 kilometre on the ground. When converted into an R.F. this statement of scale becomes 1:100 000.

3. By a linear scale which is a horizontal line divided into sections, each of which represents a unit of measurement on the ground. The smaller divisions are used for measuring fractions of the units used.

0   1   2   3   4 kilometres

The above example would be used on a map with a scale of 1:100 000

Use of a smaller scale increases the area covered on a map of the same size, but also reduces the amount of detail that can be included. This is illustrated by the map extracts reproduced on the left. These extracts of St. George's on Grenada are at scales of 1:10 000, 1:50 000 and 1: 150 000.

The 1:10 000 map is very accurate and shows a great deal of detail. All roads are shown and most of them are named. Buildings are either generalised to form a built-up area or if isolated or significant, shown individually with their correct shape. Many features and buildings are named and on this particular map, which is for use by tourists, many buildings are numbered and listed elsewhere on the map for reference.

On the 1:50 000 map a much larger area is shown. Most roads are shown and they are classified according to their importance, but there is no room to name them. Buildings are mostly shown as a built-up area, although important buildings are identified by a small block with only the very largest having any actual shape.

The 1:150 000 map is very generalised. Settlements are shown as a built-up area or as a group of building symbols – no individual buildings are shown – and it is only possible to show major roads.

Fixing Direction

Direction can be indicated in one of two ways:
1. By reference to the points of the compass.
2. By use of bearings. A bearing is the horizontal angle measured in degrees clockwise from north to a direction line.

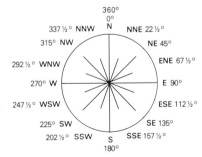

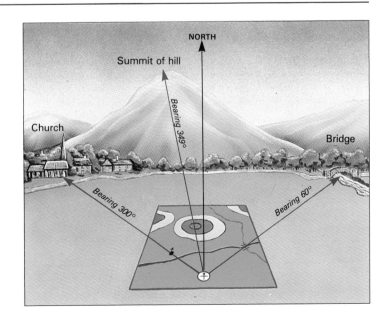

Look at the diagram on the right.
To fix your position using a map and compass, place your compass on the map with the compass north pointing in the direction of the map north. Orient your map so that three features shown on it are in their correct positions relative to the same features on the ground. You will be at the point where imaginary lines drawn from the features through these symbols on the map intersect.

MAP READING

Map Orientation

Just as you had to learn to read words, so you have to learn to read a map. Not only do you need to be able to identify features on a map, you need to say where those features are. The main points of a magnetic compass can be used to measure or calculate *bearing* to describe the position of one feature on a map in relation to another feature.

The needle of a magnetic compass is free to turn. It always points to magnetic north.

Geographic north is represented by the north pole. Another name for geographic north is true north.

The difference between true north and magnetic north is an angle, which is known as the magnetic declination.

For all places in the Caribbean, magnetic north is to the west of geographic north.

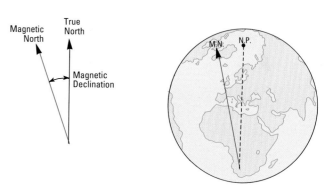

Measuring True Bearing

Look at the diagram below
On a map, true or geographic bearing is measured by using a protractor. True bearing is expressed as an angle, which is measured clockwise from the geographic north pole or true north (0°).
1. Establish the point from which the true bearing is to be measured (A).
2. Through this point, draw a line indicating true north. Most maps are drawn with north at the top of the map.
3. Join the two points between which the true bearing is being measured (AB).
4. Use a protractor to measure the true or geographic bearing.

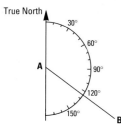

The true or geographic bearing from A to B is 125°

Calculating Magnetic Bearing

Look at the diagram below
1. Measure the true bearing. In this case, the true or geographic bearing is 230°.
2. The magnetic declination is printed on the side of topographic maps. In this case the magnetic declination is 24° west of true north.
3. If magnetic north is west of true north, the magnetic declination must be added to the true bearing to calculate the magnetic bearing.
4. If magnetic north is east of true north, the magnetic declination must be subtracted from the true bearing to calculate the magnetic bearing.

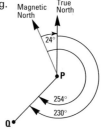

Measured true bearing from P to Q = 230°
Magnetic declination = 24° west of true north
Magnetic bearing from P to Q = 24° + 230° = 254°

Direction

You must know the main directions on a compass to determine direction.
Look at the diagram below
The direction from the bridge to the lake is south; from the bridge to the village is north-east; from the station to the bridge is south-east.

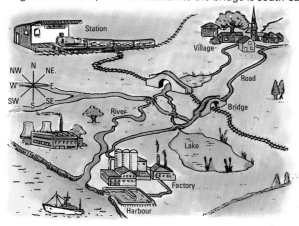

Grid References

Lines of Latitude and Longitude fix position on small scale maps (see page 5), however, on large scale maps, Grid References are more commonly used. A grid reference is given with the easting first and the northing last. In the diagram below 'x' is located east of easting 73 and north of northing 26. The Grid Reference for this position is 7326 and is called a 4 figure grid reference, but a more accurate measurement can be made by dividing the area between the grid lines into 10. 'x' can now be more accurately referenced as easting 736 and northing 262. This gives a 6 figure grid reference of 736262.

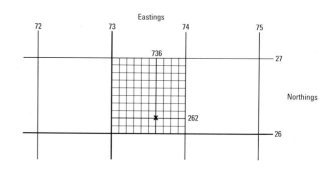

Aerial photograph of Cantaro, Trinidad
Scale 1: 25 000

Aerial photograph of St. George's, Grenada
Scale 1: 10 560

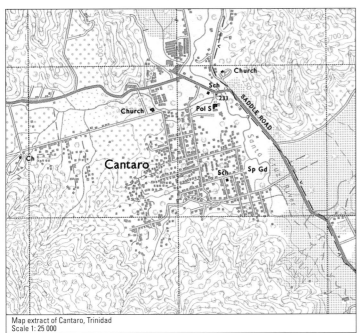

Map extract of Cantaro, Trinidad
Scale 1: 25 000

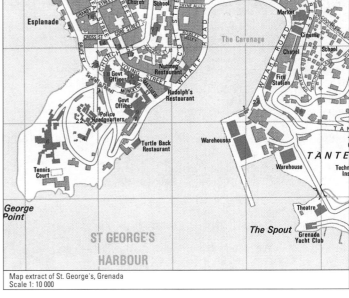

Map extract of St. George's, Grenada
Scale 1: 10 000

Aerial Photographs

Aerial photographs provide an accurate representation of an area of land and are extensively used in modern map making. Aerial photographs are taken from an aircraft with the lens of the camera pointing vertically over a point on the ground. The scale of the photograph depends on the height of the aircraft from the ground, the higher the aircraft the smaller the scale of the photograph. A map combines information selected from an aerial photograph with information from ground survey. By the use of symbols, lines and colour it is possible to represent physical features, to distinguish different types of communications and to locate settlement. Compare the map extracts and aerial photographs reproduced above.

Cantaro

The aerial photograph, top left, shows the settlement of Cantaro in the San Juan Regional Corporation on Trinidad. The map dates from 1970, while the photograph was taken in 1994. During the intervening years considerable development has occurred and this can be clearly seen in the centre of the photograph where buildings and roads have replaced a citrus orchard which is shown on the map as open green circles. Cantaro has grown on the flat land in the river valley, while forest covers the land surrounding the settlement. The shadows on the western slopes of the hills in the photograph gives a clue to their relative steepness.

St. George's

The aerial photograph, top right, shows part of the town and harbour of St. George's on Grenada. The photograph was taken in 1970, while the map was produced in 1992, but as the area is built-up, very little change is evident apart from where an area of land has been reclaimed from the sea to build a warehouse in the docks area.

Many boats can be seen in the photograph, including 2 large vessels berthed at the docks and the channel, which gives access for boats from the lagoon, in the bottom right hand corner, to the main harbour is clearly visible.

Photographs at this scale are extremely useful aids to making maps because not only are road patterns easily identifiable, but major buildings such as the warehouses on the quay, the theatre and the cinema can also be seen.

Aerial photograph and map extract of Cantaro reproduced with the permission of the Director of the Lands and Surveys Department, Port of Spain, Trinidad

Aerial photograph and map extract of St. George's reproduced with the permission of the Director of the Lands and Surveys Department, St. George's, Grenada

SATELLITE IMAGES

A

Satellite Imagery

Data gathered by scanning systems aboard satellites can be processed into false colour images which reveal detailed information about the earth's surface. The images on this page are from the U.S. Landsat satellite which orbits the earth at an altitude of 930 kilometres and repeats its orbital pattern every 18 days.

Satellite data is a valuable source of information on natural resources and can be used extensively to monitor environmental deterioration. The images assist in the location of mineral resources and ground water, and are invaluable during the planning stages of development projects. Progress of crop growth can also be revealed, thereby contributing to accurate estimates of agricultural production.

(A) Western Caribbean

The image at the top of the page covers the western half of the Caribbean Sea. In the north is Florida and the scattered islands of the Bahamas. In the centre are the major islands of Cuba, Hispaniola and Jamaica, while in the bottom left hand corner is part of Honduras and Nicaragua on the mainland of central America. Compare the image with the map on pages 14/15.

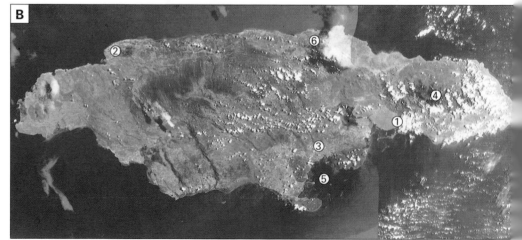

B

(B) Jamaica

Whereas the image of the western Caribbean has been given false natural colours, the image of Jamaica above has been taken in the infrared range. This shows vegetation as red, clouds appear white and water more than 5 metres deep is a dark blue or black. The image is a mosaic made up of 2 separate images taken at different times and the join between the 2 can be clearly seen as a line running north/south across the island to the west of Kingston.

1. Kingston appears as a blue/grey area.
2. Montego Bay.
3. Agricultural land appears as a patchwork pattern.
4. The Blue Mountains are shrouded in cloud.
5. Great Goat Island in the Portland Bight.
6. Clouds give a shadow which can be clearly seen on the ground.

This page explains the relief representation and most important symbols and lettering styles used in this atlas. Please note however, that for the Caribbean section of the atlas, reference should be made to legends accompanying individual maps.
The scale of the map is stated on each page. Abbreviations appear at the beginning of the index.

Relief Representation

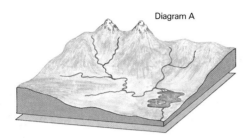

Diagram A

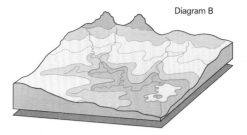

Diagram B

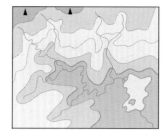

Diagram A illustrates an imaginary landscape. It shows an area of mountain peaks, hills, valleys and a river system that flows into a lake in the lowlands.

Diagram B shows the same landscape but the relief is shown by a series of coloured layers known as hypsometric layers.

This map is derived from Diagram B, it shows a map of exactly the same area. The lines separating the hypsometric layers are called contour lines. These are lines that join all the places on a map which are at the same height above sea level.

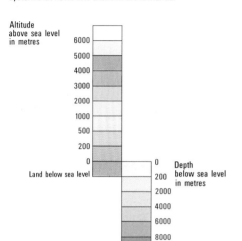

Altitude above sea level in metres
6000
5000
4000
3000
2000
1000
500
200
0
Land below sea level

Depth below sea level in metres
0
200
2000
4000
6000
8000

Physical Features

- Land contour
- ▲ Spot height (elevation in metres)
- Sea contour
- + Ocean depth (in metres)
- Permanent lake, reservoir
- Intermittent, seasonal lake
- Salt pan
- Marsh, swamp

- River
- Intermittent, seasonal river
- Waterfall, cataract
- Dam
- Canal
- Pass
- Permanent ice cap

Political and Administrative

- International boundary
- Undefined or disputed international boundary
- State boundary

Communications

- Principal road
- Railway
- ✈ International airport

Thematic Map Symbols

These are a selection of symbols used on the thematic maps; additional symbols are explained in a key accompanying each map.

Energy

- ● Coal
- ⊗ Nuclear power station
- Hydro-electric power station
- Oil
- ▢ Natural gas
- ▢ Uranium

Iron ore, ferro-alloys and steel

- ⊠ Chrome
- ▽ Nickel
- ◖ Cobalt
- ▬ Steel
- I Iron ore
- H Tungsten
- ◄ Manganese
- ▽ Vanadium
- ►◄ Molybdenum

Other minerals

- ▲ Antimony
- ✧ Mica
- Ω Asbestos
- ⊗ Nitrates
- △ Bauxite
- P Phosphates
- B Beryllium
- ◄ Platinum
- ▼ Copper
- P Potash
- ◇ Diamonds
- ◆ Pyrites
- ⊙ Gold
- ○ Silver
- ⊖ Lead and zinc
- ⊂ Sulphur
- ▬ Lithium
- × Tin
- Ⅲ Mercury
- T Titanium

Settlement

Each settlement is allocated a town symbol according to its population. Symbols contained within squares denote capital cities.

- ▣ ■ over 1 000 000 inhabitants
- ◉ ◉ 500 000–1 000 000 inhabitants
- ◎ ○ 100 000–500 000 inhabitants
- ▣ ● 25 000–100 000 inhabitants
- ▢ ○ less than 25 000 inhabitants

The size of lettering used for each settlement is graded to correspond with the appropriate town symbol.

- ■ **Rio de Janeiro**
- ◉ **Frankfurt**
- ◎ Edinburgh
- ● Luxor
- ○ Yorkton

Lettering

SAUDI ARABIA	Country name
TEXAS	State name
Réunion (Fr.)	Sovereignty of dependent territory
Madrid	Capital city
Boston Venice	Settlement
Andes	Major physical feature
Laurentian Plateau	Other physical feature
Mt. Everest 8848m	Mountain, peak
C. Horn	Cape, point, peninsular
Java	Island
INDIAN OCEAN	Ocean, sea
G. OF ADEN	Gulf
Lake Victoria	Bay, lake
Mississippi	River

WEATHER OBSERVATION

The Weather

When we say it is wet, or hot, we are saying something about the weather. Weather refers to the condition of the atmosphere: its temperature, pressure and humidity for a place for a short period of time. If we want to find out what the weather is like, we must examine temperature, pressure, humidity, wind direction and strength, rainfall, sunshine and the cloud cover.

A weather station is a site where all the components of weather are measured and recorded.

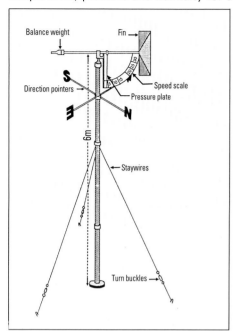

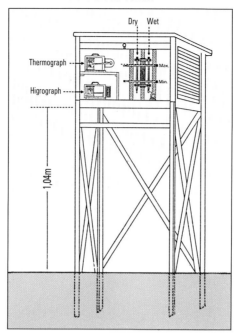

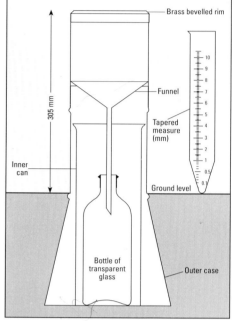

Anemometer

The direction and speed of the wind can be determined by means of an anemometer. It is recorded according to eight directions, namely N, NE, E, SE, S, SW, W and NW. Winds are named according to the direction from which they blow, eg. a wind which blows from the north to the south is called a north wind.

Wind speed is recorded in knots or metres per second (1 knot = 1,3 km/h).

Stevenson Screen

Every weather station has a Stevenson screen in which thermometers, a thermograph and hygrometers are placed.

It is a wooden box whose four sides are louvred to allow free entry of air. It is placed on a stand, 1,04m above the ground.

The roof is made of double boarding to prevent the sun's heat from reaching the inside of the screen. Insolation is improved by painting the outside white.

Rain Gauge

Rainfall is measured by means of a rain gauge and the quantity of rain is registered in millimetres. Each weather station has a rain gauge.

The rain gauge comprises a cylinder on which a funnel is placed. The rainwater is transported through the funnel into a container in the cylinder.

The water in the container is poured into the measuring cylinder so that the amount can be read off in millimetres.

Synoptic Weather Charts

A synoptic weather chart is a summary of the weather conditions at a certain time. The chart below shows the situation in the Caribbean when Hurricane Hugo passed through in 1989.

The meteorological data needed to draw up these synoptic charts is obtained from a network of weather stations all over the Caribbean, as well as from ships at sea and weather satellites.

The information on the synoptic weather chart is very important for making forecasts. Each weather station is indicated on the chart by a small circle, accompanied by a number.

SYNOPTIC WEATHER MAP – Showing the position of Hurricane Hugo 20/9/89

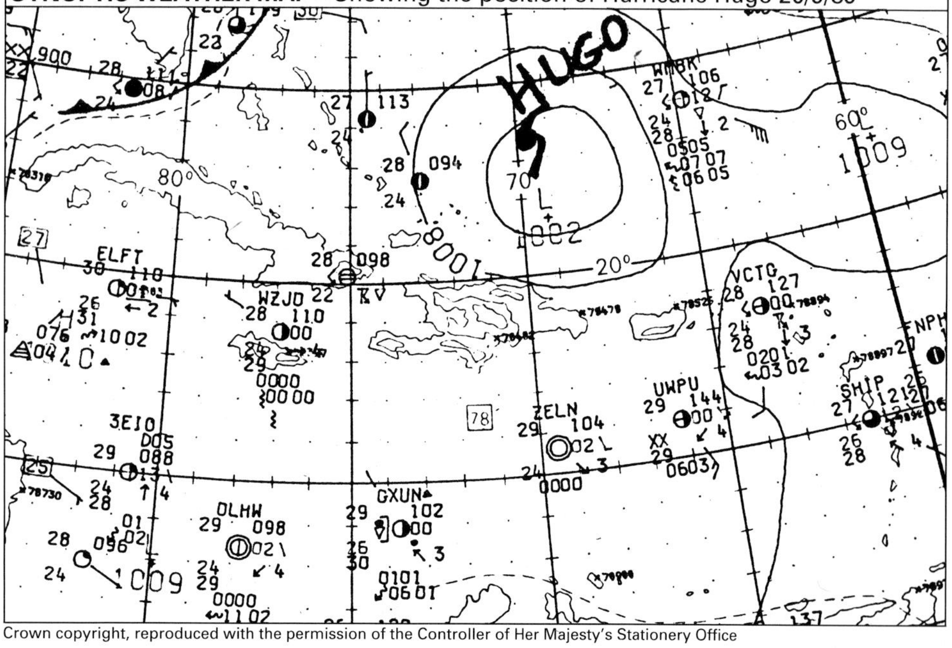

Crown copyright, reproduced with the permission of the Controller of Her Majesty's Stationery Office

Weather Symbols used on Synoptic Charts

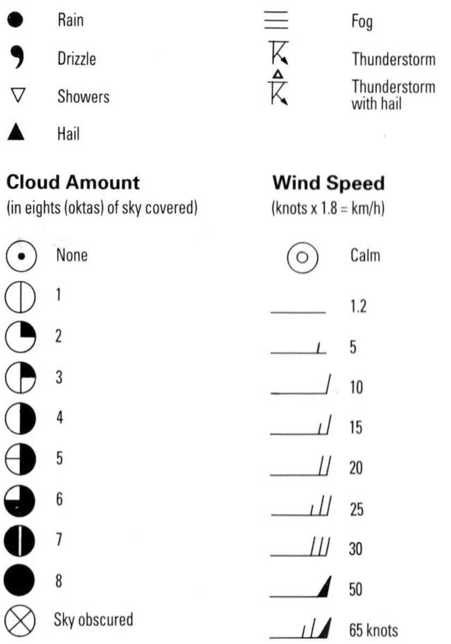

●	Rain	☰	Fog
❡	Drizzle	�	Thunderstorm
▽	Showers		Thunderstorm with hail
▲	Hail		

Cloud Amount
(in eights (oktas) of sky covered)

⊙	None
�earth1	1
	2
	3
	4
	5
	6
	7
●	8
⊗	Sky obscured

Wind Speed
(knots x 1.8 = km/h)

⊙	Calm
—	1.2
—⌐	5
—/	10
—//	15
—///	20
—////	25
—/////	30
◢	50
◢/	65 knots

CARIBBEAN – GEOLOGY, STRUCTURE AND SEISMIC ACTIVITY

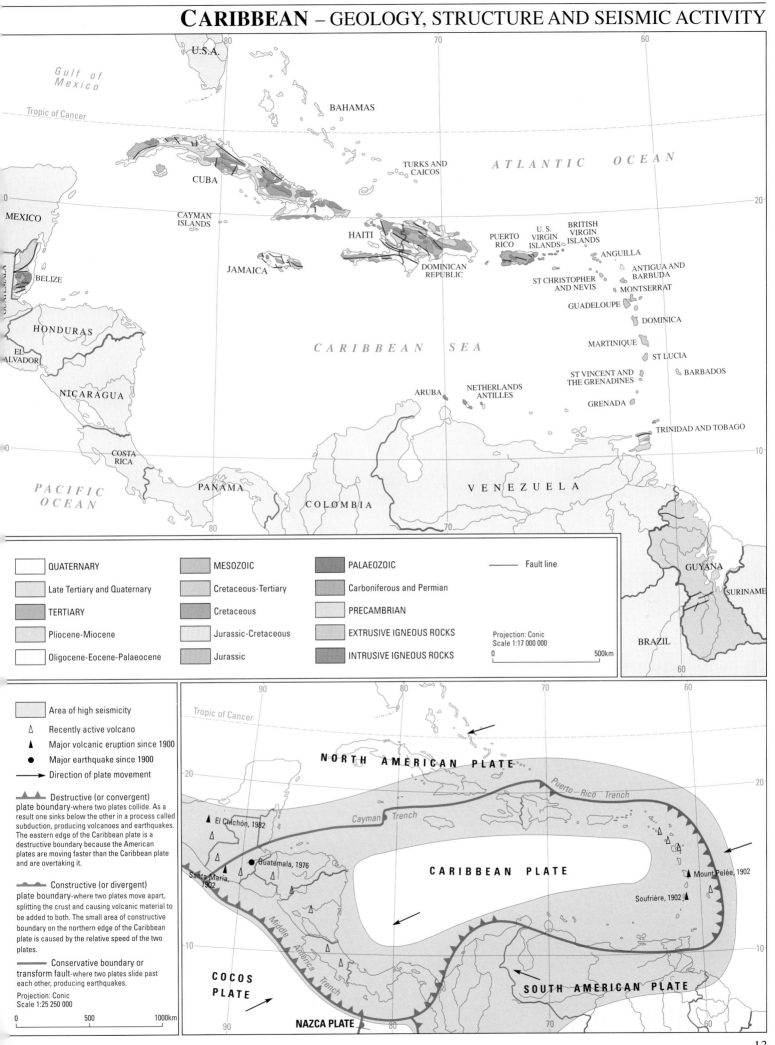

Legend:

QUATERNARY

Late Tertiary and Quaternary

TERTIARY

Pliocene-Miocene

Oligocene-Eocene-Palaeocene

MESOZOIC

Cretaceous-Tertiary

Cretaceous

Jurassic-Cretaceous

Jurassic

PALAEOZOIC

Carboniferous and Permian

PRECAMBRIAN

EXTRUSIVE IGNEOUS ROCKS

INTRUSIVE IGNEOUS ROCKS

—— Fault line

Projection: Conic
Scale 1:17 000 000
0   500km

Area of high seismicity

△ Recently active volcano

▲ Major volcanic eruption since 1900

● Major earthquake since 1900

→ Direction of plate movement

🔺 Destructive (or convergent) plate boundary-where two plates collide. As a result one sinks below the other in a process called subduction, producing volcanoes and earthquakes. The eastern edge of the Caribbean plate is a destructive boundary because the American plates are moving faster than the Caribbean plate and are overtaking it.

🔺 Constructive (or divergent) plate boundary-where two plates move apart, splitting the crust and causing volcanic material to be added to both. The small area of constructive boundary on the northern edge of the Caribbean plate is caused by the relative speed of the two plates.

━━ Conservative boundary or transform fault-where two plates slide past each other, producing earthquakes.

Projection: Conic
Scale 1:25 250 000
0   500   1000km

NORTH AMERICAN PLATE

CARIBBEAN PLATE

COCOS PLATE

SOUTH AMERICAN PLATE

NAZCA PLATE

Puerto-Rico Trench

Cayman Trench

Middle America Trench

▲ El Chichón, 1982

● Guatemala, 1976

▲ Santa María, 1902

▲ Mount Pelée, 1902

Soufrière, 1902 ▲

Tropic of Cancer

CARIBBEAN – PHYSICAL AND POLITICAL

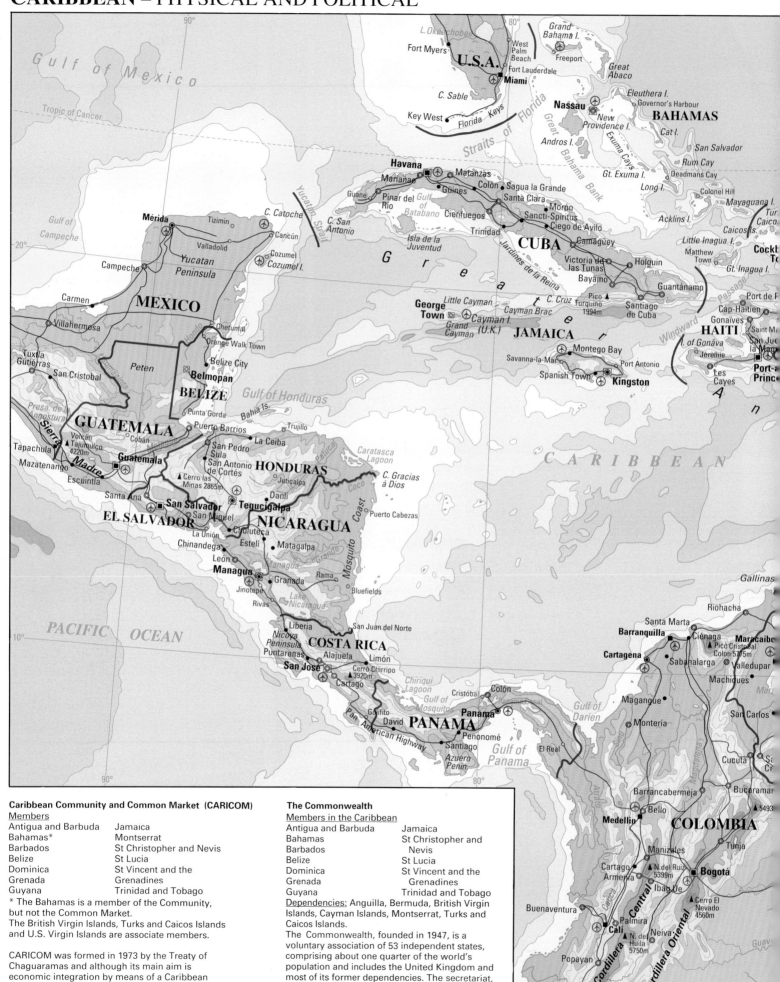

Caribbean Community and Common Market (CARICOM)

Members

Antigua and Barbuda	Jamaica
Bahamas*	Montserrat
Barbados	St Christopher and Nevis
Belize	St Lucia
Dominica	St Vincent and the
Grenada	Grenadines
Guyana	Trinidad and Tobago

* The Bahamas is a member of the Community, but not the Common Market.
The British Virgin Islands, Turks and Caicos Islands and U.S. Virgin Islands are associate members.

CARICOM was formed in 1973 by the Treaty of Chaguaramas and although its main aim is economic integration by means of a Caribbean Common Market, it also co-operates in areas such as foreign affairs, agriculture, industry and tourism.

The Commonwealth

Members in the Caribbean

Antigua and Barbuda	Jamaica
Bahamas	St Christopher and
Barbados	Nevis
Belize	St Lucia
Dominica	St Vincent and the
Grenada	Grenadines
Guyana	Trinidad and Tobago

Dependencies: Anguilla, Bermuda, British Virgin Islands, Cayman Islands, Montserrat, Turks and Caicos Islands.
The Commonwealth, founded in 1947, is a voluntary association of 53 independent states, comprising about one quarter of the world's population and includes the United Kingdom and most of its former dependencies. The secretariat, established in 1965, is the central co-ordinating body and has twelve divisions for areas such as economic affairs and science and technology.

14

COUNTRY	CAPITAL	AREA	NATIONALITY	LANGUAGE
Anguilla	The Valley	96 sq km	British	English
Antigua & Barbuda	St John's	442 sq km	Independent	English
Aruba	Oranjestad	193 sq km	Dutch	Dutch & Papiamento
Bahamas	Nassau	13 939 sq km	Independent	English
Barbados	Bridgetown	430 sq km	Independent	English
Belize	Belmopan	22 965 sq km	Independent	English
Bermuda	Hamilton	53 sq km	British	English
British Virgin Islands	Road Town	153 sq km	British	English
Cayman Islands	George Town	259 sq km	British	English
Cuba	Havana	110 860 sq km	Independent	Spanish
Dominica	Roseau	750 sq km	Independent	English
Dominican Republic	Santo Domingo	48 422 sq km	Independent	Spanish
Grenada	St George's	344 sq km	Independent	English
Guadeloupe	Basse-Terre	1 780 sq km	French	French

COUNTRY	CAPITAL	AREA	NATIONALITY	LANGUAGE
Guyana	Georgetown	214 969 sq km	Independent	English
Haiti	Port-au-Prince	27 750 sq km	Independent	French & Creole
Jamaica	Kingston	10 991 sq km	Independent	English
Martinique	Fort-de-France	1 100 sq km	French	French
Montserrat	Plymouth	102 sq km	British	English
Netherlands Antilles	Willemstad	800 sq km	Dutch	Dutch & Papiamento
Puerto Rico	San Juan	8 959 sq km	American	Spanish &English
St Christopher and Nevis	Basseterre	267 sq km	Independent	English
St Lucia	Castries	616 sq km	Independent	English
St Vincent and the Grenadines	Kingstown	389 sq km	Independent	English
Trinidad & Tobago	Port of Spain	5 128 sq km	Independent	English
Turks & Caicos	Cockburn Town	430 sq km	British	English
U.S. Virgin Islands	Charlotte Amalie	355 sq km	American	English

Organisation of Eastern Caribbean States (OECS)
Members
Antigua and Barbuda   St Christopher and Nevis
Dominica   St Lucia
Grenada   St Vincent and the
Montserrat   Grenadines

The OECS was set up in 1981 by the seven states
which originally belonged to the West Indies
Associated States. Its aims are to promote trade
and provide a common market for ideas and
policies between its members. The British Virgin
Islands is an associate member.

**The Lomé Convention for African, Caribbean and
Pacific (ACP) Countries**
Under the first Lomé Convention (1975) the
European Community (now called the European
Union), committed funds to developing countries for
aid and investment. A special provision has been
made for over 99% of ACP exports to enter the EU
market, duty free. All the Caribbean countries with
the exception of Cuba, Puerto Rico and the U.S.
Virgin Islands are ACP states.

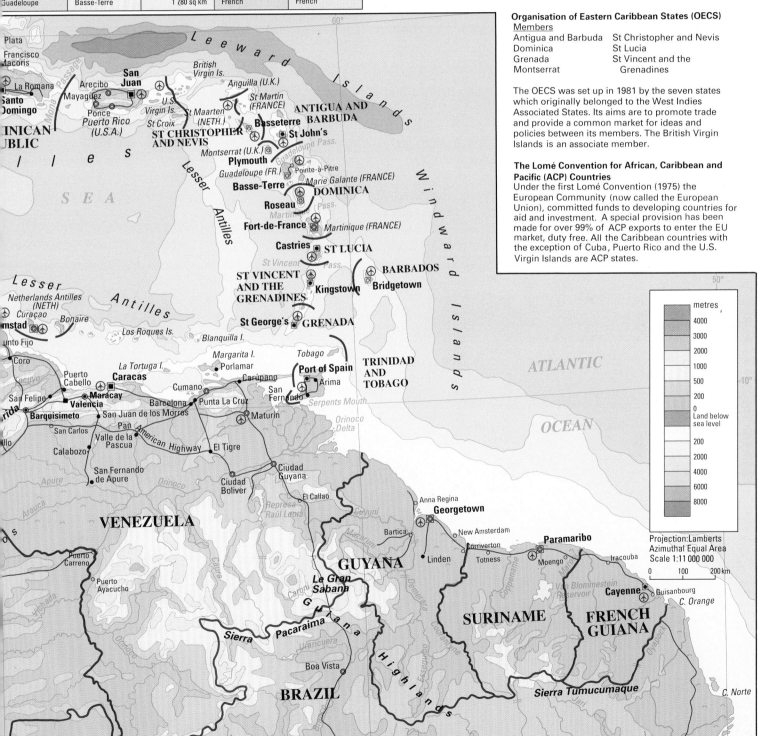

CARIBBEAN – CLIMATE

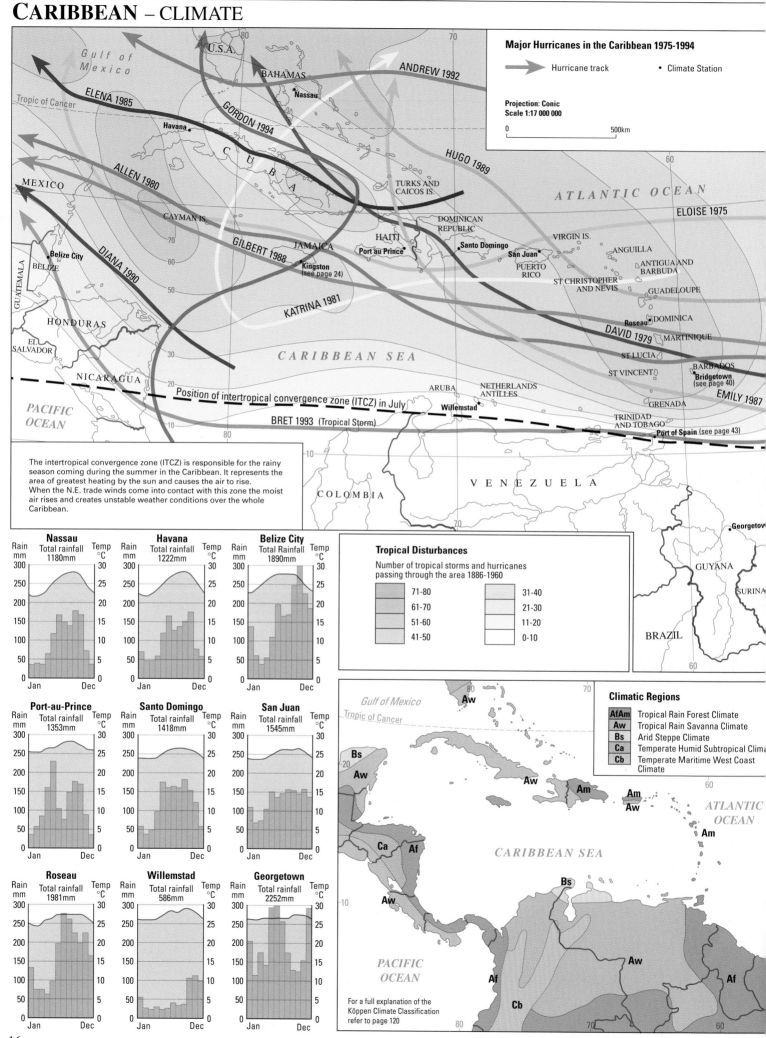

Major Hurricanes in the Caribbean 1975-1994

→ Hurricane track   • Climate Station

Projection: Conic
Scale 1:17 000 000

0   500km

ELENA 1985
ANDREW 1992
GORDON 1994
HUGO 1989
ALLEN 1980
ELOISE 1975
DIANA 1990
GILBERT 1988
KATRINA 1981
DAVID 1979
EMILY 1987
BRET 1993 (Tropical Storm)

Gulf of Mexico
Tropic of Cancer
U.S.A.
BAHAMAS
Nassau
Havana
C U B A
CAYMAN IS.
MEXICO
BELIZE
Belize City
GUATEMALA
HONDURAS
EL SALVADOR
NICARAGUA
PACIFIC OCEAN
JAMAICA
Kingston (see page 24)
HAITI
Port au Prince
TURKS AND CAICOS IS.
DOMINICAN REPUBLIC
Santo Domingo
PUERTO RICO
San Juan
VIRGIN IS.
ANGUILLA
ST CHRISTOPHER AND NEVIS
ANTIGUA AND BARBUDA
GUADELOUPE
Roseau
DOMINICA
MARTINIQUE
ST LUCIA
ST VINCENT
BARBADOS
Bridgetown (see page 40)
GRENADA
ATLANTIC OCEAN
CARIBBEAN SEA
ARUBA
NETHERLANDS ANTILLES
Willemstad
TRINIDAD AND TOBAGO
Port of Spain (see page 43)
VENEZUELA
COLOMBIA

Position of intertropical convergence zone (ITCZ) in July

The intertropical convergence zone (ITCZ) is responsible for the rainy season coming during the summer in the Caribbean. It represents the area of greatest heating by the sun and causes the air to rise. When the N.E. trade winds come into contact with this zone the moist air rises and creates unstable weather conditions over the whole Caribbean.

Tropical Disturbances

Number of tropical storms and hurricanes passing through the area 1886-1960

71-80	31-40
61-70	21-30
51-60	11-20
41-50	0-10

Nassau
Total rainfall 1180mm

Havana
Total rainfall 1222mm

Belize City
Total rainfall 1890mm

Port-au-Prince
Total rainfall 1353mm

Santo Domingo
Total rainfall 1418mm

San Juan
Total rainfall 1545mm

Roseau
Total rainfall 1981mm

Willemstad
Total rainfall 586mm

Georgetown
Total rainfall 2252mm

Climatic Regions

AfAm	Tropical Rain Forest Climate
Aw	Tropical Rain Savanna Climate
Bs	Arid Steppe Climate
Ca	Temperate Humid Subtropical Clim
Cb	Temperate Maritime West Coast Climate

Gulf of Mexico
Tropic of Cancer
ATLANTIC OCEAN
CARIBBEAN SEA
PACIFIC OCEAN
GUYANA
SURINA
BRAZIL
Georgetow

For a full explanation of the Köppen Climate Classification refer to page 120

16 © COPYRIGHT MACMILLAN EDUCATION LTD

Map

ATLANTIC OCEAN

Gulf of Mexico

U.S.A.

BERMUDA

Tropic of Cancer

BAHAMAS

CUBA

TURKS AND CAICOS IS.

U.S. VIRGIN ISLANDS

ANGUILLA

CAYMAN ISLANDS

HAITI

DOMINICAN REPUBLIC

PUERTO RICO

BRITISH VIRGIN ISLANDS

ANTIGUA AND BARBUDA

MEXICO

BELIZE

JAMAICA

ST. CHRISTOPHER AND NEVIS

MONTSERRAT

GUADELOUPE

DOMINICA

HONDURAS

CARIBBEAN SEA

MARTINIQUE

ST. LUCIA

EL SALVADOR

NICARAGUA

BARBADOS

ST. VINCENT AND THE GRENADINES

ARUBA

NETHERLANDS ANTILLES

GRENADA

TRINIDAD AND TOBAGO

COSTA RICA

PACIFIC OCEAN

PANAMA

COLOMBIA

VENEZUELA

GUYANA

SURINAME

BRAZIL

Legend

Land Use

Percentage of each major land use type

- Other Land
- Arable Land
- Forest/Woodland
- Pasture

Major Crops

- Aloes
- Arrowroot
- Avocados
- Bananas
- Citrus Fruit
- Cocoa
- Coconuts
- Coffee
- Fish
- Mace
- Mangoes
- Melons
- Nutmeg
- Pineapples
- Rice
- Sugar
- Tobacco

Projection: Conic
1:17 000 000

0   500   1000 km

Value of Agriculture to the Economy - Percentage of G.D.P. 1992

Agriculture has a minimal input to the economies of Aruba, Bermuda, Cayman Islands and U.S.V.I.

- Anguilla
- Antigua & Barbuda
- Bahamas
- Barbados
- Belize
- British Virgin Islands
- Cuba
- Dominica
- Dominican Republic
- Grenada
- Guadeloupe
- Guyana
- Haiti
- Jamaica
- Netherlands Antilles
- Martinique
- Montserrat
- Puerto Rico
- Christopher & Nevis
- St. Lucia
- St. Vincent
- Trinidad & Tobago
- Turks & Caicos Islands

0   10   20   30   40%

Major Agricultural Product Exporters, 1991/2

Million U.S. $

- Bananas
- Sugar

1200
1000
800
600
400
200
0

Cuba, Dominican Republic, Guyana, Jamaica, Martinique, St. Lucia, Guadeloupe, Belize, St. Vincent, Barbados, Trinidad & Tobago, Dominica

Sugar Production by Country, 1992

- Belize 1.8%
- Trinidad & Tobago 1.9%
- Jamaica 3.9%
- Guyana 4.3%
- Dominican Republic 10.6%
- Other 4.1%
- Cuba 73.4%

Total Production: Caribbean 1 579 000 metric tonnes
World 49 630 000 metric tonnes

Banana Production by Country, 1992

- Puerto Rico 4.1%
- Dominica 4.5%
- St. Vincent 5.3%
- Guadeloupe 7.1%
- St. Lucia 7.6%
- Jamaica 8.6%
- Haiti 11.0%
- Cuba 12.7%
- Martinique 16.0%
- Dominican Republic 18.1%
- Other 5.0%

Total Production: Caribbean 5 716 000 metric tonnes
World 115 939 000 metric tonnes

CARIBBEAN – INDUSTRY, TRADE AND COMMUNICATIONS

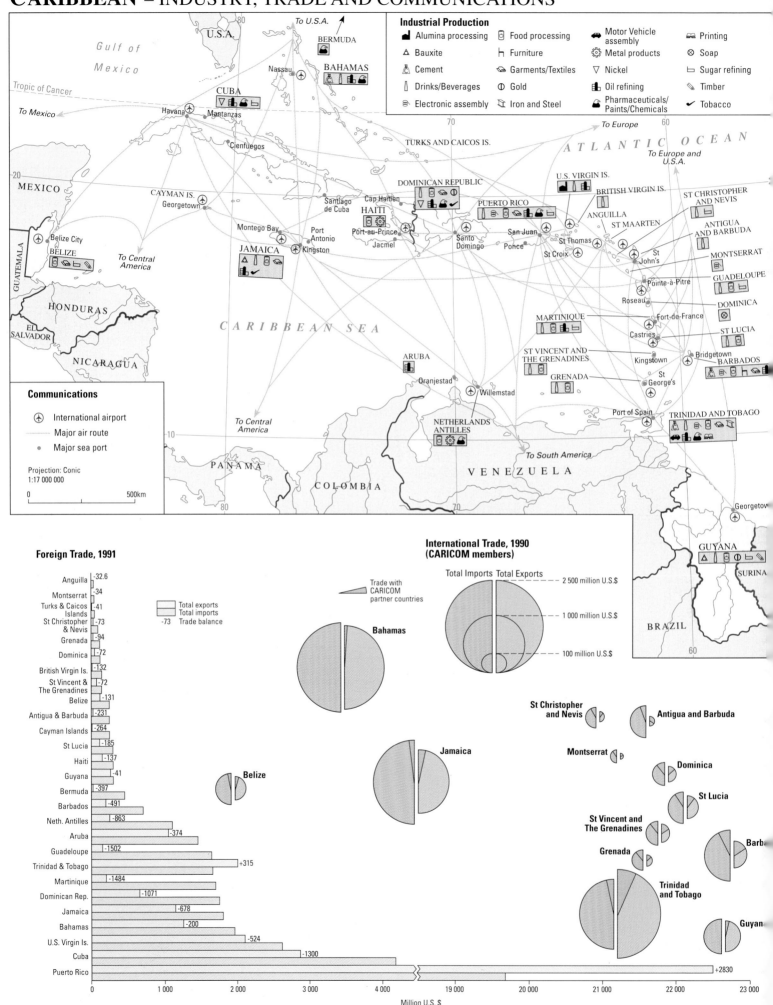

Industrial Production

- 🏭 Alumina processing
- △ Bauxite
- ⚗ Cement
- 🍾 Drinks/Beverages
- ⊟ Electronic assembly
- 🗄 Food processing
- ⊢ Furniture
- ✎ Garments/Textiles
- ⊕ Gold
- ⚒ Iron and Steel
- 🚗 Motor Vehicle assembly
- ⚙ Metal products
- ▽ Nickel
- ⬛ Oil refining
- ⬛ Pharmaceuticals/Paints/Chemicals
- ▭ Printing
- ⊗ Soap
- ⊟ Sugar refining
- ✎ Timber
- ✔ Tobacco

Communications

- ⊕ International airport
- —— Major air route
- • Major sea port

Projection: Conic
1:17 000 000

0 ——— 500km

Foreign Trade, 1991

Total exports
Total imports
-73 Trade balance

Anguilla	-32.6
Montserrat	-34
Turks & Caicos Islands	-41
St Christopher & Nevis	-73
Grenada	-94
Dominica	-72
British Virgin Is.	-132
St Vincent & The Grenadines	-72
Belize	-131
Antigua & Barbuda	-231
Cayman Islands	-264
St Lucia	-185
Haiti	-137
Guyana	-41
Bermuda	-397
Barbados	-491
Neth. Antilles	-863
Aruba	-374
Guadeloupe	-1502
Trinidad & Tobago	+315
Martinique	-1484
Dominican Rep.	-1071
Jamaica	-678
Bahamas	-200
U.S. Virgin Is.	-524
Cuba	-1300
Puerto Rico	+2830

Million U.S. $

International Trade, 1990 (CARICOM members)

Trade with CARICOM partner countries

Total Imports   Total Exports

2 500 million U.S.$
1 000 million U.S.$
100 million U.S.$

Bahamas

Belize

Jamaica

St Christopher and Nevis

Antigua and Barbuda

Montserrat

Dominica

St Lucia

St Vincent and The Grenadines

Grenada

Trinidad and Tobago

Barb...

Guyan...

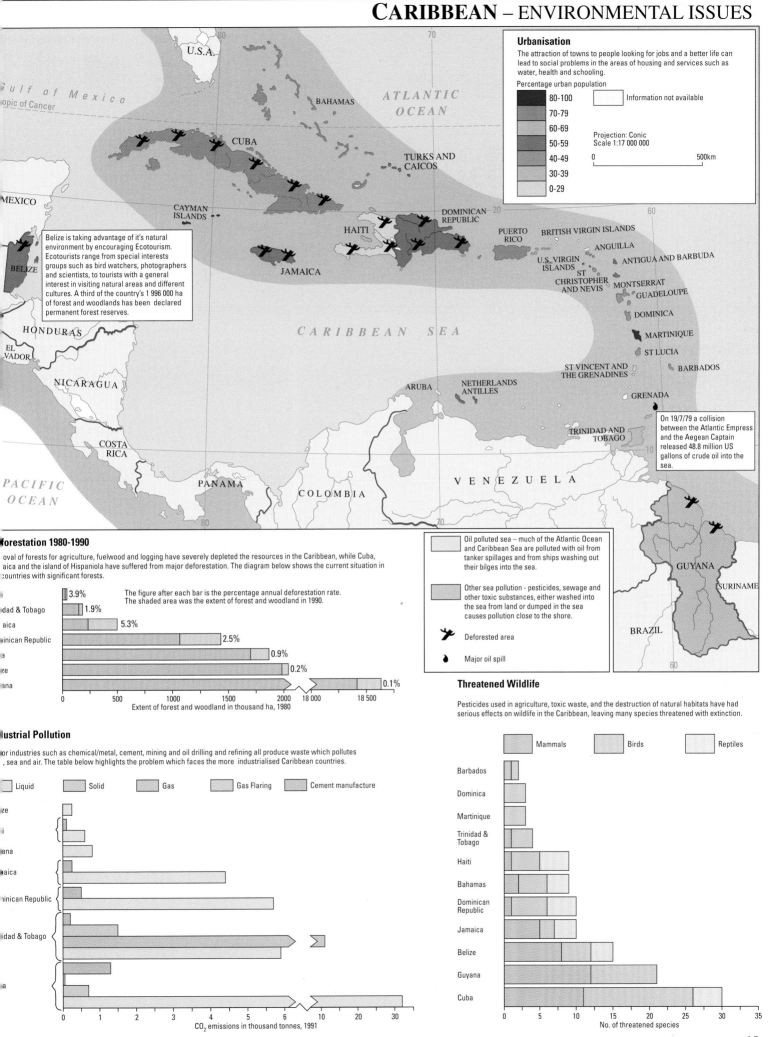

Urbanisation

The attraction of towns to people looking for jobs and a better life can lead to social problems in the areas of housing and services such as water, health and schooling.

Percentage urban population

- 80-100
- 70-79
- 60-69
- 50-59
- 40-49
- 30-39
- 0-29
- Information not available

Projection: Conic
Scale 1:17 000 000

0   500km

Belize is taking advantage of it's natural environment by encouraging Ecotourism. Ecotourists range from special interests groups such as bird watchers, photographers and scientists, to tourists with a general interest in visiting natural areas and different cultures. A third of the country's 1 996 000 ha of forest and woodlands has been declared permanent forest reserves.

On 19/7/79 a collision between the Atlantic Empress and the Aegean Captain released 48.8 million US gallons of crude oil into the sea.

Oil polluted sea – much of the Atlantic Ocean and Caribbean Sea are polluted with oil from tanker spillages and from ships washing out their bilges into the sea.

Other sea pollution - pesticides, sewage and other toxic substances, either washed into the sea from land or dumped in the sea causes pollution close to the shore.

🦌 Deforested area

🝰 Major oil spill

Forestation 1980-1990

...oval of forests for agriculture, fuelwood and logging have severely depleted the resources in the Caribbean, while Cuba, ...aica and the island of Hispaniola have suffered from major deforestation. The diagram below shows the current situation in ...countries with significant forests.

The figure after each bar is the percentage annual deforestation rate. The shaded area was the extent of forest and woodland in 1990.

- 3.9%
- ...dad & Tobago 1.9%
- ...aica 5.3%
- ...inican Republic 2.5%
- ...a 0.9%
- ...ze 0.2%
- ...ana 0.1%

Extent of forest and woodland in thousand ha, 1980
(0, 500, 1000, 1500, 2000, 18 000, 18 500)

Industrial Pollution

...or industries such as chemical/metal, cement, mining and oil drilling and refining all produce waste which pollutes ..., sea and air. The table below highlights the problem which faces the more industrialised Caribbean countries.

- Liquid
- Solid
- Gas
- Gas Flaring
- Cement manufacture

...ze
...i
...ana
...aica
...minican Republic
...idad & Tobago
...a

CO_2 emissions in thousand tonnes, 1991
(0, 1, 2, 3, 4, 5, 6, 10, 20, 30)

Threatened Wildlife

Pesticides used in agriculture, toxic waste, and the destruction of natural habitats have had serious effects on wildlife in the Caribbean, leaving many species threatened with extinction.

- Mammals
- Birds
- Reptiles

Barbados
Dominica
Martinique
Trinidad & Tobago
Haiti
Bahamas
Dominican Republic
Jamaica
Belize
Guyana
Cuba

No. of threatened species
(0, 5, 10, 15, 20, 25, 30, 35)

CARIBBEAN – POPULATION AND SETTLEMENT

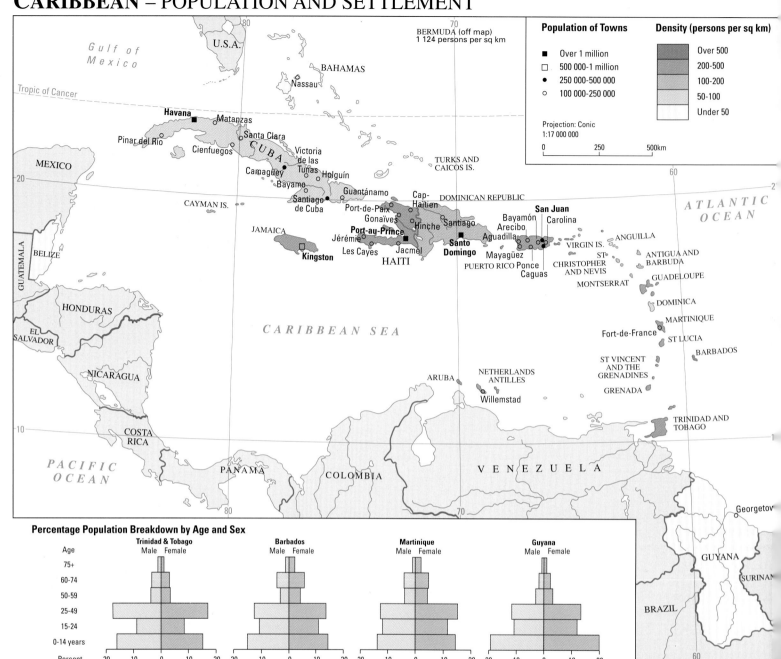

Population of Towns

- ■ Over 1 million
- □ 500 000-1 million
- ● 250 000-500 000
- ○ 100 000-250 000

Density (persons per sq km)

- Over 500
- 200-500
- 100-200
- 50-100
- Under 50

Projection: Conic
1:17 000 000

0   250   500km

BERMUDA (off map)
1 124 persons per sq km

Percentage Population Breakdown by Age and Sex

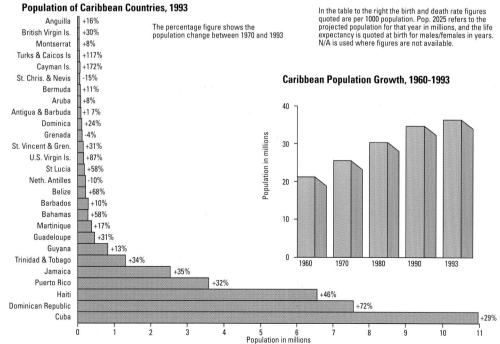

Age	Trinidad & Tobago	Barbados	Martinique	Guyana
75+				
60-74				
50-59				
25-49				
15-24				
0-14 years				

Each chart: Male / Female, Percent 20 10 0 10 20

Population of Caribbean Countries, 1993

The percentage figure shows the population change between 1970 and 1993

Anguilla	+16%
British Virgin Is.	+30%
Montserrat	+8%
Turks & Caicos Is	+117%
Cayman Is.	+172%
St. Chris. & Nevis	-15%
Bermuda	+11%
Aruba	+8%
Antigua & Barbuda	+17%
Dominica	+24%
Grenada	-4%
St. Vincent & Gren.	+31%
U.S. Virgin Is.	+87%
St Lucia	+58%
Neth. Antilles	-10%
Belize	+68%
Barbados	+10%
Bahamas	+58%
Martinique	+17%
Guadeloupe	+31%
Guyana	+13%
Trinidad & Tobago	+34%
Jamaica	+35%
Puerto Rico	+32%
Haiti	+46%
Dominican Republic	+72%
Cuba	+29%

Population in millions (0 to 11)

In the table to the right the birth and death rate figures quoted are per 1000 population. Pop. 2025 refers to the projected population for that year in millions, and the life expectancy is quoted at birth for males/females in years. N/A is used where figures are not available.

Caribbean Population Growth, 1960-1993

Population in millions (0 to 40): 1960, 1970, 1980, 1990, 1993

Population Statistics, 1992

Country	Birth Rate	Death Rate	Pop. 2025	Life Expect.	Urban P
Anguilla	25	10	N/A	71/77	N/A
Antigua & Barbuda	14	6	0.1	70/74	58%
Aruba	15	6	N/A	72/80	N/A
Bahamas	19	5	0.4	69/76	75%
Barbados	16	9	0.3	70/76	32%
Belize	37	5	0.4	67/72	52%
Bermuda	16	7	N/A	72/78	N/A
British Virgin Is.	20	6	N/A	72/77	N/A
Cayman Is.	15	4	N/A	74/80	N/A
Cuba	18	6	12.9	74/78	73%
Dominica	20	7	0.1	73/79	N/A
Dom. Republic	30	7	11.4	66/69	58%
Grenada	33	8	0.1	69/74	N/A
Guadeloupe	20	6	0.4	71/78	48%
Guyana	25	7	1.2	61/67	35%
Haiti	45	16	12.3	53/56	29%
Jamaica	25	5	3.6	71/75	51%
Martinique	18	6	0.5	74/81	82%
Montserrat	17	10	N/A	74/80	N/A
Neth. Antilles	19	6	0.2	72/76	53%
Puerto Rico	19	7	4.2	70/80	72%
St Chris. & Nevis	23	11	0.1	63/69	45%
St Lucia	23	6	0.3	69/74	46%
St Vincent & Gren.	23	6	0.2	70/73	21%
Trinidad & Tobago	21	7	1.7	67/73	64%
Turks & Caicos Is.	26	4	N/A	72/78	N/A
U.S. Virgin Is.	18	5	N/A	70/76	N/A

Gulf of Mexico

Tropic of Cancer

U.S.A.
Miami
Key West
Nassau

BAHAMAS

BERMUDA

PUERTO RICO

TURKS AND CAICOS IS.

DOMINICAN REPUBLIC

BRITISH VIRGIN IS.

ANGUILLA

HAITI

U.S. VIRGIN ISLANDS

ANTIGUA AND BARBUDA

CUBA

Cozumel

MEXICO

CAYMAN ISLANDS
Grand Cayman

Ocho Rios

JAMAICA

ATLANTIC OCEAN

St Thomas
San Juan
St John
St Maarten
St Kitts
Antigua
Montserrat
Guadeloupe
Dominica
Martinique
St Lucia
Barbados
Grenada
Tobago

ST CHRISTOPHER AND NEVIS
MONTSERRAT
DOMINICA

GUADELOUPE

BARBADOS

BELIZE

HONDURAS

EL SALVADOR

NICARAGUA

CARIBBEAN SEA

ARUBA

NETHERLANDS ANTILLES

MARTINIQUE

ST LUCIA

ST VINCENT AND THE GRENADINES

Aruba
Curaçao

GRENADA

Grenada

TRINIDAD AND TOBAGO

GUYANA

Cruise route

Major port of call

Projection: Conic
1:17 000 000
0   250   500km

Panama Canal
PANAMA
COLOMBIA
VENEZUELA

© COPYRIGHT MACMILLAN EDUCATION LTD

Tourist Accommodation: Capacity and Occupation, 1993

The shaded area represents those rooms occupied for countries where statistics are available.

Guyana
Montserrat
Dominica
Anguilla
Turks & Caicos Is.
British Virgin Is.
St Vincent and The Grenadines
Grenada
Haiti
St Christopher & Nevis
Trinidad & Tobago
St Lucia
Netherlands Antilles
Antigua & Barbuda
Belize
Cayman Islands
St Maarten
Bermuda
U.S. Virgin Islands
Barbados
Aruba
Martinique
Guadeloupe
Puerto Rico
Bahamas
Jamaica
Cuba
Dominican Republic

0   5 000   10 000   15 000   20 000   25 000   30 000
Number of rooms

Country of origin
U.S.A.
Canada
Caribbean
Venezuela
Brazil
U.K.
Netherlands
France
Other Europe
Europe
Others

Tourist Arrivals, 1993

2 500 000
2 000 000
1 000 000
500 000
250 000
100 000

BRAZIL
SURINAME

Tourist Arrivals by Country of Origin, 1993
Total tourist arrivals 12.2 million

Canada 5.8%   Caribbean 8.3%   France   Europe 17.0%
U.K.
Germany
Italy
Netherlands
Spain
U.S.A. 52.4%
Others
Others 16.5%

Growth of Tourism 1989-1993

Cruise passengers
Stopover tourists

Visitors in millions

15

0
1989   1990   1991   1992   1993

Visitor Expenditure, 1989-1993

Million U.S. $

12 000
10 000
8 000
6 000
4 000
2 000
0
1989   1990   1991   1992   1993

Visitor Expenditure by Country, 1993
Total expenditure U.S.$ 11145.4 million

Puerto Rico 14.6%   Bahamas 11.7%   Dominican Republic 11.0%
Jamaica 8.5%
U.S. Virgin Is. 8.2%
Cuba 6.4%
Others 26.3%   Barbados 4.7%
Aruba 4.1%   Bermuda 4.5%

21

CUBA

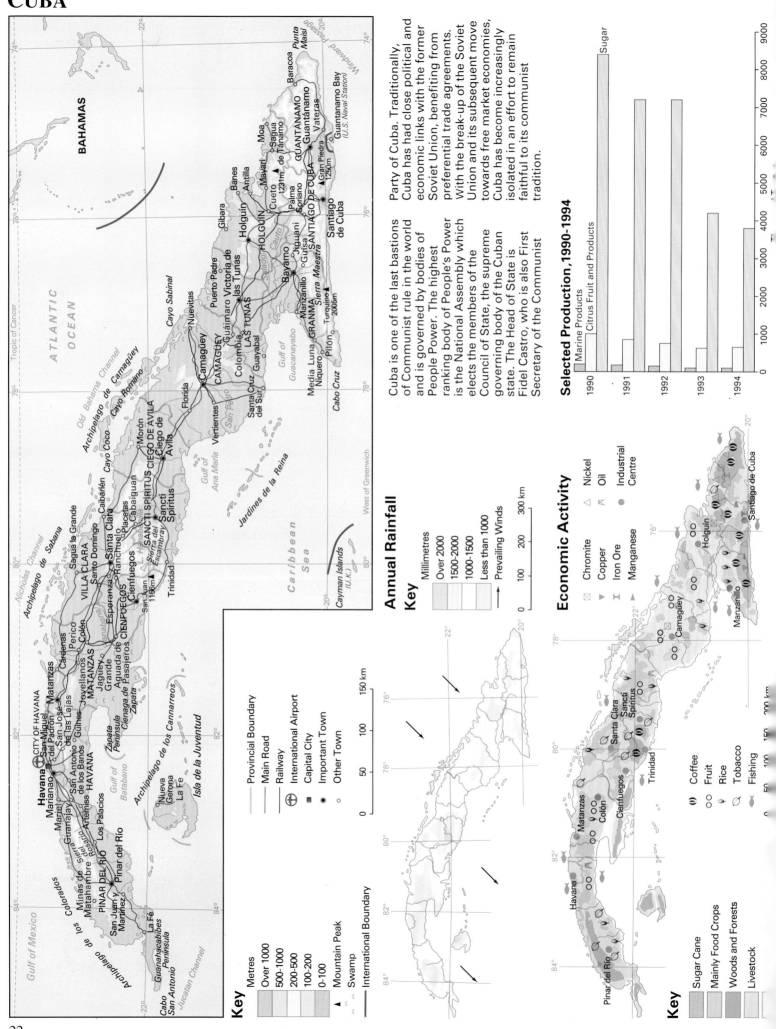

Party of Cuba. Traditionally, Cuba has had close political and economic links with the former Soviet Union, benefiting from preferential trade agreements. With the break-up of the Soviet Union and its subsequent move towards free market economies, Cuba has become increasingly isolated in an effort to remain faithful to its communist tradition.

Cuba is one of the last bastions of Communist rule in the world and is governed by bodies of People's Power. The highest ranking body of People's Power is the National Assembly which elects the members of the Council of State, the supreme governing body of the Cuban state. The Head of State is Fidel Castro, who is also First Secretary of the Communist

Selected Production, 1990-1994

Key

Metres
- Over 1000
- 500-1000
- 200-500
- 100-200
- 0-100
- ▲ Mountain Peak
- Swamp
- — International Boundary

- — Provincial Boundary
- — Main Road
- — Railway
- ⊕ International Airport
- ■ Capital City
- ● Important Town
- ○ Other Town

Annual Rainfall

Key

Millimetres
- Over 2000
- 1500-2000
- 1000-1500
- Less than 1000
- → Prevailing Winds

Economic Activity

- ⊠ Chromite
- ▶ Copper
- I Iron Ore
- △ Nickel
- ⋌ Oil
- ● Industrial Centre
- Manganese

Key

- Sugar Cane
- Mainly Food Crops
- Woods and Forests
- Livestock

- Coffee
- Fruit
- Rice
- Tobacco
- Fishing

...dominated the Cuban economy, providing 80% of export earnings, but without the preferential prices given by the former Soviet Union, Cuba has to compete on the world market and the industry has suffered badly. A combination of poor weather conditions and a lack of finance to buy fertilisers and pesticides has seen increasingly poor harvests, but it is hoped that with the opening of the industry to foreign investment in 1994 things will improve.

Tourist Arrivals, 1989-1993

(bar chart, 1989-1993; y-axis 100-600)

Origin of Tourists, 1993

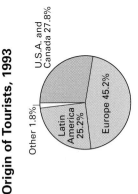

U.S.A. and Canada 27.8%
Europe 45.2%
Latin America 25.2%
Other 1.8%

Tourist Accommodation, 1989-1993

(bar chart, Thousand Rooms, 1989-1993; y-axis 5-25)

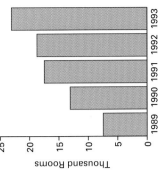

largest in the world and are the country's third largest earner of foreign exchange after tourism and sugar. Before 1990, nickel was exported, almost exclusively, to the Soviet Bloc, but new markets have opened up in Western Europe and with foreign finance being used to modernise the industry, it is expected that recovery will take place from 1995.

(area/bar chart, Thousand Tonnes, 1990-1994; y-axis 10-50)

(area/bar chart, Million U.S. $, 1990-1994; y-axis 100-400)

Tourism

The tourism sector of the Cuban economy is growing rapidly and has replaced sugar as the major earner of foreign exchange. The decline in traditional areas of the economy has made the government realise the potential of tourism and it has begun a programme of major hotel and nightclub construction with the aim of providing 30 000 rooms by 1995. Tourist expenditure in 1993 was U.S. $720 million, an increase of over 250% since 1989.

Total area: 110 860 sq. km.
Total population: 10 822 000 (1992)
Population density: 98 people per sq. km.
Capital City: Havana
Capital Population: 2 096 054 (1989)

Tourist Expenditure, 1989-1993

(bar chart, Million U.S. $, 1989-1993; y-axis 100-800)

Balance of Trade, 1989-1994

Exports
Imports

(bar chart, Billion Pesos, y-axis 0-10)

Year	Balance
1994	-0.4
1993	-0.6
1992	-0.5
1991	-1.3
1990	-2.0
1989	-2.7

Imports 1992-Total Value U.S. $2315 million

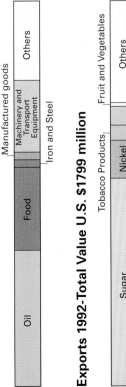

Oil | Food | Iron and Steel | Machinery and Transport Equipment | Manufactured goods | Others

Exports 1992-Total Value U.S. $1799 million

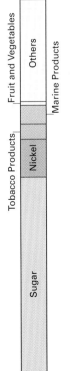

Sugar | Nickel | Tobacco Products | Fruit and Vegetables | Marine Products | Others

(area chart, Million U.S. $, 1990-1994; y-axis 1-5)

Tourism

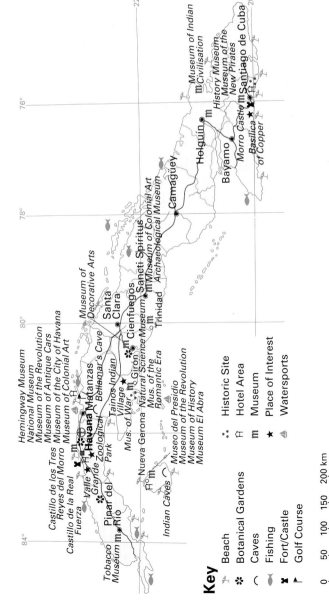

Hemingway Museum
National Museum
Museum of the Revolution
Museum of Antique Cars
Museum of the City of Havana
Museum of Colonial Art
Castillo de los Tres Reyes del Morro
Castillo de la Real Fuerza
Pinar del Rio
Tobacco Museum
Indian Caves
Valle Grande
Zoological Park
Tainos Indian Village
Nueva Gerona
Museo del Presidio
Museum of the Revolution
Museum of History
Museum El Abra
Havana
Matanzas
Mus. of War
Girón
Mus. of the Romantic Era
Natural Science Museum
Bellamar's Cave
Cienfuegos
Santa Clara
Museum of Decorative Arts
Sancti Spiritus
Trinidad
Museum of Colonial Art
Archaeological Museum
Camagüey
Holguín
Bayamo
Museum of Indian Civilisation
History Museum
Museum of the New Pirates
Morro Castle
Santiago de Cuba
Basilica of Copper

Key

- ∴ Beach
- ❋ Botanical Gardens
- (Caves
- ➤ Fishing
- ✖ Fort/Castle
- ▲ Golf Course
- ∴ Historic Site
- ♟ Hotel Area
- m Museum
- ★ Place of Interest
- ◣ Watersports

JAMAICA

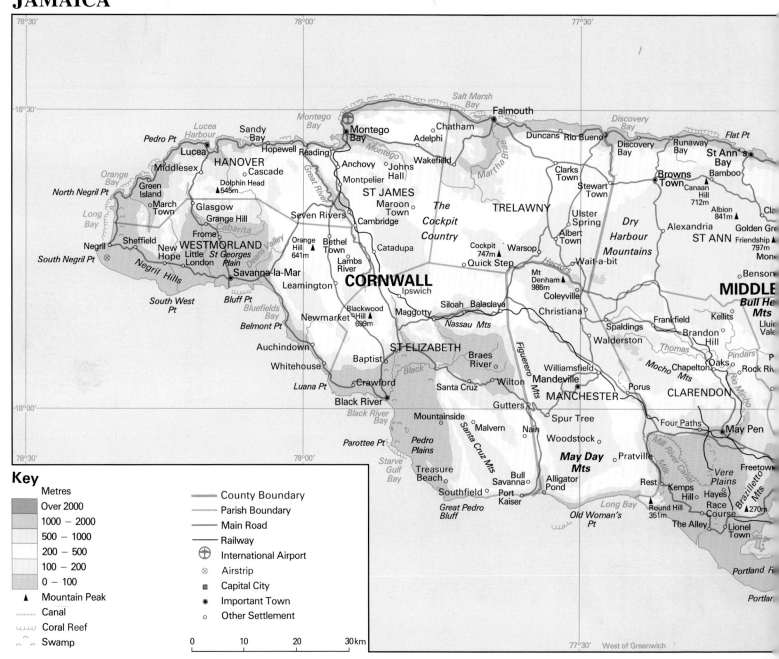

Key

Metres	
	Over 2000
	1000 – 2000
	500 – 1000
	200 – 500
	100 – 200
	0 – 100
▲	Mountain Peak
	Canal
	Coral Reef
	Swamp

	County Boundary
	Parish Boundary
	Main Road
	Railway
⊕	International Airport
⊗	Airstrip
■	Capital City
⊙	Important Town
○	Other Settlement

0   10   20   30km

West of Greenwich

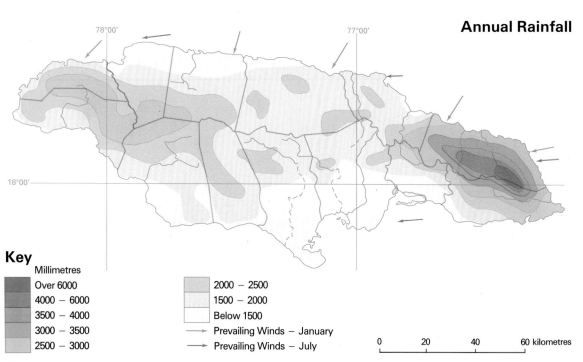

Annual Rainfall

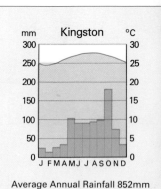

Average Annual Rainfall 852mm

Key

Millimetres	
	Over 6000
	4000 – 6000
	3500 – 4000
	3000 – 3500
	2500 – 3000
	2000 – 2500
	1500 – 2000
	Below 1500
→	Prevailing Winds – January
→	Prevailing Winds – July

0   20   40   60 kilometres

Total area: 10 991 sq. km.
Total population: 2 374 193 (1991)
Population density: 215 people
    per sq. km.

The capital city, Kingston, lies on the
south coast sheltered by a natural
sand spit which is the site of
Jamaica's International Airport. The
population of Kingston metropolitan
area is 587 798 (1991).

Jamaica is the world's third largest producer of bauxite and alumina, with estimated reserves of over 2 billion tonnes in 1980. They accounted for 75.9% of exports in 1992, but production and earnings peaked in 1991, since when the industry has suffered a decline as a result of losing Soviet contracts and falling world prices.

Tourism is now the principal earner of foreign exchange and the importance of the industry has increased steadily since the mid 1970's. The sugar industry has gradually declined since its production peaked at over 500 000 tonnes in 1965. To encourage production of goods for export, the government has established Free Trade Zones in Kingston, Montego Bay and Spanish Town, which all enjoy duty and income tax relief as incentives to attract business.

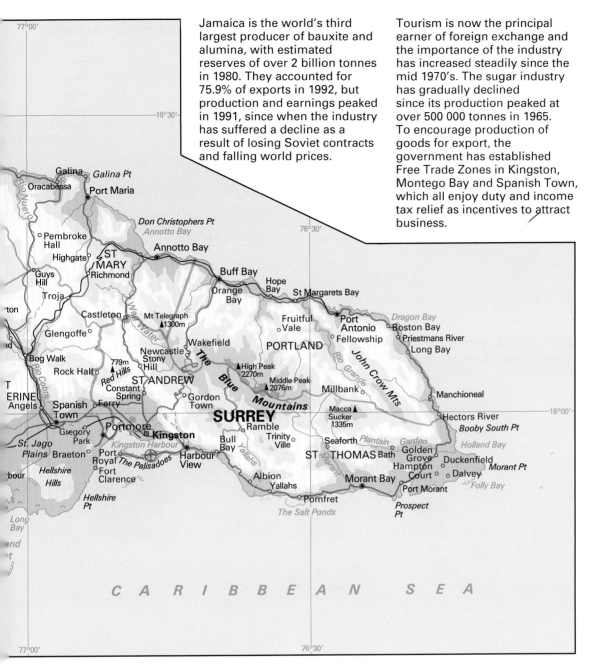

Gross Domestic Product by Economic Activity, 1992

Government Services 5.7%
Financial and Business Services 11.6%
Transport & Communication 7.2%
Distributive Trade 22.1%
Other Services 4.2%
Agriculture 7.6%
Mining and Quarrying 8.8%
Manufacturing 18.4%
Utilities 2.3%
Construction 12.1%

Agricultural Production, 1988-1992

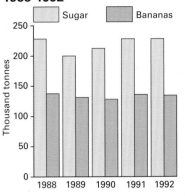

Sugar ☐   Bananas ▨

Mining Production, 1988-1992

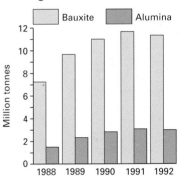

Bauxite ☐   Alumina ▨

Population

Age/Sex Pyramid, 1994 (estimate)

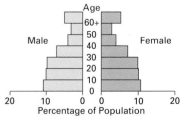

Male | Female
Age 60+ 50 40 30 20 10 0
Percentage of Population

Population by Ethnic Group

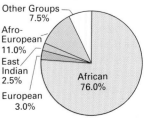

Other Groups 7.5%
Afro-European 11.0%
East Indian 2.5%
European 3.0%
African 76.0%

Key

Population Density

people per square kilometre

	Over 300
	200 – 300
	100 – 200
	20 – 100
	1 – 20
	Under 1

Population of Towns

■ Over 100 000
◉ 20 000 – 100 000
● 5 000 – 20 000
○ 2 000 – 5 000

0   20   40   60 kilometres

JAMAICA

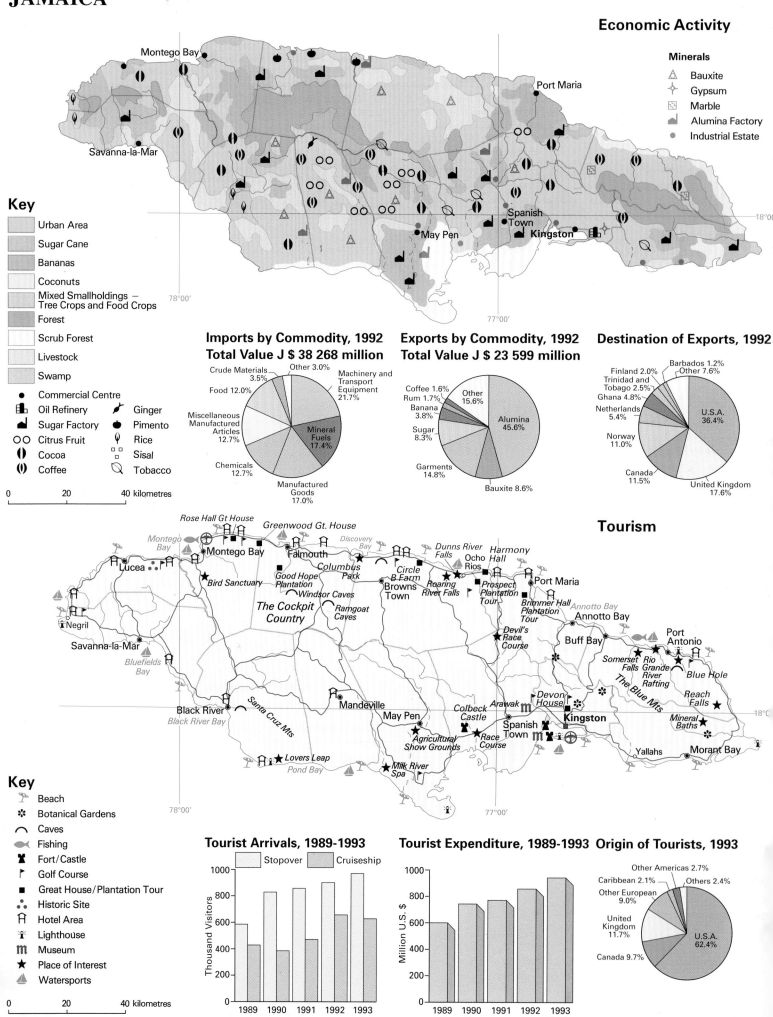

Economic Activity

Minerals
- △ Bauxite
- ✦ Gypsum
- ▦ Marble
- ◤ Alumina Factory
- ● Industrial Estate

Key

- Urban Area
- Sugar Cane
- Bananas
- Coconuts
- Mixed Smallholdings – Tree Crops and Food Crops
- Forest
- Scrub Forest
- Livestock
- Swamp

- ● Commercial Centre
- Oil Refinery
- Sugar Factory
- OO Citrus Fruit
- Cocoa
- Coffee
- ✗ Ginger
- ● Pimento
- ⚲ Rice
- ☐ Sisal
- Tobacco

0   20   40 kilometres

Imports by Commodity, 1992
Total Value J $ 38 268 million

- Crude Materials 3.5%
- Other 3.0%
- Food 12.0%
- Machinery and Transport Equipment 21.7%
- Miscellaneous Manufactured Articles 12.7%
- Mineral Fuels 17.4%
- Chemicals 12.7%
- Manufactured Goods 17.0%

Exports by Commodity, 1992
Total Value J $ 23 599 million

- Coffee 1.6%
- Rum 1.7%
- Banana 3.8%
- Other 15.6%
- Sugar 8.3%
- Alumina 45.6%
- Garments 14.8%
- Bauxite 8.6%

Destination of Exports, 1992

- Barbados 1.2%
- Finland 2.0%
- Other 7.6%
- Trinidad and Tobago 2.5%
- Ghana 4.8%
- Netherlands 5.4%
- U.S.A. 36.4%
- Norway 11.0%
- Canada 11.5%
- United Kingdom 17.6%

Tourism

Key

- ⚑ Beach
- ✳ Botanical Gardens
- ⌒ Caves
- 🐟 Fishing
- ♟ Fort/Castle
- ⚐ Golf Course
- ■ Great House/Plantation Tour
- ⋮ Historic Site
- ⌂ Hotel Area
- Lighthouse
- m Museum
- ★ Place of Interest
- ⛵ Watersports

0   20   40 kilometres

Tourist Arrivals, 1989-1993

Thousand Visitors

- Stopover
- Cruiseship

1989 1990 1991 1992 1993

Tourist Expenditure, 1989-1993

Million U.S. $

1989 1990 1991 1992 1993

Origin of Tourists, 1993

- Other Americas 2.7%
- Caribbean 2.1%
- Others 2.4%
- Other European 9.0%
- United Kingdom 11.7%
- Canada 9.7%
- U.S.A. 62.4%

26

Cayman Islands
British Dependent Territory

Caribbean Sea

81°00'

80°00'

19°30'

Little Cayman
West End Point
South Town
East Point

Cayman Brac
Spot Bay
West End

80°00'

Conch Point
West Bay
North Sound
George Town
Hutland
Grand Cayman
Old Man Bay
East End
Bodden Town
West of Greenwich
81°00'

19°30'

Total area: 260 sq. km.
Total population: 27 200 (1992)
Population density: 105 people per sq. km.

Key

	0-100 Metres		Main Road
▲	Spot Height	⊕	International Airport
■	Capital City	✈	Airport
○	Other Settlement	⊗	Airstrip

0   10   20   30 km

Tourist Expenditure, 1989-93

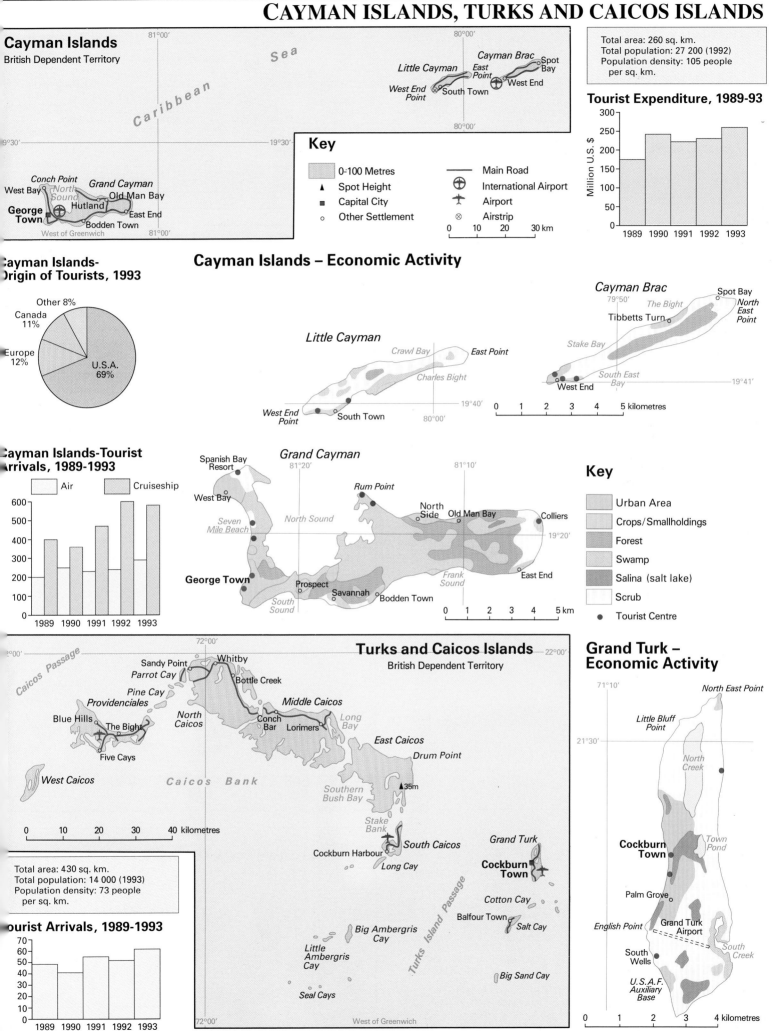

Million U.S. $
300
250
200
150
100
50
0
1989 1990 1991 1992 1993

Cayman Islands – Economic Activity

Cayman Islands-Origin of Tourists, 1993

Other 8%
Canada 11%
Europe 12%
U.S.A. 69%

Little Cayman
Crawl Bay
East Point
Charles Bight
West End Point
South Town
19°40'
80°00'

Cayman Brac
79°50'
The Bight
Spot Bay
North East Point
Tibbetts Turn
Stake Bay
South East Bay
West End
19°41'

0 1 2 3 4 5 kilometres

Cayman Islands-Tourist Arrivals, 1989-1993

Air   Cruiseship

600
500
400
300
200
100
0
1989 1990 1991 1992 1993

Grand Cayman
Spanish Bay Resort
West Bay
81°20'
Seven Mile Beach
North Sound
Rum Point
North Side
Old Man Bay
81°10'
Colliers
19°20'
George Town
Prospect
Savannah
Bodden Town
Frank Sound
East End
South Sound

0 1 2 3 4 5 km

Key

	Urban Area
	Crops/Smallholdings
	Forest
	Swamp
	Salina (salt lake)
	Scrub
●	Tourist Centre

Turks and Caicos Islands
British Dependent Territory

72°00'
22°00'

Caicos Passage
Whitby
Sandy Point
Parrot Cay
Bottle Creek
Pine Cay
Providenciales
Middle Caicos
Blue Hills
The Bight
North Caicos
Conch Bar
Lorimers
Long Bay
Five Cays
East Caicos
Drum Point
Caicos Bank
West Caicos
Southern Bush Bay
▲35m
Stake Bank
Cockburn Harbour
South Caicos
Grand Turk
Long Cay
Cockburn Town
Turks Island Passage
Cotton Cay
Balfour Town
Salt Cay
Big Ambergris Cay
Little Ambergris Cay
Big Sand Cay
Seal Cays
72°00'
West of Greenwich

0 10 20 30 40 kilometres

Total area: 430 sq. km.
Total population: 14 000 (1993)
Population density: 73 people per sq. km.

Tourist Arrivals, 1989-1993

70
60
50
40
30
20
10
0
1989 1990 1991 1992 1993

Grand Turk – Economic Activity

71°10'
North East Point
Little Bluff Point
21°30'
North Creek
Town Pond
Cockburn Town
Palm Grove
English Point
Grand Turk Airport
South Wells
South Creek
U.S.A.F. Auxiliary Base

0 1 2 3 4 kilometres

THE BAHAMAS AND BERMUDA

The Bahamas

Matanilla Reef
Little Bahama Bank
Great Sole Cay
Grand Bahama Island
Little Abaco I.
Fox Town
Coopers Town
West End
Green Turtle Cay
High Rock
Eight Mile Rock
Freeport City
Marsh Harbour
Hope Town
Moore's I.
Northwest Providence Channel
Great Isaac Bank
Gorda Cay
Sandy Point
Great Abaco Island
Crossing Rocks

Alice Town
Bimini Islands
Louis Town
Great Harbour Cay
Berry Islands
Spanish Wells
The Bluff
Dunmore Town
Alice Town
Eleuthera Island
NORTH ATLANTIC OCEAN
Orange Cay
Nicolls Town
Red Bays
Mastic Point
Stafford Creek
Coakley Town
Andros Town
Behring Point
Nassau
New Providence Island
Governor's Harbour
Rock Sound
Deep Creek
Bannerman Town
Little San Salvador
Arthur's Town
Cat Island
Great Bahama Bank
Andros Island
Moxey Town
Congo Town
Kemps Bay
Exuma Cays
Scrub Cays
Green Cay
Staniel Cay
Exuma Sound
Old Bight
Port Howe
Devil's Point
San Salvador (Watling I.)
Cockburn Town
Tongue of the Ocean
Santaren Channel
Anguilla Cays
Conception Island
Rolleville
Burnt Ground
Port Nelson
Rum Cay
Great Exuma Island
Mount Thompson
George Town
Stella Maris
Long Island
West of Greenwich
Little Exuma Island
Deadmans Cay
Clarence Town
Tropic of Cancer
Jumento Cays
Samana Cay (Atwood)
Crooked Island
Colonel Hill
Plana Cays
Long Cay
Hard Hill
Snug Corner
Betsy Bay
Abraham's Bay
Ragged Island Range
Acklins Island
Mayaguana Passage
Mayaguana Island
Duncan Town
Cay Verde
Mira Por vos Islet
Crooked Island Passage
Caicos Passage
West Caicos Island
Cay Santo Domingo
Little Inagua Island
Great Inagua Island
CUBA
Matthew Town

Grand Bahama Island

Mangrove Cay
Little Bahama Bank
HIGH ROCK DISTRICT
Water Cay
Riding Point
Comorant Point
West End
FREEPORT DISTRICT
Bootle Bay
Holmes Rock
Sea Grape
Eight Mile Rock
Pinders Point
Lucaya Estates
Bevans Town
High Rock
Freeport City
Lucaya
Smith Point
Freetown
Gold Rock Creek
Bulk Oil Site
Pelican Point
McLeans Town
Sweeting Cay
East End Point

| 0 | 10 | 20 | 30 Kilometres |

Key

- 0–100 Metres
- Coral Reef
- International Boundary
- District Boundary
- Road
- ⊕ International Airport
- ■ Capital City
- ◉ Important Town
- ○ Other Settlement
- Oil Refinery

| 0 | 50 | 100 | 150 k |

New Providence Island — Economic Activity

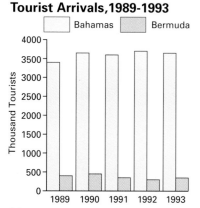

Cable Beach Tourist Centre
Gambier Village
Paradise Island
Nassau
Lyford Cay
Lake Killarney
Sandilands Village
Nassau International Airport
Adelaide
Carmichael Village
Coral Harbour

Key

- Urban Area
- Crops/Livestock
- Public Land
- Forest
- Swamp/Mangrove

- ● Tourist/Commercial Centre
- ♀ Hotel
- ♈ Dairy Cattle
- 🐖 Pigs
- ⊤ Pine Trees

| 0 | 5 | 10 | 15 km |

Tourist Arrivals, 1989-1993

Bahamas   Bermuda

Thousand Tourists

	1989	1990	1991	1992	1993

THE BAHAMAS
Total area: 13 939 sq.km.
Total population: 259 000 (1991)
Population density: 18.6 people per sq.km.
Capital City: Nassau
Capital population: 172 196

BERMUDA
Total area: 53 sq.km.
Total population: 59 549 (1993)
Population density: 1124 people per sq.km.
Capital City: Hamilton
Capital population: 1100

Bermuda

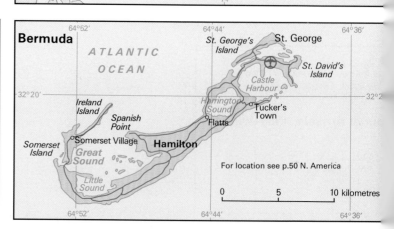

ATLANTIC OCEAN
St. George's Island
St. George
St. David's Island
Ireland Island
Castle Harbour
Harrington Sound
Spanish Point
Tucker's Town
Somerset Island
Flatts
Somerset Village
Hamilton
Great Sound
Little Sound

For location see p.50 N. America

| 0 | 5 | 10 kilometres |

HAITI AND THE DOMINICAN REPUBLIC

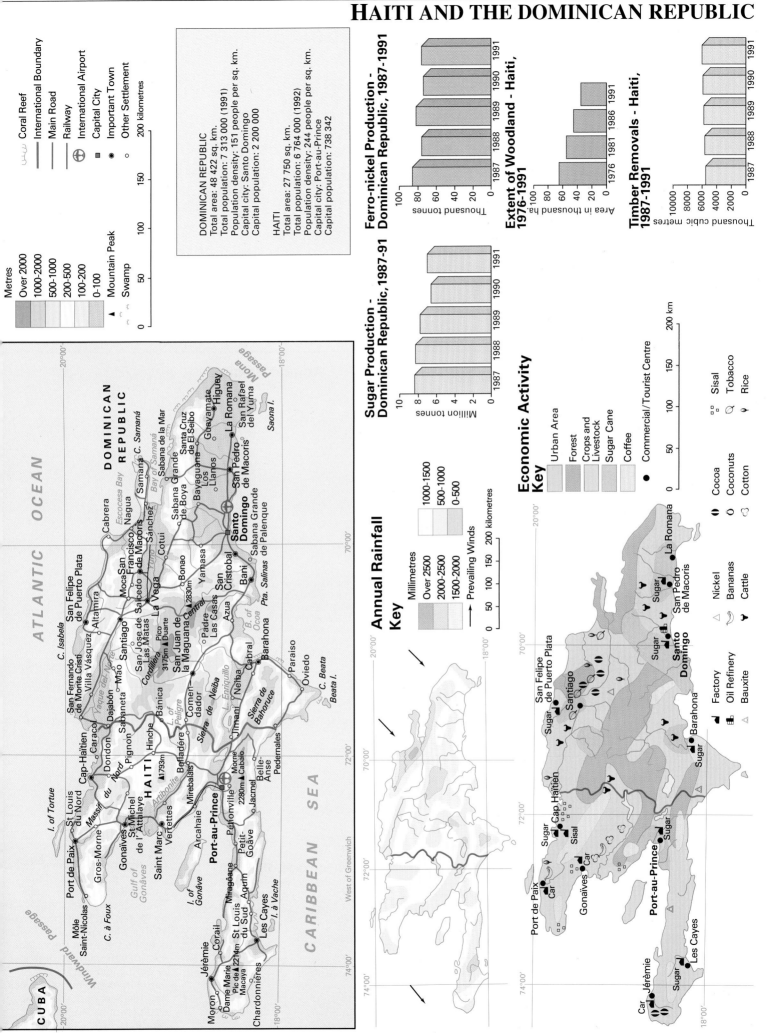

Metres
- Over 2000
- 1000-2000
- 500-1000
- 200-500
- 100-200
- 0-100
- ▲ Mountain Peak
- Swamp

0   50   100   150   200 kilometres

~ Coral Reef
— International Boundary
— Main Road
— Railway
⊕ International Airport
■ Capital City
● Important Town
○ Other Settlement

DOMINICAN REPUBLIC
Total area: 48 422 sq. km.
Total population: 7 313 000 (1991)
Population density: 151 people per sq. km.
Capital city: Santo Domingo
Capital population: 2 200 000

HAITI
Total area: 27 750 sq. km.
Total population: 6 764 000 (1992)
Population density: 244 people per sq. km.
Capital city: Port-au-Prince
Capital population: 738 342

Ferro-nickel Production - Dominican Republic, 1987-1991
Thousand tonnes (0, 20, 40, 60, 80, 100)
1987, 1988, 1989, 1990, 1991

Extent of Woodland - Haiti, 1976-1991
Area in thousand ha. (0, 20, 40, 60, 80, 100)
1976, 1981, 1986, 1991

Timber Removals - Haiti, 1987-1991
Thousand cubic metres (0, 2000, 4000, 6000, 8000, 10000)
1987, 1988, 1989, 1990, 1991

Sugar Production - Dominican Republic, 1987-91
Million tonnes (0, 2, 4, 6, 8, 10)
1987, 1988, 1989, 1990, 1991

Annual Rainfall
Key
Millimetres
- Over 2500
- 2000-2500
- 1500-2000
- 1000-1500
- 500-1000
- 0-500

→ Prevailing Winds

0   50   100   150   200 kilometres

Economic Activity
Key
- Urban Area
- Forest
- Crops and Livestock
- Sugar Cane
- Coffee
- ● Commercial/Tourist Centre

0   50   100   150   200 km

- Cocoa
- Coconuts
- Cotton
- Sisal
- Tobacco
- Rice
- Nickel
- Bananas
- Cattle
- Factory
- Oil Refinery
- Bauxite

PUERTO RICO

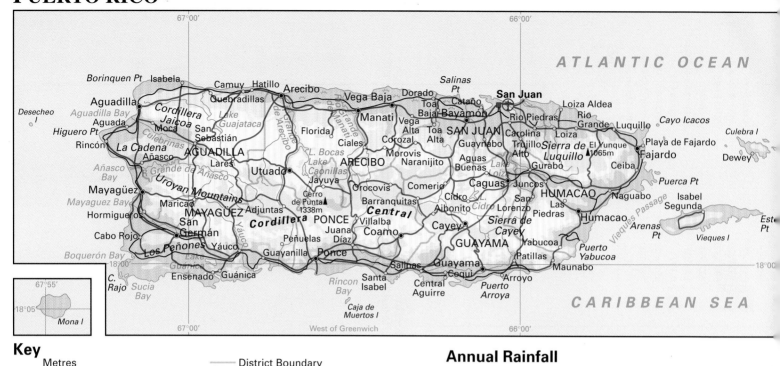

Key

Metres	
	Over 1000
	500–1000
	200–500
	100–200
	0–100
▲	Mountain Peak
	Swamp

----- District Boundary
——— Main Road
——— Railway
⊕ International Airport
■ Capital City
⦿ Important Town
○ Other Town

0 10 20 30 40 km

Annual Rainfall

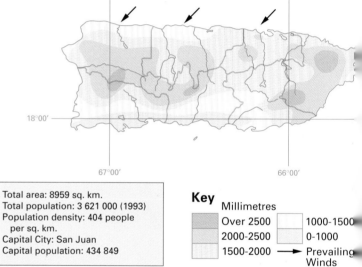

Total area: 8959 sq. km.
Total population: 3 621 000 (1993)
Population density: 404 people per sq. km.
Capital City: San Juan
Capital population: 434 849

Key

Millimetres	
Over 2500	1000–1500
2000–2500	0–1000
1500–2000	→ Prevailing Winds

0 10 20 30 40 50 kilometres

Economic Activity

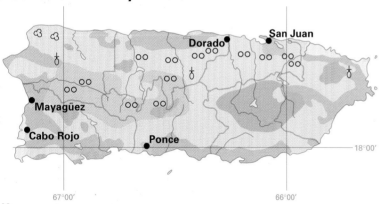

Key

Urban Area		○○	Citrus Fruit
Forest		⬡	Cotton
Crops and Livestock		⚲	Pineapples
Sugar Cane		●	Commercial/Tourist Centre
Coffee			
Coconuts		0 10 20 30 40 50 km	
Tobacco			

Trade with the U.S.A. by Commodity, 1991

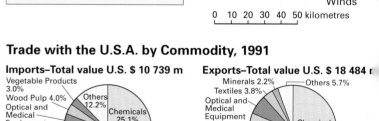

Imports–Total value U.S. $ 10 739 m

Vegetable Products 3.0%
Wood Pulp 4.0%
Optical and Medical Equipment 4.2%
Base Metals 4.3%
Animals 4.5%
Transport Equipment 4.5%
Plastic and Rubber 5.3%
Textiles 5.7%
Food, drink and Tobacco 8.4%
Machinery and Electrical Equipment 18.8%
Chemicals 25.1%
Others 12.2%

Exports–Total value U.S. $ 18 484 [m]

Minerals 2.2%
Textiles 3.8%
Optical and Medical Equipment 7.2%
Food, Drink and Tobacco 13.7%
Chemical Products 45.7%
Machinery and Electrical Equipment 21.7%
Others 5.7%

Foreign Trade, 1987-1991

The shaded area represents trade with the U.S.A.

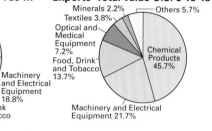

Imports   Exports

Puerto Rico's economy is close[ly] integrated with that of the United States.
The economy was industrialise[d] by Operation Bootstrap in the 1940's and now manufacturing is by far the most important sector with pharmaceuticals, scientific instruments, computers and microprocesso[rs] and medical and electronic equipment being the main products.

Gross Domestic Product by Economic Activity, 1993

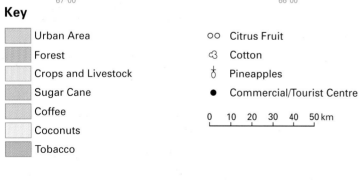

Agriculture 1.1%
Construction and Mining 2.2%
Finance, Insurance, Real Estate 13.1%
Manufacturing 39.2%
Trade 15.0%
Services 10.6%
Transportation and Public Utilities 8.1%
Government 10.7%

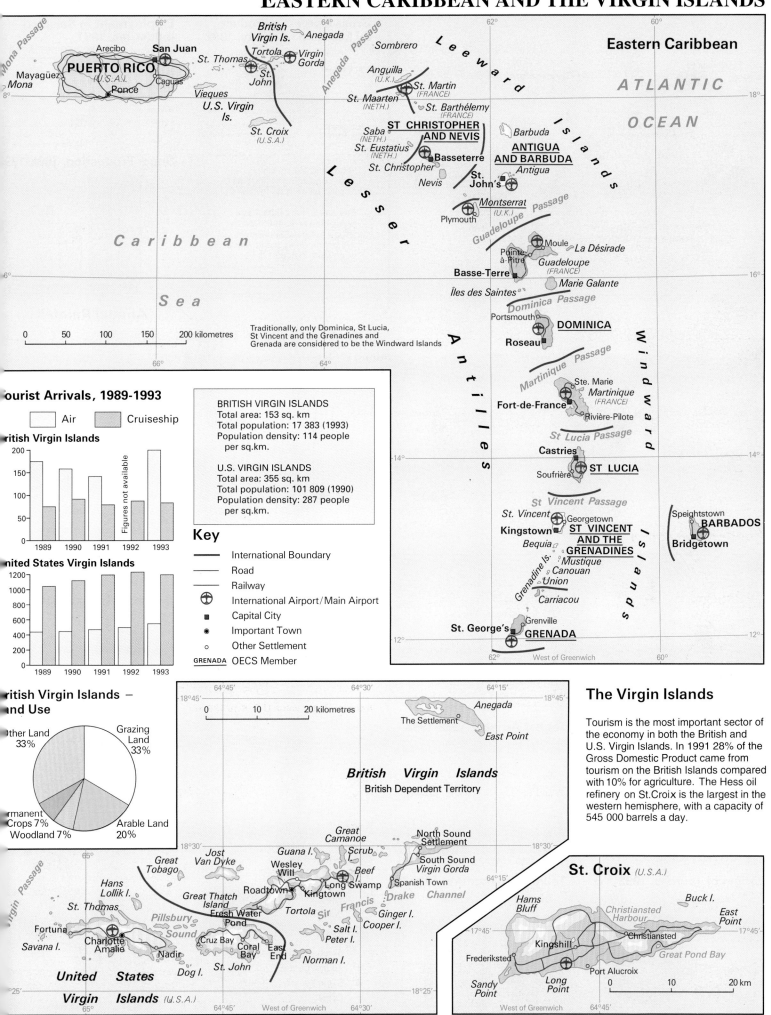

Eastern Caribbean

Traditionally, only Dominica, St Lucia, St Vincent and the Grenadines and Grenada are considered to be the Windward Islands

Tourist Arrivals, 1989-1993

Air   Cruiseship

British Virgin Islands

United States Virgin Islands

BRITISH VIRGIN ISLANDS
Total area: 153 sq. km
Total population: 17 383 (1993)
Population density: 114 people per sq.km.

U.S. VIRGIN ISLANDS
Total area: 355 sq. km
Total population: 101 809 (1990)
Population density: 287 people per sq.km.

Key

International Boundary
Road
Railway
International Airport/Main Airport
Capital City
Important Town
Other Settlement
GRENADA OECS Member

British Virgin Islands – Land Use

Other Land 33%
Grazing Land 33%
Permanent Crops 7%
Woodland 7%
Arable Land 20%

British Virgin Islands
British Dependent Territory

The Virgin Islands

Tourism is the most important sector of the economy in both the British and U.S. Virgin Islands. In 1991 28% of the Gross Domestic Product came from tourism on the British Islands compared with 10% for agriculture. The Hess oil refinery on St.Croix is the largest in the western hemisphere, with a capacity of 545 000 barrels a day.

St. Croix (U.S.A.)

United States Virgin Islands (U.S.A.)

ST CHRISTOPHER AND NEVIS

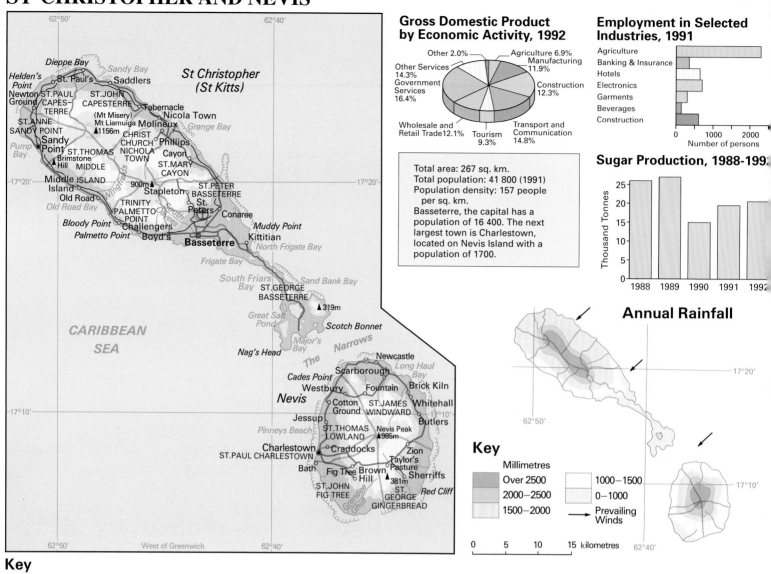

Gross Domestic Product by Economic Activity, 1992

Other 2.0%
Agriculture 6.9%
Other Services 14.3%
Manufacturing 11.9%
Government Services 16.4%
Construction 12.3%
Wholesale and Retail Trade 12.1%
Tourism 9.3%
Transport and Communication 14.8%

Employment in Selected Industries, 1991

Agriculture
Banking & Insurance
Hotels
Electronics
Garments
Beverages
Construction

0   1000   2000
Number of persons

Total area: 267 sq. km.
Total population: 41 800 (1991)
Population density: 157 people per sq. km.
Basseterre, the capital has a population of 16 400. The next largest town is Charlestown, located on Nevis Island with a population of 1700.

Sugar Production, 1988-199

Thousand Tonnes
25, 20, 15, 10, 5, 0
1988 1989 1990 1991 1992

Annual Rainfall

Key
Millimetres
Over 2500
2000–2500
1500–2000
1000–1500
0–1000
Prevailing Winds

0   5   10   15 kilometres

Key

Metres
Over 1000
500–1000
200–500
100–200
0–100
▲ Mountain Peak
Parish Boundary
Main Road

—— Railway
⊕ International Airport
⊗ Airfield
▣ Capital City
◉ Important Town
○ Other Settlement

0   5   10 kilometres

The economy of St.Christopher and Nevis has traditionally depended on sugar cultivation (on St.Christopher) and cotton and coconuts (on Nevis). Sugar is still important, accounting for about 46% of total agricultural production and earning EC$32 million in 1992. Diversification into non-sugar agriculture and manufacturing is increasing, but the greatest expansion has been seen in the tourism sector.

Tourist Arrivals, 1989-1993

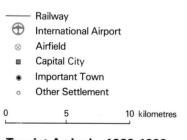

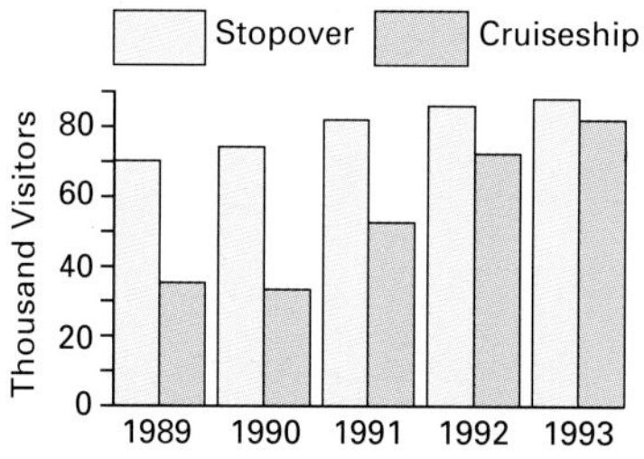

Stopover   Cruiseship

Thousand Visitors
80, 60, 40, 20, 0
1989 1990 1991 1992 1993

Origin of Tourists, 1993

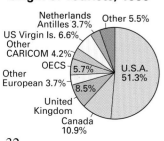

Netherlands Antilles 3.7%
Other 5.5%
US Virgin Is. 6.6%
Other CARICOM 4.2%
OECS 5.7%
Other European 3.7%
United Kingdom 8.5%
Canada 10.9%
U.S.A. 51.3%

Tourist Expenditure, 1989-93

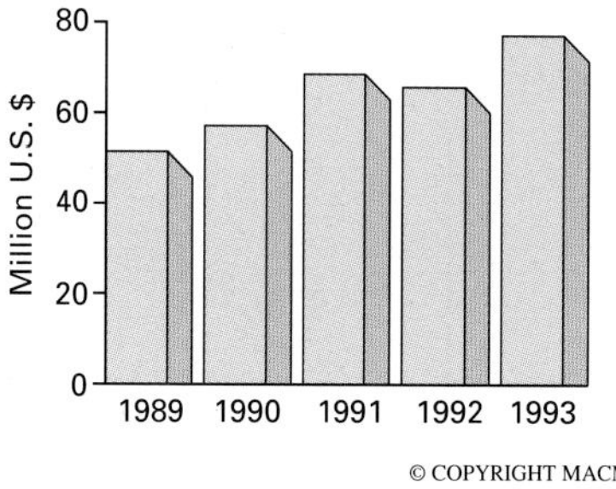

Million U.S. $
80, 60, 40, 20, 0
1989 1990 1991 1992 1993

Economic Activity

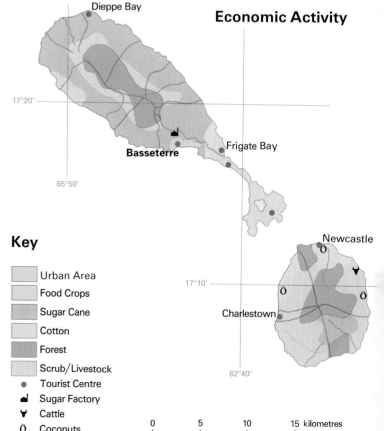

Key

Urban Area
Food Crops
Sugar Cane
Cotton
Forest
Scrub/Livestock
● Tourist Centre
⌐ Sugar Factory
� Cattle
ᵜ Coconuts

0   5   10   15 kilometres

ANTIGUA AND BARBUDA

Traditionally, agriculture was the backbone of Antigua and Barbudas's economy, but soil depletion, unfavourable market conditions and inconsistent rainfall patterns have resulted in the decline of this sector of the economy, to be replaced by tourism, which is now the main earner of foreign exchange.

Total area: 442 sq.km.
Total population: 65 962 (1991)
Population density: 149 people per sq.km.

98 per cent of the population live on Antigua. St John's, the capital city, has a population of 30 000. Codrington is the only village on Barbuda.

Antigua

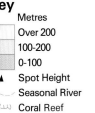

Key

Metres
- Over 200
- 100-200
- 0-100

▲ Spot Height
- Seasonal River
- Coral Reef
- Parish Boundary

- Main Road
- - - - Track
⊕ International Airport
⊗ Airstrip
■ Capital City
◉ Important Town
○ Other Settlement

Barbuda

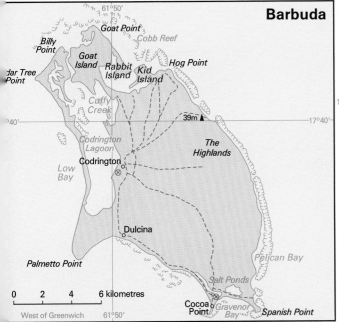

Annual Rainfall

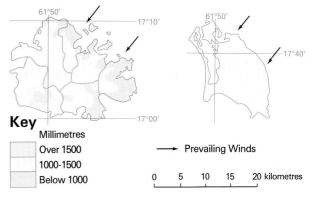

Key

Millimetres
- Over 1500
- 1000-1500
- Below 1000

→ Prevailing Winds

0   5   10   15   20 kilometres

Economic Activity

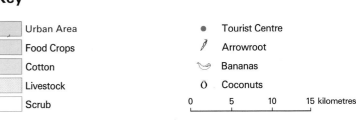

Key

- Urban Area
- Food Crops
- Cotton
- Livestock
- Scrub

● Tourist Centre
🖊 Arrowroot
🍌 Bananas
Ȣ Coconuts

0   5   10   15 kilometres

Gross Domestic Product by Economic Activity, 1992

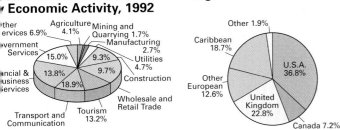

- Other Services 6.9%
- Agriculture 4.1%
- Mining and Quarrying 1.7%
- Manufacturing 2.7%
- Utilities 4.7%
- Construction
- Government Services 15.0%
- Financial & Business Services 13.8%
- Transport and Communication 18.9%
- Tourism 13.2%
- Wholesale and Retail Trade 9.7%
- 9.3%

Origin of Tourists, 1993

- Other 1.9%
- Caribbean 18.7%
- U.S.A. 36.8%
- Other European 12.6%
- United Kingdom 22.8%
- Canada 7.2%

Tourist Arrivals, 1989-1993

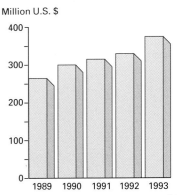

☐ Air   ☐ Cruiseship

Thousand Visitors: 250, 200, 150, 100, 50, 0

1989 1990 1991 1992 1993

Tourist Expenditure, 1989-1993

Million U.S. $

400, 300, 200, 100, 0

1989 1990 1991 1992 1993

MONTSERRAT AND ANGUILLA

Montserrat
British Dependent Territory

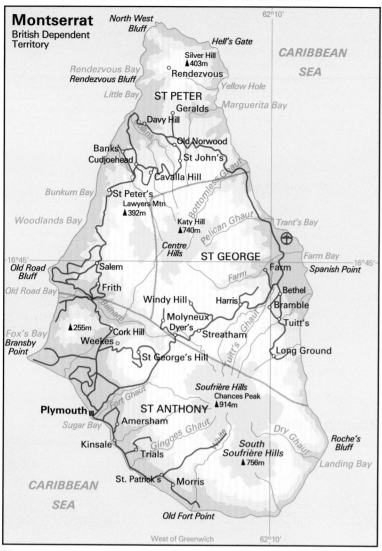

Montserrat has seen swift economic growth in recent years based largely on tourism. The objective is to promote the island as an up-market destination and the majority of tourists are villa owners from North America. Extensive damage to berthing facilities by Hurricane Hugo in 1989 severely affected the cruiseship business for several years, but with the completion of repairs to the port this has now improved.

Total area: 102 sq.km.
Total population: 11 957 (1991)
Population density: 117 people per sq.km.

Plymouth, the capital has a population of 3 500. It is also a port, situated on the more sheltered south west coast.

Annual Rainfall

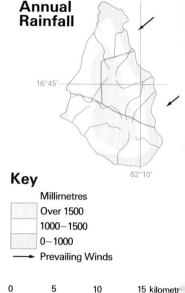

Key

Millimetres
- Over 1500
- 1000–1500
- 0–1000
- → Prevailing Winds

0   5   10   15 kilometr

Economic Activity

Key

- Urban Area
- Food Crops
- Cotton
- Forest
- Scrub/Livestock
- ● Tourist Centre
- ⋎ Cattle
- 0 Limes

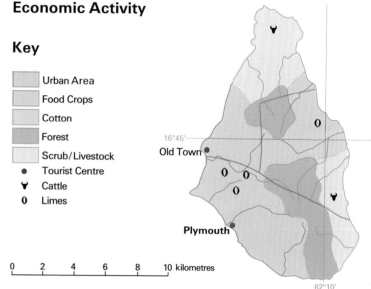
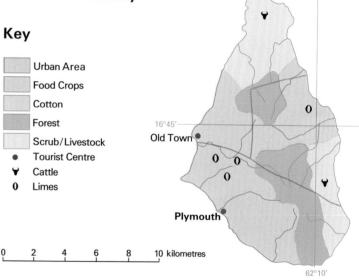

0   2   4   6   8   10 kilometres

Key

Metres
- Over 500
- 200–500
- 100–200
- 0–100
- ▲ Mountain Peak

- ---- Parish Boundary
- —— Main Road
- ⊕ International Airport
- ■ Capital City
- ○ Other Settlement

0   1   2   3   4 kilometres

Tourist Arrivals-Montserrat, 1989-1993

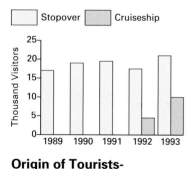

□ Stopover   ▨ Cruiseship

Tourist Arrivals-Anguilla, 1989-1993

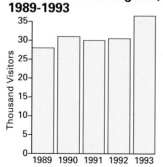

Origin of Tourists-Montserrat, 1993

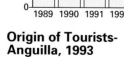

Other 3.6%
Other CARICOM 16.4%
U.S.A. 31.1%
OECS 27.9%
Canada 7.6%
United Kingdom 13.4%

Origin of Tourists-Anguilla, 1993

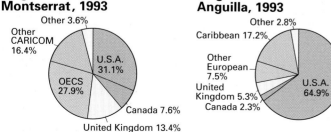

Other 2.8%
Caribbean 17.2%
Other European 7.5%
United Kingdom 5.3%
Canada 2.3%
U.S.A. 64.9%

Anguilla
British Dependent Territory

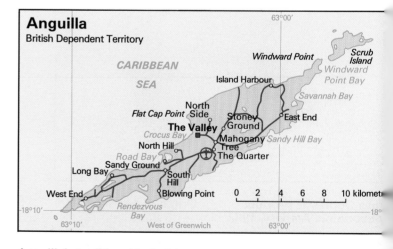

Anguilla's traditional industries were boat building, fishing, salt production and livestock rearing, but during the 1980's these were replaced by a rapid growth in tourism, which has now become the most important sector of the island's economy.

Total area: 96 sq.km
Total population: 8 960 (1992)
Population density: 93 people per sq.km.
Capital city: The Valley
Capital population: 595

Guadeloupe

ATLANTIC OCEAN

Pte de la Grande Vigie

Anse-Bertrand
Haut de la Montagne
Beauport
Port Louis
Les Mangles
Gros Cap
Ste-Marguerite
Petit-Canal
Vieux Bourg
Morne-a-L'Eau
Moule
Lasserre
Chateau-Gaillard
GRANDE-TERRE
Abymes
Douville
Pte Allègre
Ilet à Fajou
Grand Cul-de-Sac Marin
Duzer
Ste-Rose
M Rouge
Lamentin
Deshaies
Bis
▲758m
Belle Hôtesse 777m
Baie-Mahault
Castel
Jarry
Pointe-à-Pitre
St-François
Pte des Châteaux
Morne Jeanneton 744m
Pointe Noire
Mahaut
Petit Cul-de-Sac Marin
Gosier
Ste-Anne
Petit-Bourg
Vernou
BASSE-TERRE
Goyave
ouillante
Grand Sans-Toucher 1354m
Ste-Marie
Marigot
Capesterre
Soufrière 1467m
Vieux-Habitants
Matouba
St Claude Routhiers
Capesterre-Belle-Eau
Baillif
St Sauveur
Gourbeyre
Bananier
Basse Terre
Vieux-Fort
Trois-Rivières
Pte du Vieux Fort
West of Greenwich 61°30'

Marie Galante

Grosse Pointe
Caye Plate
Grelin
Anse Coudrier
St-Louis
St Louis
Château Murat
Capesterre
Grand-Bourg
Pte des Basses

Key

Metres	
	Over 1000
	500–1000
	200–500
	100–200
	0–100
▲	Mountain Peak
	Coral Reef
	Swamp

- - - Arrondissement Boundary
——— Main Road
⊕ International Airport
⊗ Airfield
■ Capital City
◉ Important Town
○ Other Settlement

0   5   10   15   20 kilometres

Martinique

Grand Rivière
Macouba
Basse-Pointe
Cape St Martin
Le Lorrain
Marigot
Le Precheur
Mt Pelée 1397m
Ajoupa-Bouillon
ATLANTIC OCEAN
Le Morne Rouge
TRINITE
Ste-Marie
Pte du Diable
Champ Flore
Morne des Esses
Madras
St-Pierre
Fond St-Denis
Morne Bellevue 694m
La Trinité
Baie du Galion
Le Carbet
Piton Lacroix 1196m
Dumaine
Gros-Morne
Le Morne-Vert
Bellefontaine
FORT-DE-FRANCE
St-Joseph
Le Robert
Pelletier
Ilet Ramville ou Chancel
Pte de la Rose
Case-Pilote
Redoute
Le Lamentin
Le François
Schoelcher
Fort-de-France
Ducos
Le St-Esprit
Baie de Fort-de-France
Petit Bourg
MARIN
Montagne du Vauclin 504m
Le Vauclin
Pte Blanche
Les Trois Ilets
Rivière-Salée
Josseaud
Grand Anse
Desmarinières
Le Cap
Les Anses D'Arlets
Rivière-Pilote
Le Marin
Le Diamant
Ste-Luce
Pte du Diamant
Ste-Anne
Pte des Salines
West of Greenwich 61°00'

CARIBBEAN SEA

Annual Rainfall

16°20'
16°00'
61°30'
61°15'
14°40'
61°00'

Key

Millimetres	
Over 4000	2000–2500
3000–3500	1500–2000
2500–3000	Below 1500

→ Prevailing Winds

0   20   40   60 km

Economic Activity

Moule
Pointe-à-Pitre
Ste-Anne
St-François
Basse Terre
16°20'
16°00'
61°30'
61°15'

St-Pierre
La Trinité
Fort-de-France
Anse-Mitan/ Pointe du Bout
Le Diamant
Le Marin
Ste-Anne
14°40'
61°00'

Key

	Urban Area		Forest
	Mixed Crops		Scrub/ Livestock
	Sugar Cane		

● Commercial Centre
🛢 Oil Refinery
⚒ Sugar Factory
● Tourist Centre
🍌 Bananas
🐂 Cattle
◖◗ Cocoa
◖◗ Coffee
🍍 Pineapples
Vanilla

0   10   20   30   40 km

GUADELOUPE
Total area: 1780 sq.km.
Total population: 387 034 (1990)
Population density: 217 people per sq. km.
Capital city: Basse-Terre
Capital population: 14 003

MARTINIQUE
Total area: 1100 sq.km.
Total population: 359 579 (1990)
Population density: 327 people per sq. km.
Capital city: Fort-de-France
Capital population: 101 540

Tourist Arrivals, 1989-1993

GUADELOUPE
MARTINIQUE
Stopover   Cruiseship

Thousand Visitors

800
600
400
200
0

1989   1990   1991   1992   1993

35

DOMINICA

Dominica's economy is dominated by bananas, which accounted for over 55% of the country's exports in 1993. Lower prices though, have meant a gradual decrease in banana revenues, despite an increase in production. Coconuts are also an important crop, and are used primarily for the production of soap, another significant export. Tourism is increasingly becoming a visible part of the economy, but as a result of the islands mountainous character, the emphasis is on flora, fauna and diving, not beaches — in other words, Ecotourism.

Total area: 750 sq. km.
Total population: 71 183 (1991)
Population density: 95 people per sq. km.

Most Dominicans live in coastal areas. The rugged interior landscape is not generally habitable. The largest settlement is Roseau the capital, with 20 755 people living in the town and it's immediate surroundings. 3 000 acres of land are set aside on the windward side of the island for the Carib population.

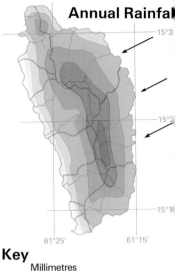

Annual Rainfa

Key
Millimetres

	Over 4000
	3500–4000
	3000–3500
	2500–3000
	2000–2500
	1500–2000
	Below 1500
→	Prevailing Winds

0   10   20 kilometres

Economic Activit

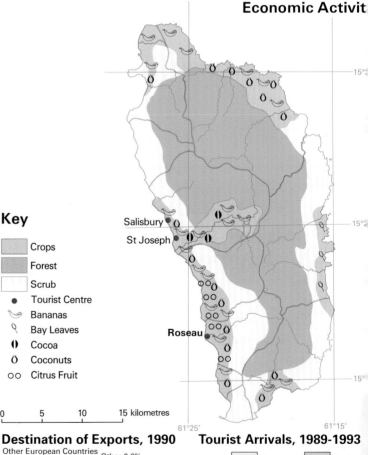

Key

	Crops
	Forest
	Scrub
●	Tourist Centre
➳	Bananas
✎	Bay Leaves
◖	Cocoa
♨	Coconuts
○○	Citrus Fruit

0   5   10   15 kilometres

Key

Metres

	Over 1000
	500–1000
	200–500
	100–200
	0–100
▲	Mountain Peak
⋯⋯	Parish Boundary
−−−−	National Park/Reserve Boundary

▬▬	Main Road
⊕	International Airport
■	Capital City
●	Important Town
○	Other Settlement

0   5   10 kilometres

Gross Domestic Product by Economic Activity, 1992

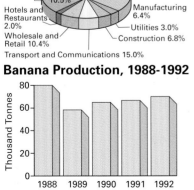

Other Services 4.4%
Government Services 16.9%
Banking & Insurance 10.5%
Crops 20.1%
Agriculture 24.6%
Manufacturing 6.4%
Utilities 3.0%
Construction 6.8%
Hotels and Restaurants 2.0%
Wholesale and Retail 10.4%
Transport and Communications 15.0%

Domestic Exports, 1988-1992

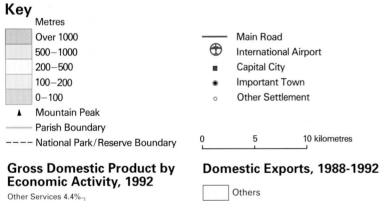

	Others
	Toilet and Laundry Soap
	Bananas

Million EC$

150

100

50

0

1988   1989   1990   1991   1992

Banana Production, 1988-1992

Thousand Tonnes

80

60

40

20

0

1988   1989   1990   1991   1992

Destination of Exports, 1990

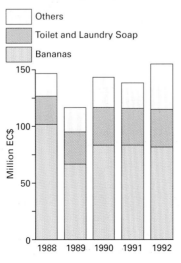

Other European Countries 7.2%
Other 0.6%
U.S.A. 9.7%
Other Caribbean Countries 7.8%
United Kingdom 49.4%
Rest of CARICOM 18.1%
OECS 7.2%

Tourist Arrivals, 1989-1993

	Stopover
	Cruises

Thousand Visitors

100

80

60

40

20

0

1989   1990   1991   1992   199

St. Lucia's economy is dominated by bananas with tourism and manufacturing also making significant contributions. Banana production has fluctuated in recent years, but output grew by 34% in 1992 to 133,000 tonnes bringing in earnings of EC$184 million, with the United Kingdom being the main market. Other important crops are coconuts, (including copra), cocoa, mangoes, root crops and vegetables.

Tourism is growing and provided earnings of EC$565 million in 1993, but with an occupancy rate of 68% in hotel rooms there is still room for expansion.

Total area: 616 sq.km.
Total population: 138 151 (1992)
Population density: 224 people per sq. km.

Nearly half of the people of St Lucia live in urban areas. The largest urban area is around the capital city Castries, (Population 51 994). Other important towns are Soufrière, Gros Islet and Vieux Fort. Castries was destroyed by fire in 1948, but was rebuilt as a planned, modern city in the 1950s.

Annual Rainfall

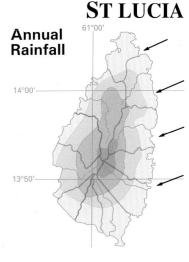

Key

Millimetres
- Over 3000
- 2500–3000
- 2000–2500
- Below 2000
- → Prevailing Winds

0   5   10   15   20 kilometres

Economic Activity

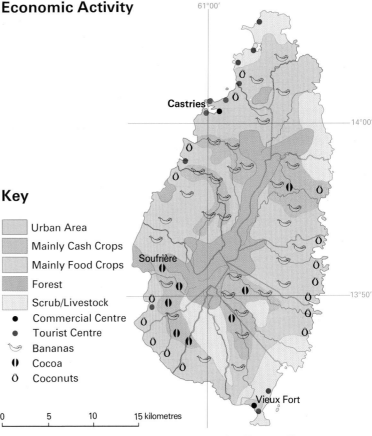

Key

- Urban Area
- Mainly Cash Crops
- Mainly Food Crops
- Forest
- Scrub/Livestock
- ● Commercial Centre
- ● Tourist Centre
- 🍌 Bananas
- ❮❯ Cocoa
- ᕮ Coconuts

0   5   10   15 kilometres

Key

Metres
- Over 500
- 200–500
- 100–200
- 0–100
- ▲ Mountain Peak
- Parish Boundary
- — Main Road

⊕ International Airport
■ Capital City
◉ Important Town
○ Other Settlement

0   5   10 kilometres

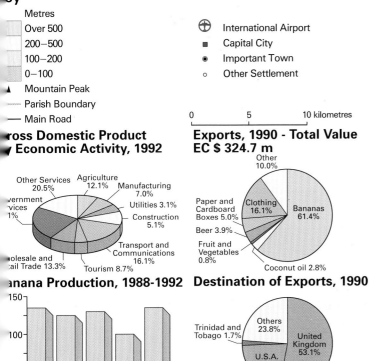

Gross Domestic Product by Economic Activity, 1992

- Other Services 20.5%
- Agriculture 12.1%
- Manufacturing 7.0%
- Utilities 3.1%
- Construction 5.1%
- Transport and Communications 16.1%
- Tourism 8.7%
- Wholesale and Retail Trade 13.3%
- Government Services ...1%

Exports, 1990 - Total Value EC $ 324.7 m

- Other 10.0%
- Clothing 16.1%
- Paper and Cardboard Boxes 5.0%
- Beer 3.9%
- Fruit and Vegetables 0.8%
- Coconut oil 2.8%
- Bananas 61.4%

Banana Production, 1988-1992

(bar chart: 1988, 1989, 1990, 1991, 1992; values approximately 135, 125, 130, 100, 135)

Destination of Exports, 1990

- Others 23.8%
- Trinidad and Tobago 1.7%
- United Kingdom 53.1%
- U.S.A. 21.4%

Tourist Arrivals, 1989-1993

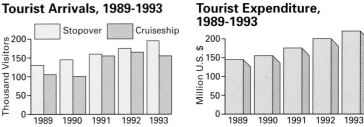

□ Stopover   ■ Cruiseship

Thousand Visitors
1989, 1990, 1991, 1992, 1993

Tourist Expenditure, 1989-1993

Million U.S. $
1989, 1990, 1991, 1992, 1993

ST VINCENT AND THE GRENADINES

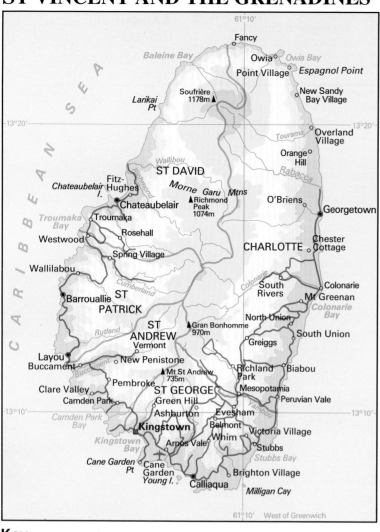

The economy of St.Vincent and the Grenadines is largely reliant on the production of bananas which provided earnings of over EC$98 million in 1992. The dismantling of preferential arrangements under the Lomé Convention though, makes the future of the industry uncertain and there is a drive towards diversification into other crops. Arrowroot, a major export in the mid 1980's, has seen a recovery in production in 1993 after several years of decline.

Total area: 389 sq.km.
Total population: 107 598 (1991)
Population density: 277 people per sq. km.

The capital city is Kingstown on the island of St. Vincent; its population is estimated to be about 15 670. Approximately 12 000 of the total population of the islands live on the Grenadines, the largest islands of which are Bequia, Mustique, Canouan, Mayreau and Union.

Annual Rainfall

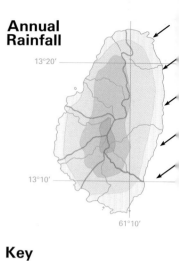

Key

Millimetres
- Over 3000
- 2500–3000
- 2000–2500
- Below 2000
- → Prevailing Winds

```
0    4    8    12    16 kilometres
```

Key

Metres
- Over 1000
- 500–1000
- 200–500
- 100–200
- 0–100
- ▲ Mountain Peak
- Parish Boundary

- —— Main Road
- ✈ Airport
- ▣ Capital City
- ◉ Important Town
- ○ Other Settlement

```
0    2    4    6    8 kilometres
```

Economic Activity

Key

- Urban Area
- Cotton
- Mainly Cash Crops
- Mainly Food Crops
- Forest
- ● Tourist Centre
- Arrowroot
- Bananas
- Cocoa
- Coconuts

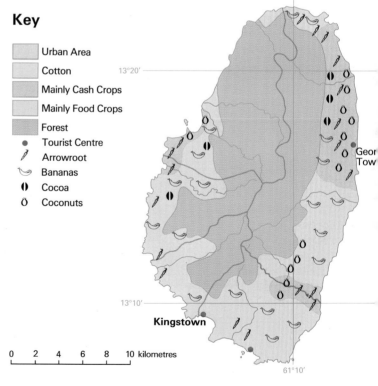

```
0    2    4    6    8    10 kilometres
```

Bequia

```
0    1    2    3    4    5 kilometres
```

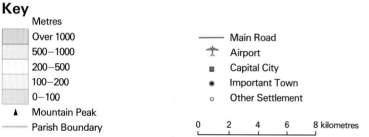

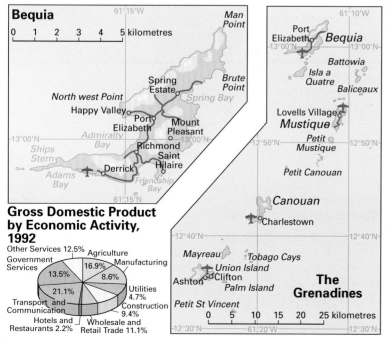

The Grenadines

```
0    5    10    15    20    25 kilometres
```

Gross Domestic Product by Economic Activity, 1992

Other Services 12.5%
Agriculture 16.9%
Manufacturing 8.6%
Utilities 4.7%
Construction 9.4%
Wholesale and Retail Trade 11.1%
Hotels and Restaurants 2.2%
Transport and Communication 21.1%
Government Services 13.5%

Banana Production, 1988 -1992

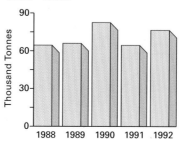

Thousand Tonnes

```
90

60

30

0
   1988  1989  1990  1991  1992
```

Exports, 1992 - Total Value EC $ 211.4m

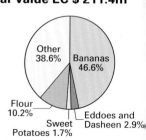

Other 38.6%
Bananas 46.6%
Flour 10.2%
Sweet Potatoes 1.7%
Eddoes and Dasheen 2.9%

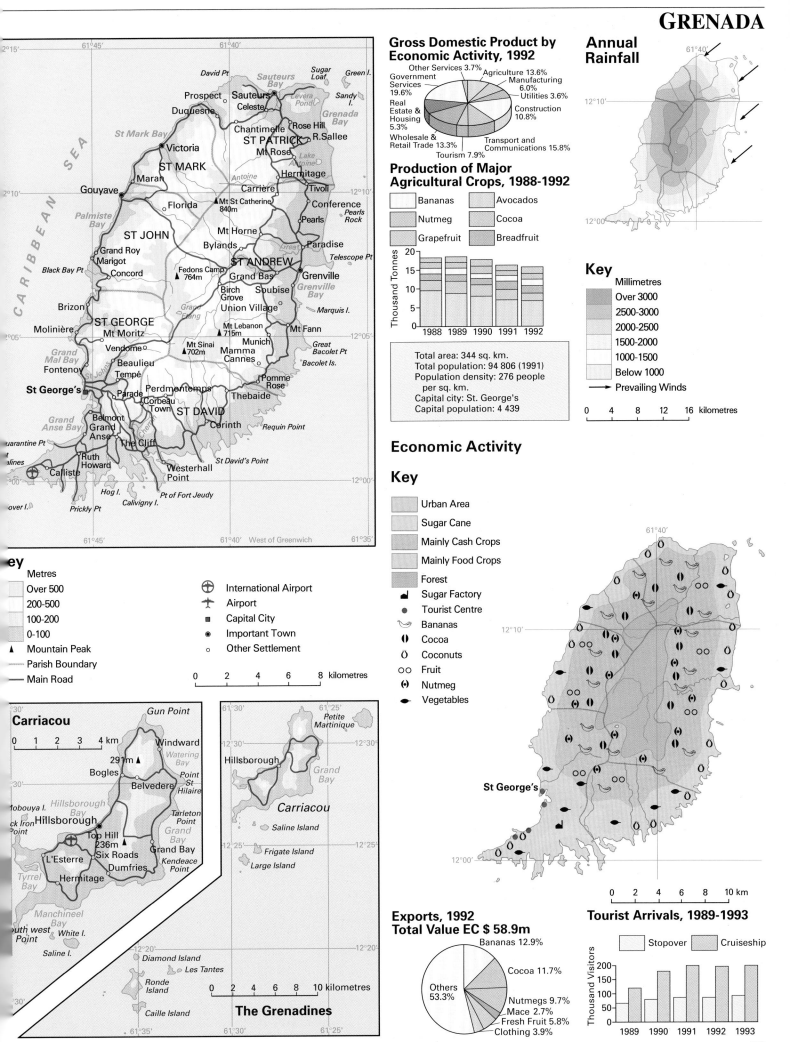

Gross Domestic Product by Economic Activity, 1992

- Other Services 3.7%
- Government Services 19.6%
- Real Estate & Housing 5.3%
- Wholesale & Retail Trade 13.3%
- Tourism 7.9%
- Transport and Communications 15.8%
- Construction 10.8%
- Utilities 3.6%
- Manufacturing 6.0%
- Agriculture 13.6%

Production of Major Agricultural Crops, 1988-1992

- Bananas
- Nutmeg
- Grapefruit
- Avocados
- Cocoa
- Breadfruit

Thousand Tonnes (0–20), years 1988, 1989, 1990, 1991, 1992

Total area: 344 sq. km.
Total population: 94 806 (1991)
Population density: 276 people per sq. km.
Capital city: St. George's
Capital population: 4 439

Annual Rainfall

Key
Millimetres
- Over 3000
- 2500-3000
- 2000-2500
- 1500-2000
- 1000-1500
- Below 1000
- → Prevailing Winds

0   4   8   12   16 kilometres

Key
Metres
- Over 500
- 200-500
- 100-200
- 0-100
- ▲ Mountain Peak
- Parish Boundary
- Main Road
- ⊕ International Airport
- ✈ Airport
- ■ Capital City
- ◉ Important Town
- ○ Other Settlement

0   2   4   6   8 kilometres

Economic Activity

Key
- Urban Area
- Sugar Cane
- Mainly Cash Crops
- Mainly Food Crops
- Forest
- Sugar Factory
- Tourist Centre
- Bananas
- Cocoa
- Coconuts
- Fruit
- Nutmeg
- Vegetables

0   2   4   6   8   10 km

Carriacou

0   1   2   3   4 km

The Grenadines

0   2   4   6   8   10 kilometres

Exports, 1992
Total Value EC $ 58.9m

- Bananas 12.9%
- Cocoa 11.7%
- Nutmegs 9.7%
- Mace 2.7%
- Fresh Fruit 5.8%
- Clothing 3.9%
- Others 53.3%

Tourist Arrivals, 1989-1993

- Stopover
- Cruiseship

Thousand Visitors (0–200), years 1989, 1990, 1991, 1992, 1993

BARBADOS

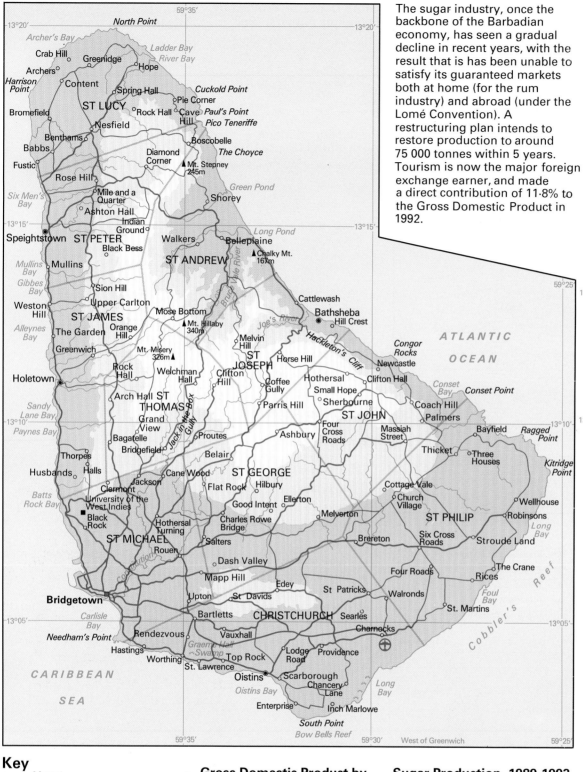

The sugar industry, once the backbone of the Barbadian economy, has seen a gradual decline in recent years, with the result that is has been unable to satisfy its guaranteed markets both at home (for the rum industry) and abroad (under the Lomé Convention). A restructuring plan intends to restore production to around 75 000 tonnes within 5 years. Tourism is now the major foreign exchange earner, and made a direct contribution of 11·8% to the Gross Domestic Product in 1992.

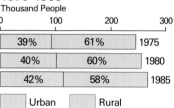

Total area: 430 sq. km.
Total population: 259 300 (1992)
Population density: 603 people per sq. km.
Bridgetown, the capital is the only town of any size and has a population of 7 516.

Urban/Rural Population, 1975-1985

Thousand People

39%	61%	1975
40%	60%	1980
42%	58%	1985

Urban   Rural

Annual Rainfa[ll]

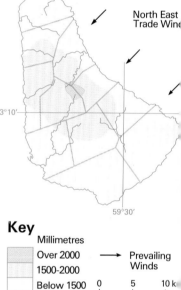

North East Trade Wind[s]

Key

Millimetres

Over 2000
1500-2000
Below 1500

Prevailing Winds

0   5   10 k[m]

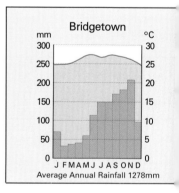

Bridgetown

Average Annual Rainfall 1278mm

Key

Metres

Over 200
100-200
0-100
▲ Mountain Peak
Swamp
Parish Boundary
Main Road
Other Road
⊕ International Airport
■ Capital City
◉ Important Town
○ Other Settlement

0   2   4   6 km

Gross Domestic Product by Economic Activity, 1992

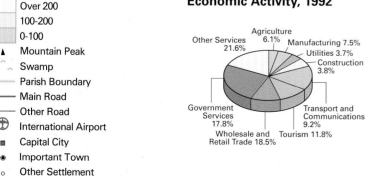

Agriculture 6.1%
Manufacturing 7.5%
Utilities 3.7%
Construction 3.8%
Transport and Communications 9.2%
Tourism 11.8%
Wholesale and Retail Trade 18.5%
Government Services 17.8%
Other Services 21.6%

Sugar Production, 1989-1993

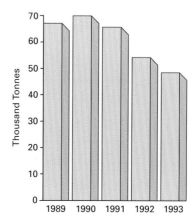

Thousand Tonnes

1989 1990 1991 1992 1993

Destination of Exports, 199[3]

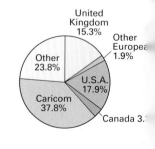

United Kingdom 15.3%
Other Europea[n] 1.9%
U.S.A. 17.9%
Canada 3.[%]
Caricom 37.8%
Other 23.8%

Population

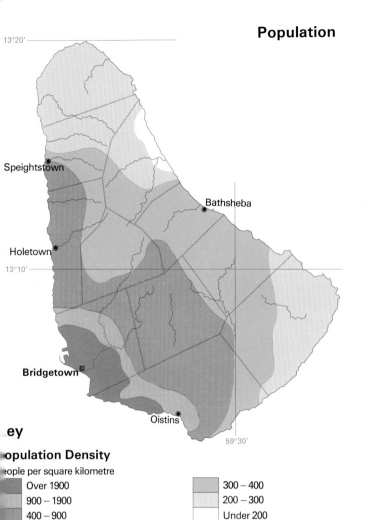

13°20'
13°10'
59°30'

Speightstown
Bathsheba
Holetown
Bridgetown
Oistins

Key

Population Density
people per square kilometre

Over 1900	300 – 400
900 – 1900	200 – 300
400 – 900	Under 200

Economic Activity

- ● Cement Factory
- ● Industrial Estate
- ⚒ Oil Field
- Sugar Factory
- Y Cattle
- V Sheep
- Vegetables
- Fishing

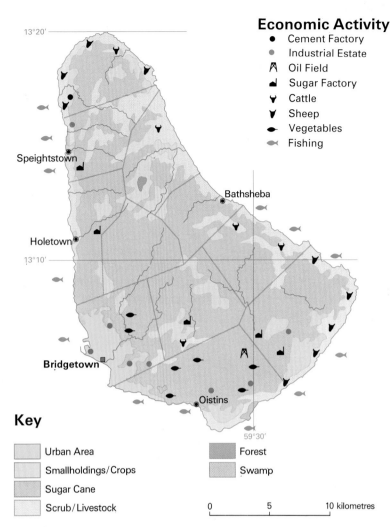

13°20'
Speightstown
Bathsheba
Holetown
13°10'
Bridgetown
Oistins
59°30'

Key

Urban Area	Forest
Smallholdings/Crops	Swamp
Sugar Cane	
Scrub/Livestock	

0   5   10 kilometres

Tourism

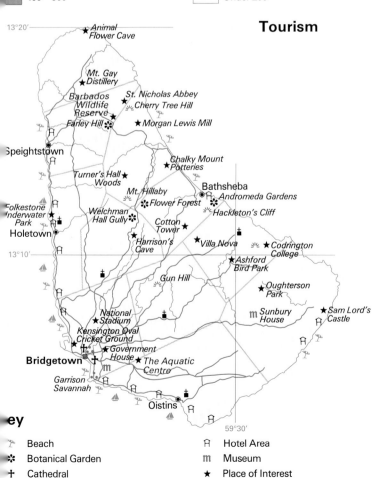

13°20'
Animal Flower Cave
Mt. Gay Distillery
Barbados Wildlife Reserve
St. Nicholas Abbey
Cherry Tree Hill
Farley Hill
Morgan Lewis Mill
Speightstown
Turner's Hall Woods
Chalky Mount Potteries
Mt. Hillaby
Flower Forest
Bathsheba
Andromeda Gardens
Hackleton's Cliff
Folkestone Underwater Park
Welchman Hall Gully
Cotton Tower
Holetown
Harrison's Cave
Villa Nova
Codrington College
13°10'
Ashford Bird Park
Gun Hill
Oughterson Park
National Stadium
Sunbury House
Sam Lord's Castle
Kensington Oval Cricket Ground
Government House
The Aquatic Centre
Bridgetown
Garrison Savannah
Oistins
59°30'

Key

Beach	Hotel Area
Botanical Garden	m Museum
† Cathedral	★ Place of Interest
Church	View Point
Historic Site	Watersports

Principal Exports and Imports

Exports by Commodity, 1993
Total Value BDS$ 272 242 000

| Sugar | Rum | | Chemicals | Electrical Components | Other Manufactures | Other |

Other Food & Beverages

Imports by Commodity, 1993
Total Value BDS$ 1 065 880 000

| Food and Beverages | | Other Manufactured Goods | | | | Machinery | Other |

Motor Cars   Fuels   Chemicals
Electrical Components   Construction Materials

Tourist Arrivals, 1989-1993

Stopover   Cruiseship

Thousand Visitors
500
400
300
200
100
0
1989 1990 1991 1992 1993

Origin of Tourists, 1993

Other CARICOM 9.2%
Other 5.0%
Trinidad and Tobago 4.0%
U.S.A. 28.5%
Other European 15.6%
Canada 12.4%
United Kingdom 25.3%

Tourist Expenditure, 1989-1993

Million U.S.$
600
500
400
300
200
100
0
1989 1990 1991 1992 1993

Tourist Accommodation, 1989-1993

The shaded area indicates the no. of rooms occupied

Number of Rooms
7000
6000
5000
4000
3000
2000
1000
0
1989 1990 1991 1992 1993

TRINIDAD AND TOBAGO

The economy of Trinidad and Tobago is dominated by petroleum, which contributed over 20% of the country's GDP in 1992 and over 60% of foreign exchange earnings. Production has gradually been falling though, and there have been no major oil discoveries since the early 1970's. Petrochemicals is another important earner of foreign exchange with production and export of methanol reaching record levels in 1992 and ammonia exports being the second largest in the world. Iron and steel is produced at Point Lisas by the Iron and Steel Company of Trinidad and Tobago (ISCOTT), but after experiencing marketing and production problems the sale of the plant to the Caribbean Ispat company was agreed in 1994.

Tourism is the country's largest untapped resource, but in 1993 a new state agency, The Tourism and Industrial Development Company of Trinidad and Tobago (TIDCO) was created to promote the opportunities.

Gross Domestic Product by Economic Activity, 1992

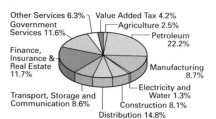

- Other Services 6.3%
- Value Added Tax 4.2%
- Government Services 11.6%
- Agriculture 2.5%
- Petroleum 22.2%
- Finance, Insurance & Real Estate 11.7%
- Manufacturing 8.7%
- Transport, Storage and Communication 8.6%
- Electricity and Water 1.3%
- Construction 8.1%
- Distribution 14.8%

Key

Metres
- Over 500
- 200-500
- 100-200
- 0-100
- ▲ Mountain Peak
- ● Pitch Lake
- Canal
- Swamp
- International Boundary

- Regional Corporation Boundary
- Main Road
- ⊕ International Airport
- ■ Capital City
- ◉ Important Town
- ○ Other Settlement
- Penal Main Administrative Area

Total area: 5 128 sq. km.
Total population: 1 169 572 (1990)
Population density: 228 people per sq. km.

The population of the capital city, Port of Spain is about 52 000. The most densely populated areas are in the north-west and west of Trinidad.

0 5 10 15 20 kilometres

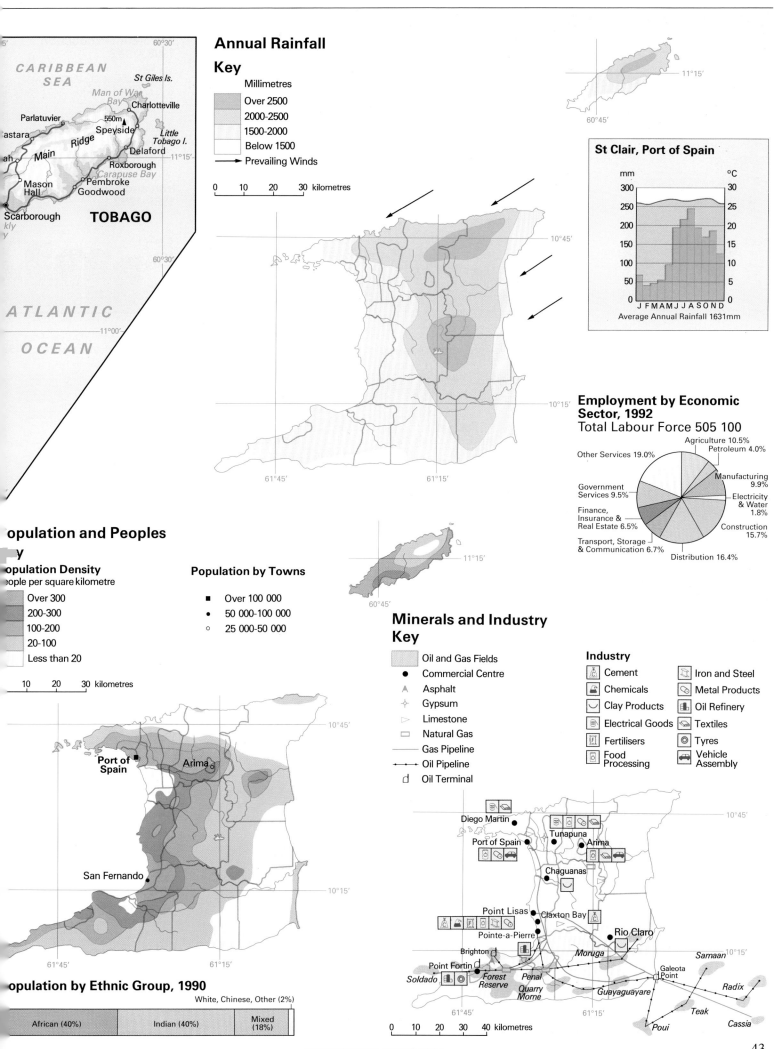

Annual Rainfall

Key

Millimetres
- Over 2500
- 2000-2500
- 1500-2000
- Below 1500
- → Prevailing Winds

0 10 20 30 kilometres

St Clair, Port of Spain

mm / °C chart, months J F M A M J J A S O N D

Average Annual Rainfall 1631mm

Employment by Economic Sector, 1992
Total Labour Force 505 100

- Agriculture 10.5%
- Petroleum 4.0%
- Manufacturing 9.9%
- Electricity & Water 1.8%
- Construction 15.7%
- Distribution 16.4%
- Transport, Storage & Communication 6.7%
- Finance, Insurance & Real Estate 6.5%
- Government Services 9.5%
- Other Services 19.0%

TOBAGO

- CARIBBEAN SEA
- St Giles Is.
- Man of War Bay
- Charlotteville
- Parlatuvier
- 550m
- Speyside
- Little Tobago I.
- Delaford
- Ridge
- Roxborough
- Carapuse Bay
- Main
- Pembroke
- Mason Hall
- Goodwood
- Scarborough
- ATLANTIC OCEAN

Population and Peoples

Key

Population Density
people per square kilometre
- Over 300
- 200-300
- 100-200
- 20-100
- Less than 20

10 20 30 kilometres

Population by Towns
- ■ Over 100 000
- ● 50 000-100 000
- ○ 25 000-50 000

- Port of Spain
- Arima
- San Fernando

Population by Ethnic Group, 1990

White, Chinese, Other (2%)

African (40%)	Indian (40%)	Mixed (18%)	

Minerals and Industry

Key

- Oil and Gas Fields
- ● Commercial Centre
- ⋏ Asphalt
- ✦ Gypsum
- ▷ Limestone
- ▭ Natural Gas
- — Gas Pipeline
- Oil Pipeline
- ⊐ Oil Terminal

Industry
- Cement
- Chemicals
- Clay Products
- Electrical Goods
- Fertilisers
- Food Processing
- Iron and Steel
- Metal Products
- Oil Refinery
- Textiles
- Tyres
- Vehicle Assembly

- Diego Martin
- Tunapuna
- Port of Spain
- Arima
- Chaguanas
- Point Lisas
- Claxton Bay
- Rio Claro
- Pointe-a-Pierre
- Brighton
- Moruga
- Samaan
- Point Fortin
- Galeota Point
- Soldado
- Forest Reserve
- Penal
- Radix
- Quarry Morne
- Guayaguayare
- Teak
- Cassia
- Poui

0 10 20 30 40 kilometres

43

TRINIDAD AND TOBAGO
Agriculture and Economic Activity

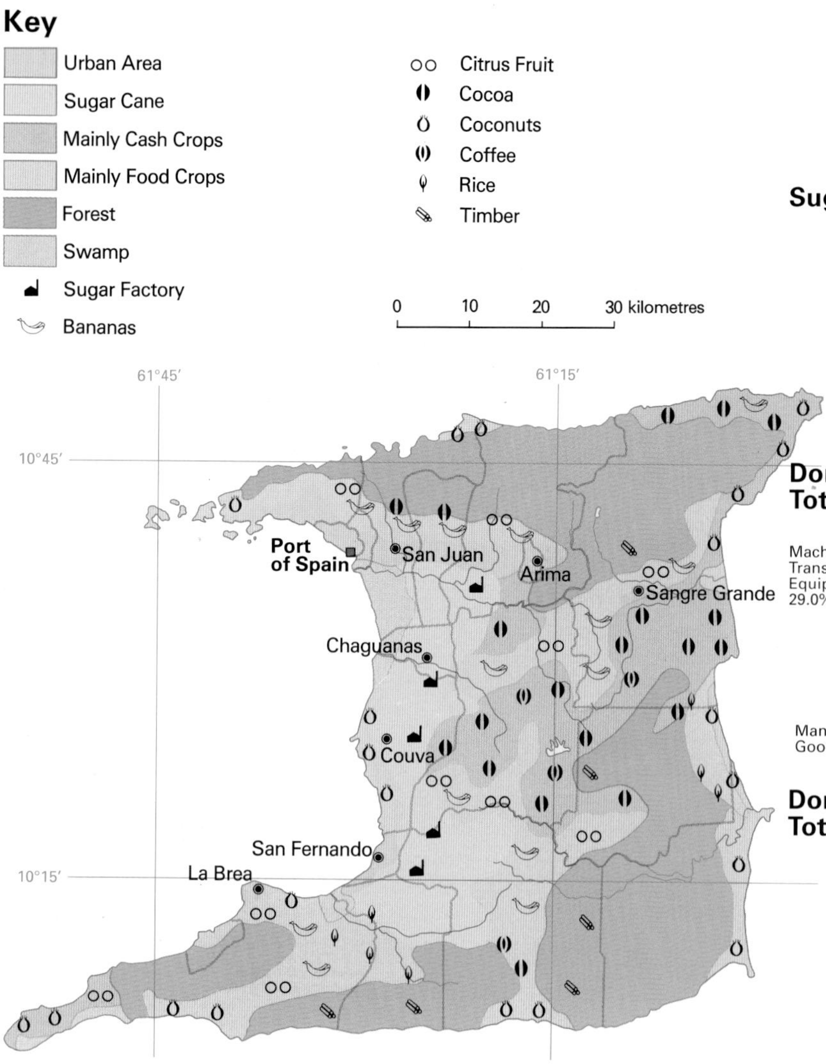

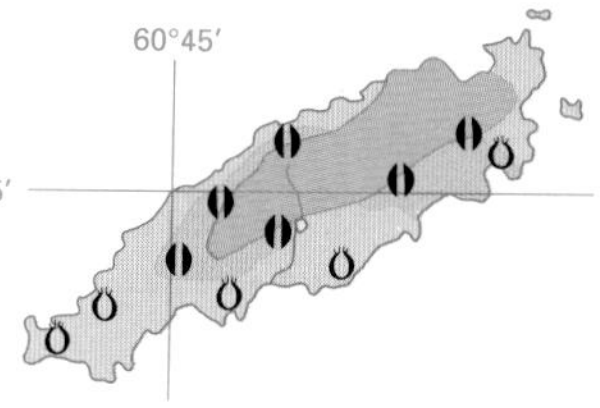

Key

- Urban Area
- Sugar Cane
- Mainly Cash Crops
- Mainly Food Crops
- Forest
- Swamp
- Sugar Factory
- Bananas

- ○○ Citrus Fruit
- ◑ Cocoa
- ◔ Coconuts
- ◉ Coffee
- ⚲ Rice
- ⬱ Timber

0 10 20 30 kilometres

Petroleum Production, 1988-1992

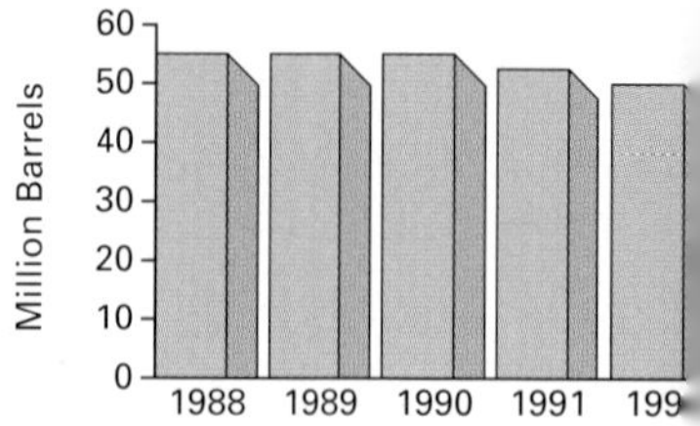

(bar chart, Million Barrels)
1988, 1989, 1990, 1991, 199[2]

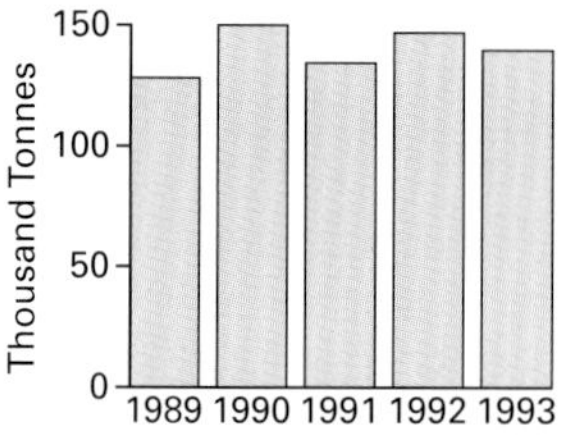

Iron and Steel Production, 1988-1992

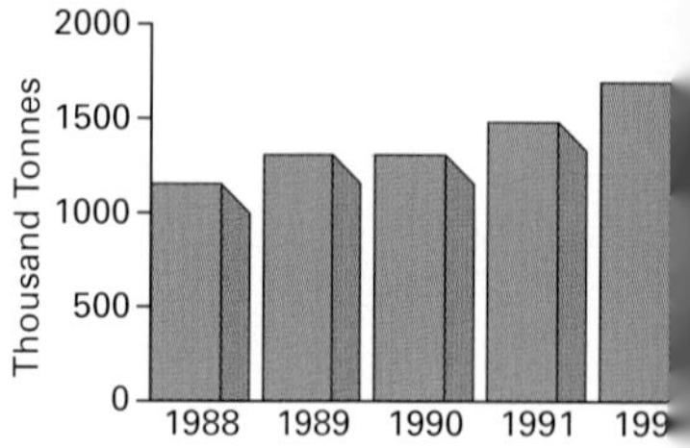

(bar chart, Thousand Tonnes)
1988, 1989, 1990, 1991, 199[2]

Sugar Production, 1989-1993

(bar chart, Thousand Tonnes)
1989, 1990, 1991, 1992, 1993

Domestic Imports, 1992
Total Value $TT 6081 million

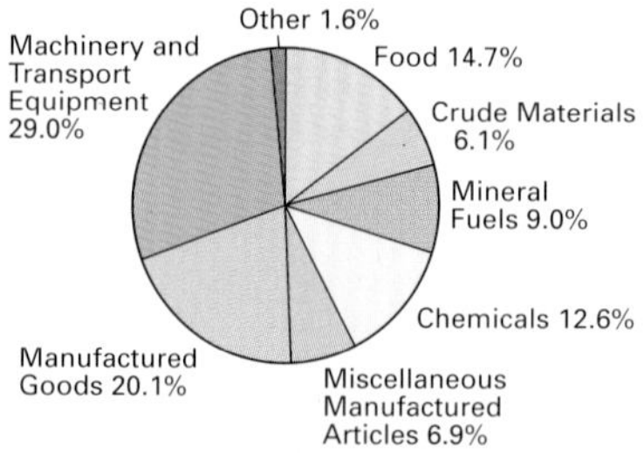

(pie chart)
- Other 1.6%
- Machinery and Transport Equipment 29.0%
- Food 14.7%
- Crude Materials 6.1%
- Mineral Fuels 9.0%
- Chemicals 12.6%
- Miscellaneous Manufactured Articles 6.9%
- Manufactured Goods 20.1%

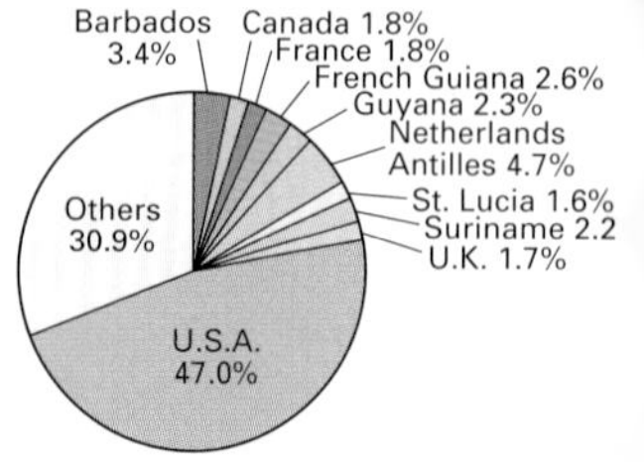

Domestic Exports, 1992
Total Value $TT 7812 million

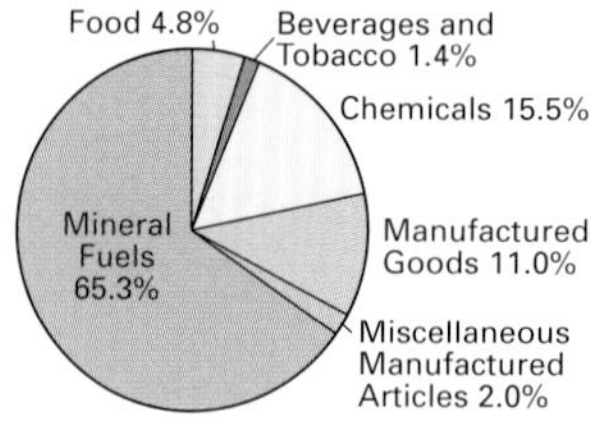

(pie chart)
- Food 4.8%
- Beverages and Tobacco 1.4%
- Chemicals 15.5%
- Manufactured Goods 11.0%
- Miscellaneous Manufactured Articles 2.0%
- Mineral Fuels 65.3%

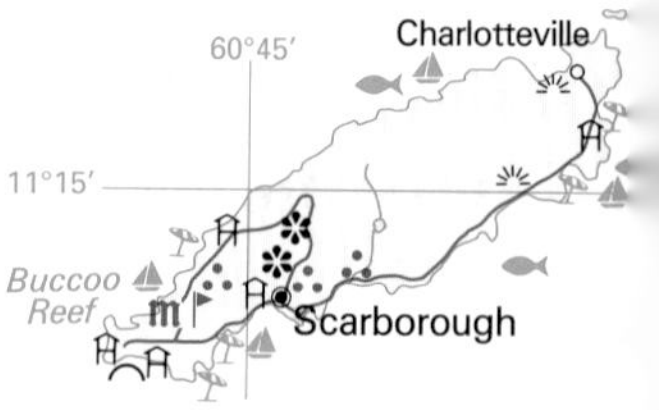

Destination of Exports, 1993

(pie chart)
- Barbados 3.4%
- Canada 1.8%
- France 1.8%
- French Guiana 2.6%
- Guyana 2.3%
- Netherlands Antilles 4.7%
- St. Lucia 1.6%
- Suriname 2.2
- U.K. 1.7%
- Others 30.9%
- U.S.A. 47.0%

(Map of Trinidad with place names: Port of Spain, San Juan, Arima, Sangre Grande, Chaguanas, Couva, San Fernando, La Brea)

(Map of Tobago with place names: Charlotteville, Buccoo Reef, Scarborough)

Tourist Arrivals, 1989-1993

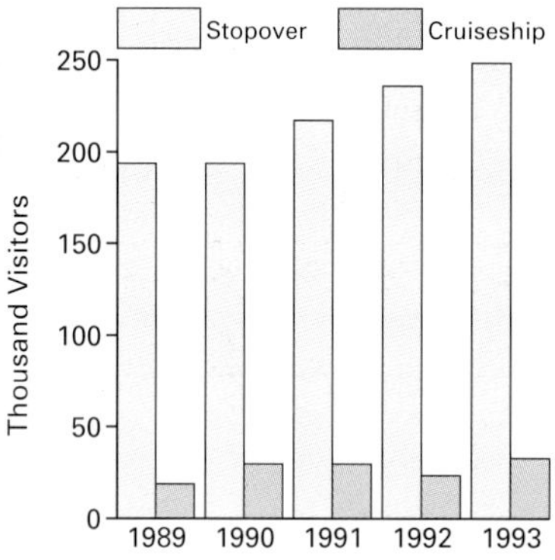

(bar chart, Thousand Visitors)
Stopover / Cruiseship
1989, 1990, 1991, 1992, 1993

Tourist Expenditure, 1989-1993

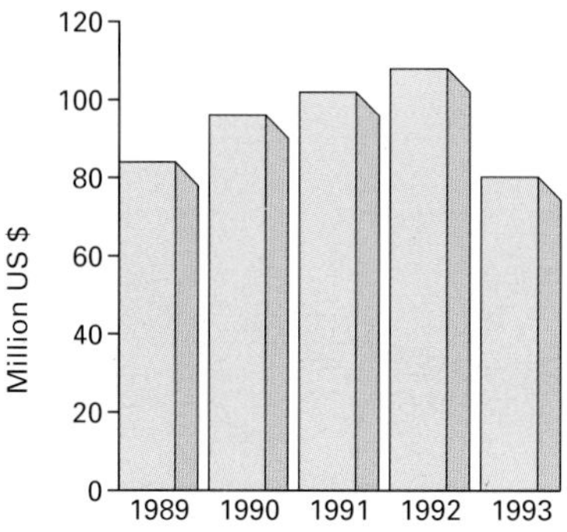

(bar chart, Million US $)
1989, 1990, 1991, 1992, 1993

Tourism

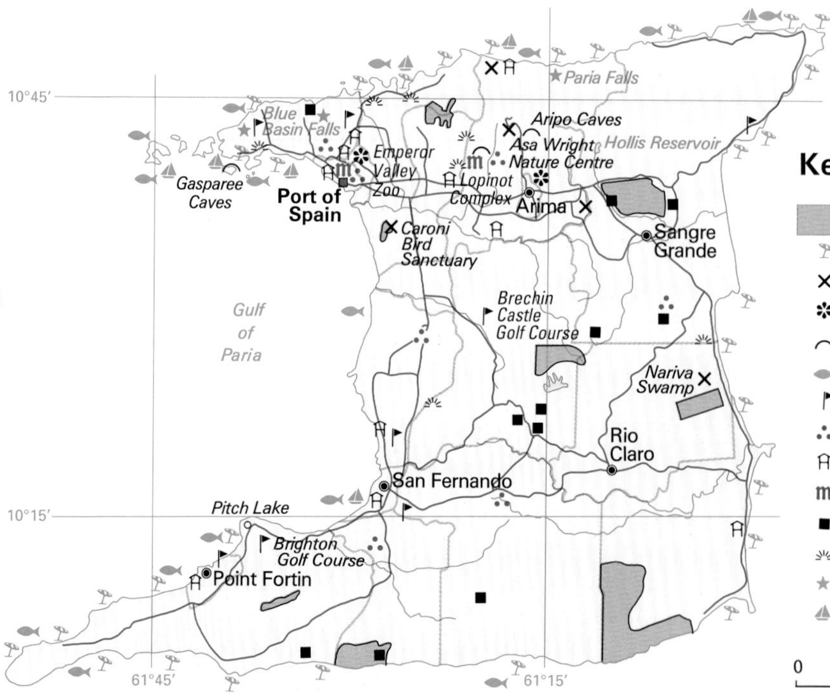

(Map of Trinidad showing tourism features with labels: Blue Basin Falls, Gasparee Caves, Emperor Valley Zoo, Port of Spain, Caroni Bird Sanctuary, Gulf of Paria, Paria Falls, Aripo Caves, Asa Wright Nature Centre, Hollis Reservoir, Lopinot Complex, Arima, Sangre Grande, Brechin Castle Golf Course, Nariva Swamp, Rio Claro, San Fernando, Pitch Lake, Brighton Golf Course, Point Fortin)

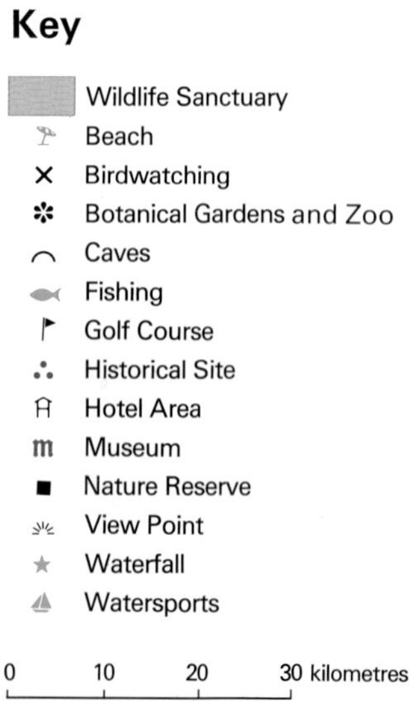

Origin of Tourists, 1993

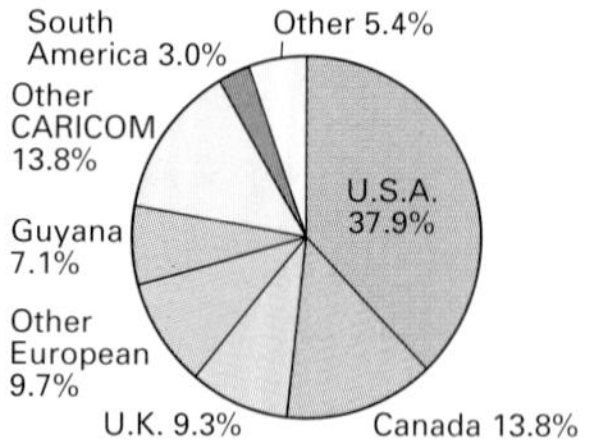

(pie chart)
- South America 3.0%
- Other 5.4%
- Other CARICOM 13.8%
- Guyana 7.1%
- Other European 9.7%
- U.K. 9.3%
- Canada 13.8%
- U.S.A. 37.9%

Key

- Wildlife Sanctuary
- Beach
- ✕ Birdwatching
- ✳ Botanical Gardens and Zoo
- ⌒ Caves
- Fishing
- ▸ Golf Course
- ∴ Historical Site
- ⌂ Hotel Area
- ɱ Museum
- ■ Nature Reserve
- View Point
- ★ Waterfall
- Watersports

0 10 20 30 kilometres

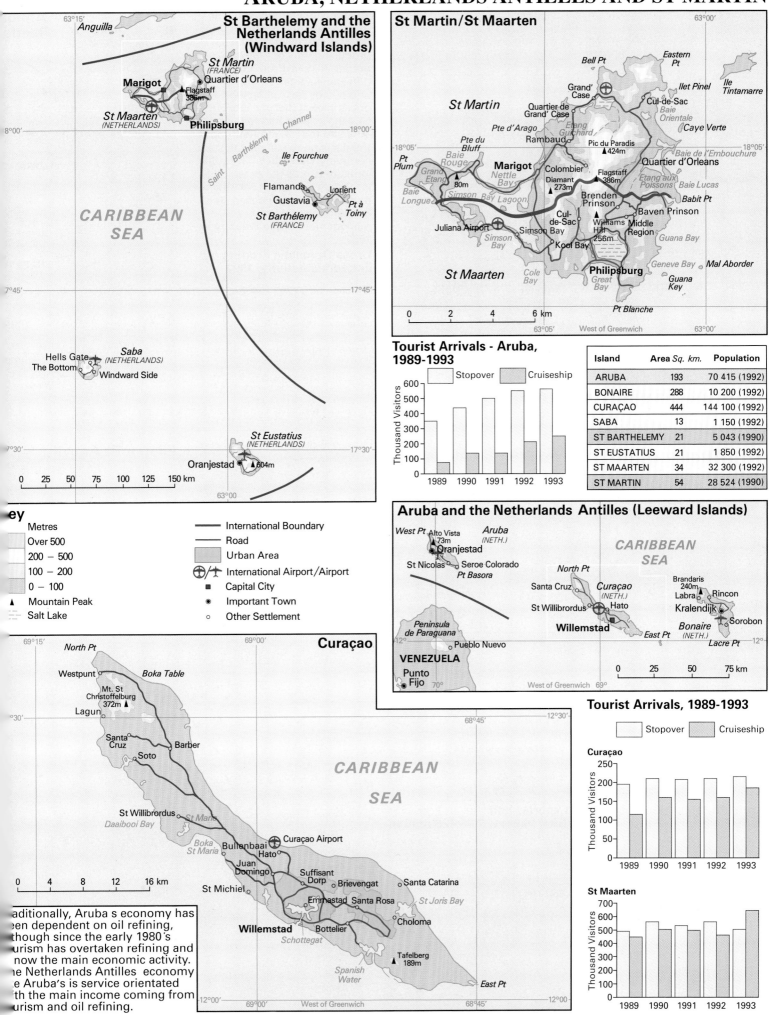

St Barthelemy and the Netherlands Antilles (Windward Islands)

Anguilla

St Martin (FRANCE)
Marigot
Quartier d'Orleans
Flagstaff 386m
St Maarten (NETHERLANDS)
Philipsburg

Saint Barthélemy Channel

Ile Fourchue

Flamands
Gustavia
Lorient
Pt à Toiny
St Barthélemy (FRANCE)

CARIBBEAN SEA

Hells Gate
The Bottom
Saba (NETHERLANDS)
Windward Side

St Eustatius (NETHERLANDS)
Oranjestad ▲604m

0 25 50 75 100 125 150 km

St Martin/St Maarten

Bell Pt
Eastern Pt
Ilet Pinel
Ile Tintamarre

St Martin
Grand' Case
Quartier de Grand' Case
Cul-de-Sac
Baie Orientale
Caye Verte

Pte d'Arago
Pte du Bluff
Rambaud
Etang Guichard
Pic du Paradis ▲424m
Baie de l'Embouchure

Pt Plum
Baie Rouge
Grand Etang ▲80m
Colombier
Diamant ▲273m
Flagstaff ▲386m
Quartier d'Orleans
Etang aux Poissons
Baie Lucas

Marigot
Nettle Bay
Baie Longue
Simson Bay Lagoon
Brenden Prinson
Babit Pt
Baven Prinson

Juliana Airport
Cul-de-Sac
Williams Hill ▲256m
Middle Region
Guana Bay

Simson Bay
Simson Bay
Kool Bay
Philipsburg
Mal Aborder

St Maarten
Cole Bay
Great Bay
Guana Key
Geneve Bay

Pt Blanche

0 2 4 6 km

63°05' West of Greenwich 63°00'

Tourist Arrivals - Aruba, 1989-1993

Stopover Cruiseship

Thousand Visitors
600 / 500 / 400 / 300 / 200 / 100 / 0
1989 1990 1991 1992 1993

Island	Area *Sq. km.*	Population
ARUBA	193	70 415 (1992)
BONAIRE	288	10 200 (1992)
CURAÇAO	444	144 100 (1992)
SABA	13	1 150 (1992)
ST BARTHELEMY	21	5 043 (1990)
ST EUSTATIUS	21	1 850 (1992)
ST MAARTEN	34	32 300 (1992)
ST MARTIN	54	28 524 (1990)

Aruba and the Netherlands Antilles (Leeward Islands)

West Pt
Alto Vista ▲73m
Oranjestad
Aruba (NETH.)

CARIBBEAN SEA

St Nicolas
Seroe Colorado
Pt Basora

North Pt
Santa Cruz
Curaçao (NETH.)
St Willibrordus
Hato
Willemstad
East Pt

Brandaris ▲240m
Labra ▲ Rincon
Kralendijk
Sorobon
Bonaire (NETH.)
Lacre Pt

Peninsula de Paraguana
Pueblo Nuevo
VENEZUELA
Punto Fijo

0 25 50 75 km

West of Greenwich 69°

Key

Metres
Over 500
200 – 500
100 – 200
0 – 100
▲ Mountain Peak
Salt Lake

International Boundary
Road
Urban Area
International Airport/Airport
■ Capital City
◉ Important Town
○ Other Settlement

Curaçao

North Pt
Westpunt
Boka Table
Mt. St Christoffelburg 372m ▲
Lagun
Santa Cruz
Barber
Soto
St Willibrordus
St Marie
Daaibooi Bay
Boka St Maria
Bullenbaai
Hato
Curaçao Airport
Juan Domingo
Suffisant Dorp
Brievengat
Santa Catarina
St Michiel
Emmastad
Santa Rosa
St Joris Bay
Willemstad
Bottelier
Choloma
Schottegat
Tafelberg ▲189m
Spanish Water
East Pt

0 4 8 12 16 km

Tourist Arrivals, 1989-1993

Stopover Cruiseship

Curaçao
Thousand Visitors
250 / 200 / 150 / 100 / 50 / 0
1989 1990 1991 1992 1993

St Maarten
Thousand Visitors
700 / 600 / 500 / 400 / 300 / 200 / 100 / 0
1989 1990 1991 1992 1993

Traditionally, Aruba's economy has been dependent on oil refining, though since the early 1980's tourism has overtaken refining and is now the main economic activity. The Netherlands Antilles economy like Aruba's is service orientated with the main income coming from tourism and oil refining.

GUYANA

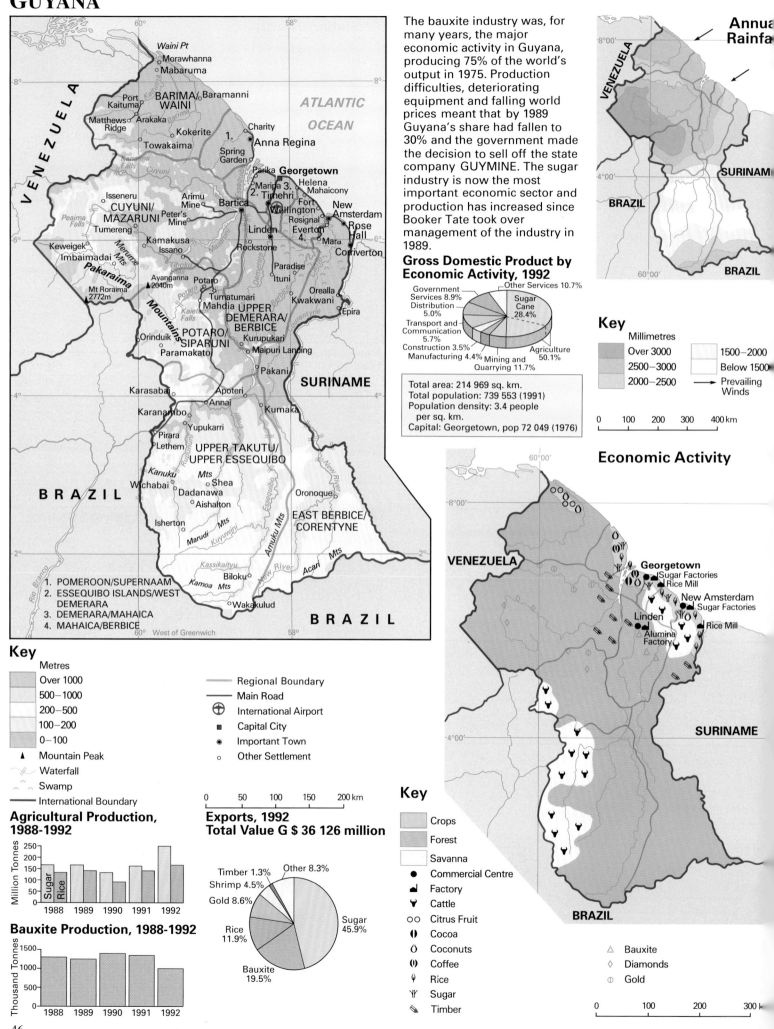

The bauxite industry was, for many years, the major economic activity in Guyana, producing 75% of the world's output in 1975. Production difficulties, deteriorating equipment and falling world prices meant that by 1989 Guyana's share had fallen to 30% and the government made the decision to sell off the state company GUYMINE. The sugar industry is now the most important economic sector and production has increased since Booker Tate took over management of the industry in 1989.

Map labels (political/physical map):

VENEZUELA
ATLANTIC OCEAN
Waini Pt
Morawhanna
Mabaruma
Baramanni
BARIMA/WAINI
Port Kaituma
Matthews Ridge
Arakaka
Kokerite
Towakaima
Charity
Anna Regina
Spring Garden
Parika
Georgetown
Marina
Timehri
Helena
Mahaicony
Isseneru
Arimu Mine
Bartica
Fort Wellington
New Amsterdam
Rose Hall
CUYUNI/MAZARUNI
Peter's Mine
Tumereng
Kamakusa
Issano
Linden
Rosignal
Everton
Mara
Corriverton
Rockstone
Keweigek
Imbaimadai
Pakaraima
Paradise
Ituni
Orealla
Kwakwani
Epira
Mt Roraima 2772m
Ayanganna 2040m
Potaro
Tumatumari
Mahdia
UPPER DEMERARA/BERBICE
Orinduik
POTARO/SIPARUNI
Kurupukari
Maipuri Landing
Paramakato
Pakani
SURINAME
Karasabai
Apoteri
Annai
Karanambo
Kumaka
Pirara
Yupukarri
Lethem
UPPER TAKUTU/UPPER ESSEQUIBO
Wichabai
Shea
Dadanawa
Aishalton
Oronoque
Isherton
Marudi Mts
EAST BERBICE/CORENTYNE
Biloku
Kamoa Mts
Wakakulud
BRAZIL
West of Greenwich

1. POMEROON/SUPERNAAM
2. ESSEQUIBO ISLANDS/WEST DEMERARA
3. DEMERARA/MAHAICA
4. MAHAICA/BERBICE

Gross Domestic Product by Economic Activity, 1992

Government Services 8.9%
Distribution 5.0%
Transport and Communication 5.7%
Construction 3.5%
Manufacturing 4.4%
Mining and Quarrying 11.7%
Agriculture 50.1%
Sugar Cane 28.4%
Other Services 10.7%

Total area: 214 969 sq. km.
Total population: 739 553 (1991)
Population density: 3.4 people per sq. km.
Capital: Georgetown, pop 72 049 (1976)

Annual Rainfa[ll]

Key
Millimetres
Over 3000
2500–3000
2000–2500
1500–2000
Below 1500
Prevailing Winds

0   100   200   300   400 km

Key
Metres
Over 1000
500–1000
200–500
100–200
0–100
▲ Mountain Peak
Waterfall
Swamp
International Boundary
Regional Boundary
Main Road
⊕ International Airport
■ Capital City
◉ Important Town
○ Other Settlement

0   50   100   150   200 km

Agricultural Production, 1988-1992

Million Tonnes
(bar chart 1988–1992: Sugar, Rice)

Bauxite Production, 1988-1992

Thousand Tonnes
(bar chart 1988, 1989, 1990, 1991, 1992)

Exports, 1992
Total Value G $ 36 126 million

Timber 1.3%
Shrimp 4.5%
Gold 8.6%
Rice 11.9%
Bauxite 19.5%
Sugar 45.9%
Other 8.3%

Economic Activity

VENEZUELA
Georgetown
Sugar Factories
Rice Mill
New Amsterdam
Sugar Factories
Linden
Rice Mill
Alumina Factory
SURINAME
BRAZIL

Key
Crops
Forest
Savanna
● Commercial Centre
⚒ Factory
🐂 Cattle
○○ Citrus Fruit
◖ Cocoa
◓ Coconuts
◔ Coffee
🌾 Rice
🌿 Sugar
🖋 Timber
△ Bauxite
◇ Diamonds
⊕ Gold

0   100   200   300 k[m]

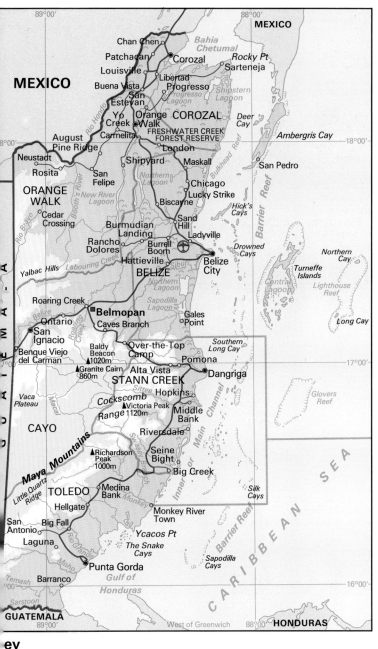

Agriculture is the dominant sector of the Belizean economy providing 67% of total foreign exchange earnings and employing 23% of the total labour force. Sugar is the most important crop and production has remained steady, while citrus fruit was processed into 2.1 million gallons of concentrate for export in 1994.

Gross Domestic Product by Economic Activity, 1994

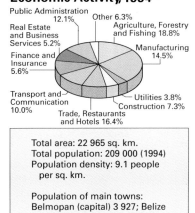

Public Administration 12.1%
Other 6.3%
Real Estate and Business Services 5.2%
Agriculture, Forestry and Fishing 18.8%
Finance and Insurance 5.6%
Manufacturing 14.5%
Transport and Communication 10.0%
Utilities 3.8%
Construction 7.3%
Trade, Restaurants and Hotels 16.4%

Total area: 22 965 sq. km.
Total population: 209 000 (1994)
Population density: 9.1 people per sq. km.

Population of main towns:
Belmopan (capital) 3 927; Belize City 48 655; Corozal 7 794; Orange Walk 12 155; Dangriga 7 103

Annual Rainfall

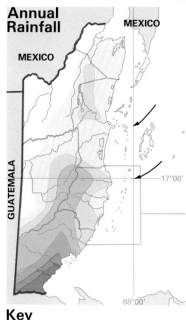

Key

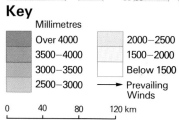

Millimetres
Over 4000
3500–4000
3000–3500
2500–3000
2000–2500
1500–2000
Below 1500
→ Prevailing Winds

0   40   80   120 km

Economic Activity

Key

Crops/Livestock
Forest
Swamp
● Commercial Centre
⬟ Factory
● Tourist Centre
🍌 Bananas
⬭ Beans
Y Cattle
ੴ Chicle
oo Citrus Fruit
◖ Cocoa
ᶁ Coconuts
⌂ Honey
⇑ Maize
φ Rice
Ψ Sugar
✎ Timber
🐟 Fishing

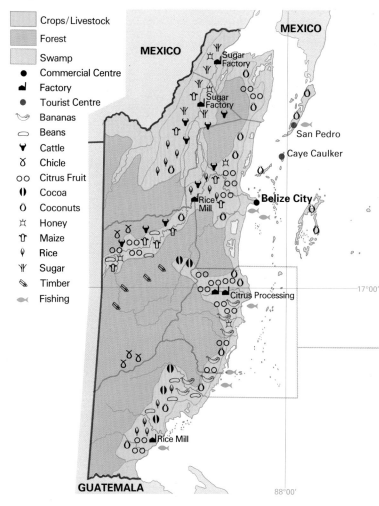

Key

Metres
Over 1000
500–1000
200–500
100–200
0–100
▲ Mountain Peak
⎍⎍⎍ Canal
Swamp
Coral Reef
— International Boundary
⋯⋯ District Boundary
— Main Road
— Other Road
⊕ International Airport
■ Capital City
⊙ Important Town
○ Other Settlement

0   20   40   60 km

Agricultural Production, 1990–1994

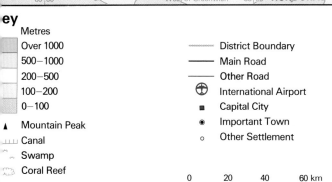

Citrus Fruit   Raw Sugar

160
120
80
40
0
1990 1991 1992 1993 1994

Domestic Exports, 1994
Total Value BZ $ 255.0 million

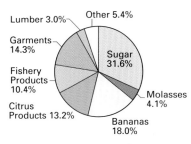

Lumber 3.0%
Other 5.4%
Garments 14.3%
Sugar 31.6%
Fishery Products 10.4%
Citrus Products 13.2%
Molasses 4.1%
Bananas 18.0%

0   20   40   60 km

TOWN PLANS – KINGSTON, BRIDGETOWN, PORT OF SPAIN AND BELMOPAN

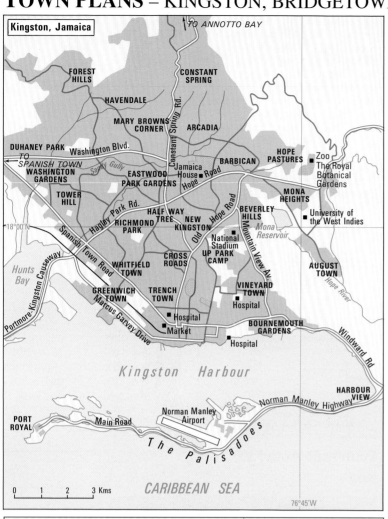

Kingston, Jamaica

TO ANNOTTO BAY

FOREST HILLS
CONSTANT SPRING
HAVENDALE
MARY BROWNS CORNER
ARCADIA
DUHANEY PARK
Washington Blvd.
TO SPANISH TOWN
WASHINGTON GARDENS
Constant Spring Rd.
Jamaica House
Hope Road
BARBICAN
HOPE PASTURES
Zoo
The Royal Botanical Gardens
EASTWOOD PARK GARDENS
TOWER HILL
Hagley Park Rd.
MONA HEIGHTS
BEVERLEY HILLS
HALF WAY TREE
RICHMOND PARK
NEW KINGSTON
Old Hope Road
Mona Reservoir
Mountain View Av.
University of the West Indies
18°00'N
Spanish Town Road
WHITFIELD TOWN
CROSS ROADS
National Stadium
UP PARK CAMP
AUGUST TOWN
Hunts Bay
Portmore-Kingston Causeway
GREENWICH TOWN
TRENCH TOWN
VINEYARD TOWN
Hope River
Marcus Garvey Drive
Hospital
Market
Hospital
BOURNEMOUTH GARDENS
Hospital
Windward Rd.
HARBOUR VIEW

Kingston Harbour

PORT ROYAL
Main Road
Norman Manley Airport
Norman Manley Highway
The Palisadoes
CARIBBEAN SEA

0   1   2   3 Kms

76°45'W

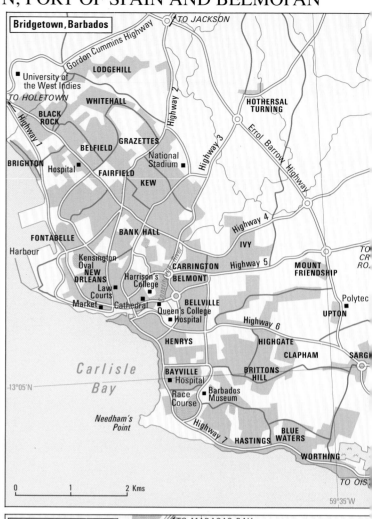

Bridgetown, Barbados

TO JACKSON
Gordon Cummins Highway
University of the West Indies
LODGEHILL
HOTHERSAL TURNING
TO HOLETOWN
WHITEHALL
BLACK ROCK
Highway 1
Highway 2
Highway 3
Errol Barrow Highway
BELFIELD
GRAZETTES
National Stadium
BRIGHTON
FAIRFIELD
Hospital
KEW
Highway 4
FONTABELLE
BANK HALL
IVY
Harbour
Kensington Oval
NEW ORLEANS
CARRINGTON
BELMONT
Highway 5
MOUNT FRIENDSHIP
TO CR RO.
Harrison's College
Law Courts
Market
Cathedral
Queen's College
BELLVILLE
Hospital
Polytec
UPTON
Highway 6
HENRYS
HIGHGATE
CLAPHAM
SARG
13°05'N
Carlisle Bay
BAYVILLE
Hospital
BRITTONS HILL
Race Course
Barbados Museum
Needham's Point
Highway 7
HASTINGS
BLUE WATERS
WORTHING
TO OIS
0   1   2 Kms
59°35'W

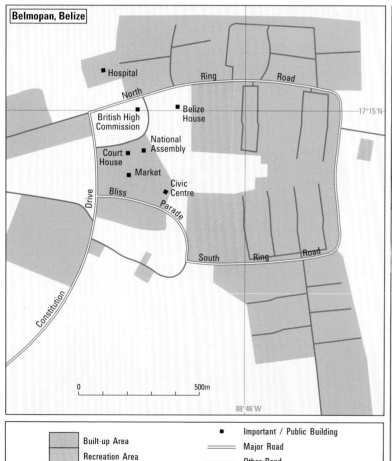

Belmopan, Belize

Hospital
Ring
Road
North
BELIZE House
British High Commission
17°15'N
Court House
National Assembly
Market
Civic Centre
Bliss
Parade
Drive
South
Ring
Road
Constitution
0   500m
88°46'W

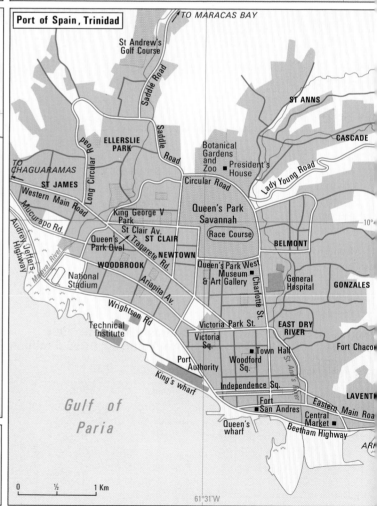

Port of Spain, Trinidad

TO MARACAS BAY
St Andrew's Golf Course
ST ANNS
Saddle Road
CASCADE
ELLERSLIE PARK
Saddle Road
Botanical Gardens and Zoo
President's House
TO CHAGUARAMAS
Long Circular Road
Circular Road
Lady Young Road
ST JAMES
Western Main Road
Mucurapo Rd.
King George V Park
Queen's Park Savannah
10°
Audrey Jeffers Highway
St Clair Av.
ST CLAIR
Race Course
BELMONT
Maraval River
Queen's Park Oval
Traqarete Rd.
NEWTOWN
Queen's Park West
WOODBROOK
Ariapita Av.
Museum & Art Gallery
General Hospital
GONZALES
National Stadium
Charlotte St.
Wrightson Rd.
Victoria Park St.
EAST DRY RIVER
Technical Institute
Victoria Sq.
Woodford Sq.
Fort Chaco
Town Hall
Port Authority
St Ann's River
King's wharf
Independence Sq.
Gulf of Paria
Fort San Andres
Queen's wharf
Central Market
LAVENT
Eastern Main Roa
Beetham Highway
ARI
0   ½   1 Km
61°31'W

Legend

▨ Built-up Area	■ Important / Public Building	
▨ Recreation Area	══ Major Road	
⌁ Marsh	── Other Road	
	── Railway	

CENTRAL AMERICA – PHYSICAL AND POLITICAL

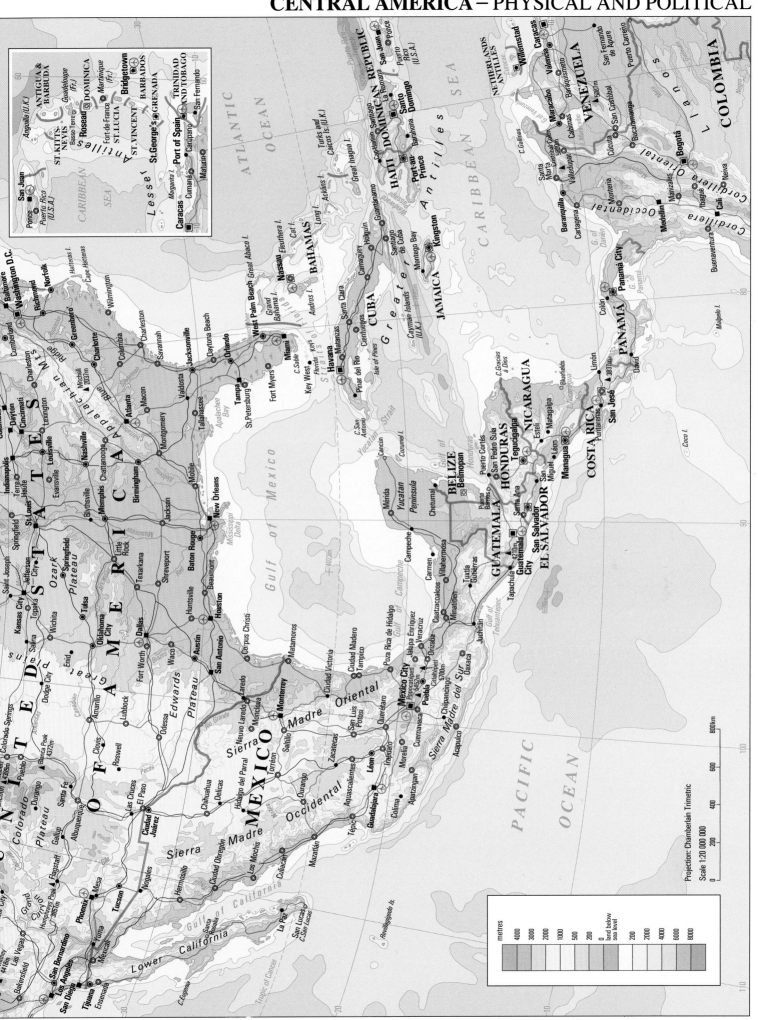

Inset map (Lesser Antilles):

Anguilla (U.K.), San Juan, Puerto Rico (U.S.A.), Ponce, ANTIGUA & BARBUDA, Guadeloupe (Fr.), ST. KITTS NEVIS, DOMINICA, Roseau, Basse-Terre, Fort-de-France, Martinique (Fr.), ST. LUCIA, ST. VINCENT, Bridgetown, BARBADOS, St. George's, GRENADA, TRINIDAD AND TOBAGO, Port of Spain, San Fernando, Margarita I., Cumaná, Carúpano, Maturín, Caracas, Lesser Antilles, CARIBBEAN SEA, ATLANTIC OCEAN

Main map labels:

UNITED STATES OF AMERICA

Baltimore, Washington D.C., Norfolk, Cumberland, Richmond, Greensboro, Charlotte, Wilmington, Hatteras I., Cape Hatteras, Dayton, Cincinnati, Indianapolis, Lexington, Mitchell 2037m, Appalachian Mts, Blue Ridge, Charleston, Columbia, Savannah, Jacksonville, Daytona Beach, Orlando, Springfield, St. Louis, Terre Haute, Louisville, Nashville, Chattanooga, Atlanta, Macon, Valdosta, Tallahassee, Montgomery, Saint Joseph, Jefferson City, Springfield, Ozark Plateau, Kansas City, Topeka, Wichita, Salina, Tulsa, Oklahoma City, Little Rock, Memphis, Birmingham, Mobile, Pensacola, Tampa, St. Petersburg, Fort Myers, Apalachee Bay, West Palm Beach, Miami, Key West, Florida Keys, C. Sable, Dodge City, Enid, Jackson, Baton Rouge, Shreveport, Beaumont, New Orleans, Mississippi Delta, Amarillo, Lubbock, Wichita Falls, Fort Worth, Dallas, Waco, Austin, Huntsville, Houston, Corpus Christi, Odessa, Edwards Plateau, San Antonio, Laredo, Nuevo Laredo, Great Plains, Colorado Springs, Pueblo, Blanca Peak 4372m, Roswell, Clovis, Santa Fe, Albuquerque, Las Cruces, El Paso, Ciudad Juárez, Carlsbad, Pecos, Rio Grande, Gila, Amistad, Denver, Grand Junction, Humphreys Peak 3851m, Flagstaff, Phoenix, Mesa, Tucson, Nogales, Mexicali, Tijuana, San Diego, San Bernardino, Los Angeles, Bakersfield, Las Vegas, Cerro 4418m

MEXICO

Chihuahua, Delicias, Hidalgo del Parral, Durango, Hermosillo, Ciudad Obregón, Los Mochis, Culiacán, Mazatlán, La Paz, San Lucas, C. San Lucas, Santa Rosalía, C. Eugenia, Lower California, Gulf of California, Sierra Madre Occidental, Torreón, Monclova, Saltillo, Monterrey, Matamoros, Ciudad Victoria, Ciudad Madero, Tampico, Zacatecas, San Luis Potosí, Aguascalientes, León, Guadalajara, Tepic, Colima, Guanajuato, Querétaro, Morelia, Irapuato, Apatzingán, Poza Rica de Hidalgo, Jalapa Enríquez, Veracruz, Orizaba, 5700m, Catemaco, Mexico City, Puebla, Cuernavaca, Chilpancingo, Acapulco, Oaxaca, Sierra Madre Oriental, Sierra Madre del Sur, Coatzacoalcos, Minatitlán, Villahermosa, Carmen, Campeche, Gulf of Campeche, 4052m, Juchitán, Tuxtla Gutiérrez, Gulf of Tehuantepec, Tapachula, Mérida, Yucatan Peninsula, Chetumal, Cancún, Cozumel I., Yucatan Strait

GULF OF MEXICO

BAHAMAS — Nassau, Grand Bahama I., Great Abaco I., Eleuthera I., Cat I., Andros I., Long I., Acklins I., Great Inagua I., Crooked I., San Salvador I., Turks and Caicos Is. (U.K.)

CUBA — Havana, Pinar del Río, Matanzas, Cienfuegos, Santa Clara, Isle of Pines, Camagüey, Holguín, Santiago de Cuba, Guantánamo, C. San Antonio, Florida Straits

JAMAICA — Kingston, Montego Bay, Cayman Islands (U.K.)

HAITI — Port-au-Prince, DOMINICAN REPUBLIC — Santo Domingo, Santiago, Cap-Haïtien, La Romana, Barahona, Windward Passage, Mona Passage

PUERTO RICO (U.S.A.) — San Juan, Ponce

Greater Antilles, Antilles, CARIBBEAN SEA

NETHERLANDS ANTILLES — Willemstad, Curaçao

BELIZE — Belmopan, Puerto Barrios

GUATEMALA — Guatemala City, 4211m

EL SALVADOR — San Salvador, Santa Ana, San Miguel

HONDURAS — Tegucigalpa, San Pedro Sula, Puerto Cortés, C. Gracias à Dios

NICARAGUA — Managua, León, Estelí, Matagalpa, Bluefields, L. Nicaragua

COSTA RICA — San José, Puntarenas, Limón, 3837m

PANAMA — Panamá City, Colón, David, G. of Panamá, G. of Darién, Coco I.

VENEZUELA — Caracas, Valencia, Maracaibo, Barquisimeto, L. de Valencia, San Fernando de Apure, San Cristóbal, Cúcuta, Puerto Carreño, G. of Venezuela, C. Gallinas, Santa Marta, Barranquilla, Cartagena

COLOMBIA — Bogotá, Medellín, Cali, Manizales, Ibagué, Neiva, Buenaventura, Bucaramanga, Valledupar, Montería, Cúcuta, Cordillera Occidental, Cordillera Oriental, LLANOS, Malpelo I., R. Negro, Magdalena

PACIFIC OCEAN, ATLANTIC OCEAN, Tropic of Cancer, Revillagigedo Is.

Projection: Chamberlain Trimetric
Scale 1:20 000 000

Scale 0 200 400 600 800km

Legend: metres — 4000, 3000, 2000, 1000, 500, 200, 0 land below sea level, 200, 2000, 4000, 6000, 8000

NORTH AMERICA – PHYSICAL AND POLITICAL

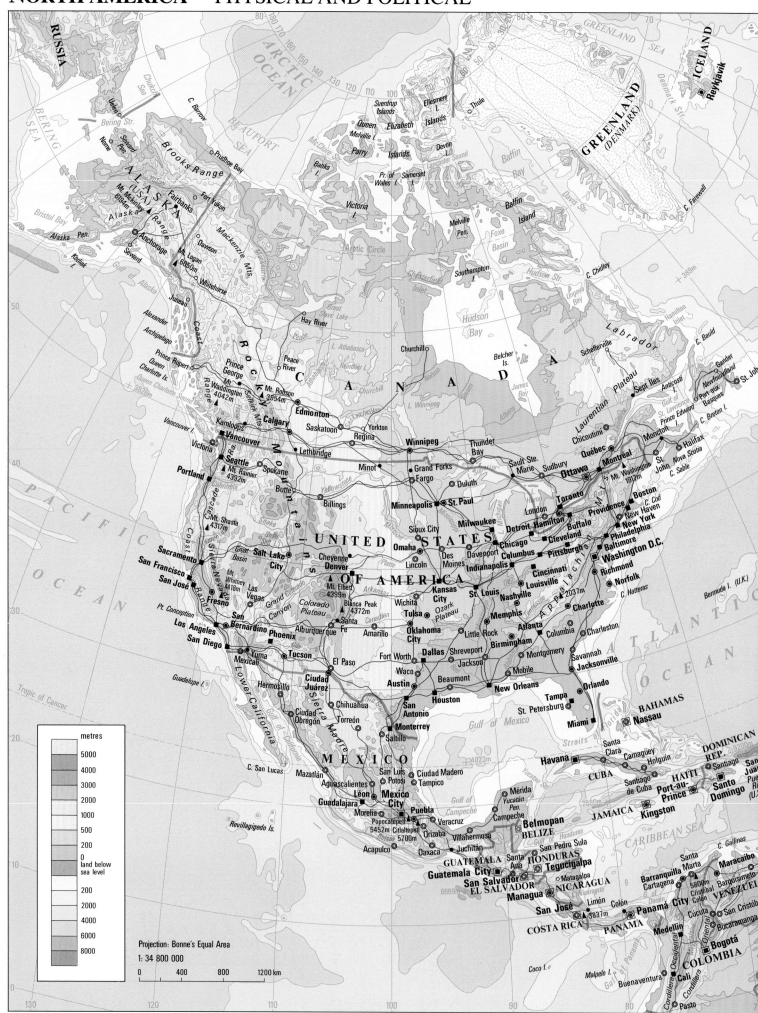

metres	
5000	
4000	
3000	
2000	
1000	
500	
200	
0	land below
	sea level
200	
2000	
4000	
6000	
8000	

Projection: Bonne's Equal Area

1: 34 800 000

0   400   800   1200 km

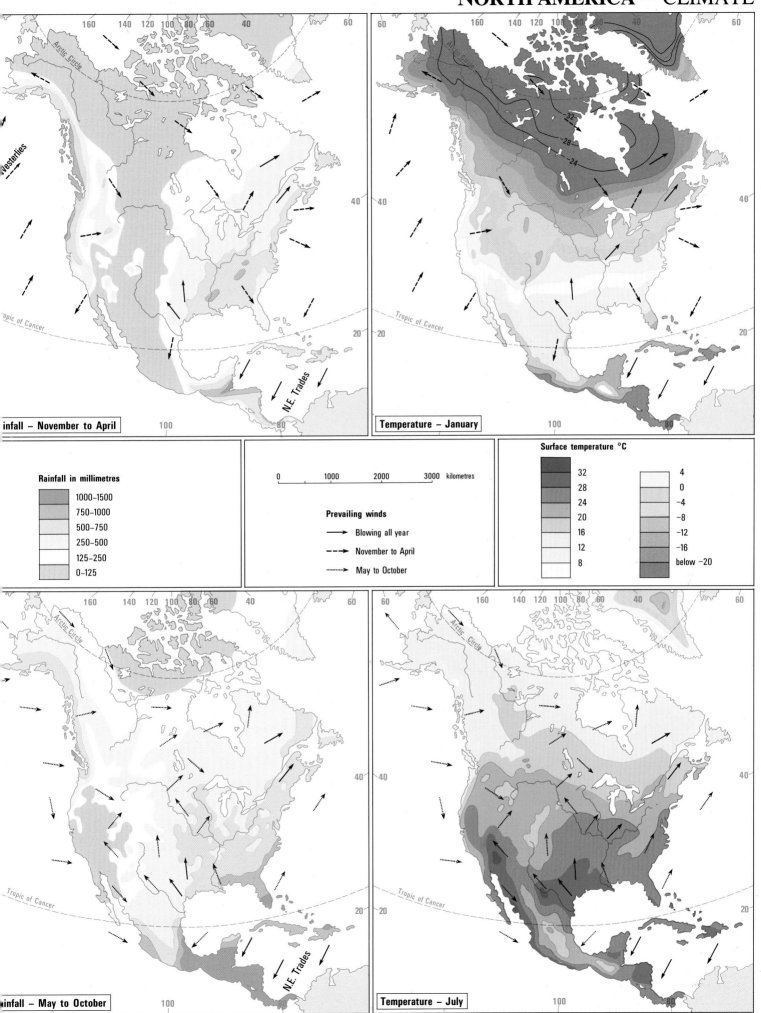

Westerlies

Tropic of Cancer

N.E. Trades

infall – November to April

Temperature – January

160 140 120 100 80 60 40 60

32
28
24

40 40

Tropic of Cancer

20 20

100 80

Rainfall in millimetres

1000–1500
750–1000
500–750
250–500
125–250
0–125

0   1000   2000   3000 kilometres

Prevailing winds

——→ Blowing all year
– – → November to April
······→ May to October

Surface temperature °C

32	4
28	0
24	−4
20	−8
16	−12
12	−16
8	below −20

Arctic Circle

Tropic of Cancer

N.E. Trades

infall – May to October

Temperature – July

NORTH AMERICA – LAND COVER

Land cover maps show a combination of natural vegetation and land use, ie how humans have affected the natural environment with their farming techniques. See also the World Natural Vegetation M.

Projection: Bonne's Equal Area
1:34 800 000

0   400   800   1200 km

Cultivated land	Forest and woodland
Cultivated land and grassland	Grassland
Cultivated land and woodland	Swamp and marsh
Scrub and sparse grassland	
Tundra	
Barren land (including permanent ice)	

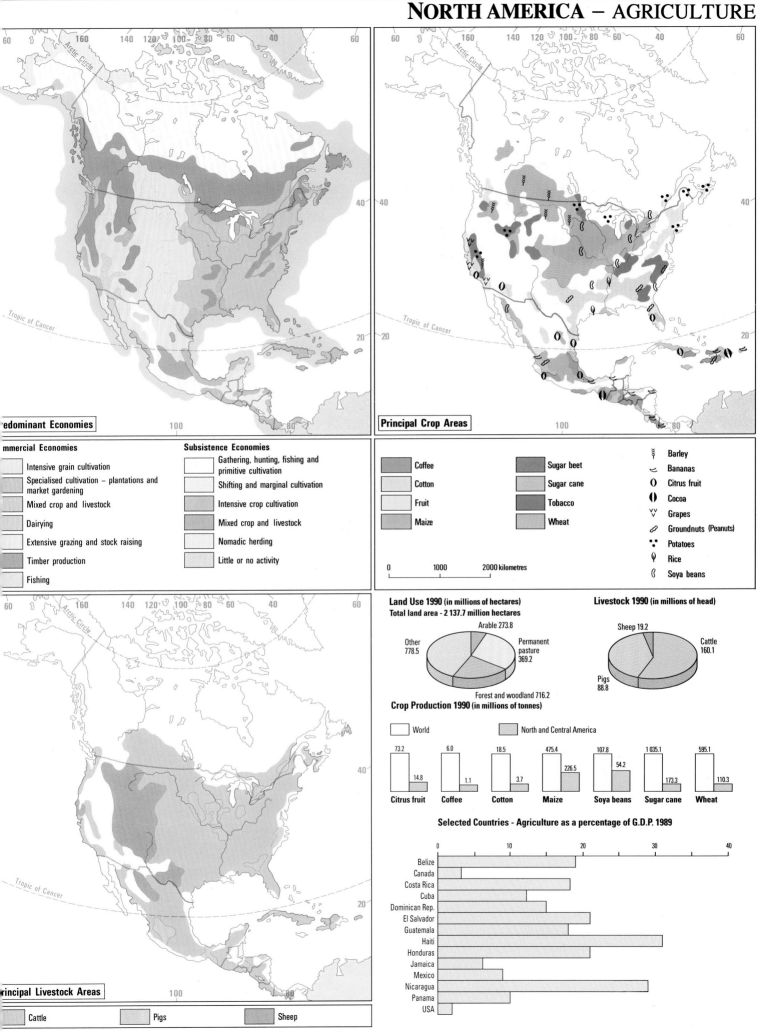

Predominant Economies

Commercial Economies

- Intensive grain cultivation
- Specialised cultivation – plantations and market gardening
- Mixed crop and livestock
- Dairying
- Extensive grazing and stock raising
- Timber production
- Fishing

Subsistence Economies

- Gathering, hunting, fishing and primitive cultivation
- Shifting and marginal cultivation
- Intensive crop cultivation
- Mixed crop and livestock
- Nomadic herding
- Little or no activity

Principal Crop Areas

- Coffee
- Cotton
- Fruit
- Maize
- Sugar beet
- Sugar cane
- Tobacco
- Wheat

- Barley
- Bananas
- O Citrus fruit
- Cocoa
- Grapes
- Groundnuts (Peanuts)
- Potatoes
- Rice
- Soya beans

0   1000   2000 kilometres

Principal Livestock Areas

- Cattle
- Pigs
- Sheep

Land Use 1990 (in millions of hectares)
Total land area - 2 137.7 million hectares

- Other 778.5
- Arable 273.8
- Permanent pasture 369.2
- Forest and woodland 716.2

Livestock 1990 (in millions of head)

- Sheep 19.2
- Cattle 160.1
- Pigs 88.8

Crop Production 1990 (in millions of tonnes)

- World
- North and Central America

Crop	World	North and Central America
Citrus fruit	73.2	14.8
Coffee	6.0	1.1
Cotton	18.5	3.7
Maize	475.4	226.5
Soya beans	107.8	54.2
Sugar cane	1 035.1	173.3
Wheat	595.1	110.3

Selected Countries - Agriculture as a percentage of G.D.P. 1989

0   10   20   30   40

- Belize
- Canada
- Costa Rica
- Cuba
- Dominican Rep.
- El Salvador
- Guatemala
- Haiti
- Honduras
- Jamaica
- Mexico
- Nicaragua
- Panama
- USA

53

NORTH AMERICA – MINERALS AND INDUSTRY

Energy
Arctic Circle
Tropic of Cancer
Prudhoe Bay (Oil & Gas)
Parma (Gas)
Medicine Hat (Gas)
Elliot Lake (Uranium)
Appalachian Basin (Coal, Oil & Gas)
Panhandle (Gas)
Monroe (Gas)
60
160
140
120
100
80
60
40
60
40
40
20
20
100
80

Iron Ore, Ferro-Alloys and Steel
Arctic Circle
Tropic of Cancer
Mesabi Range (Iron Ore)
Chicago (Steel)
Pittsburgh (Steel)
60
160
140
120
100
80
60
40
60
40
20
100
80

Energy:
- Coal
- Natural gas
- Oil
- Uranium
- H.E.P. station
- Nuclear power station

0 1000 2000 3000km

Iron Ore, Ferro-Alloys and Steel:
- Chrome
- Cobalt
- Iron ore
- Manganese
- Molybdenum
- Nickel
- Steel
- Tungsten
- Vanadium

Other Minerals
Arctic Circle
Tropic of Cancer
Pine Point (Silver, Lead & Zinc)
Pinchi Lake (Mercury)
Kimberley (Silver, Lead & Zinc)
Coeur d'Alene (Silver, Lead & Zinc)
Bingham (Copper)
Morenci (Copper)
Sudbury (Copper, Nickel & Platinum)
Jamaica (Bauxite)
60
160
140
120
100
80
60
40
60
40
40
20
20
100
80

Value of Mineral and Industrial Production
Arctic Circle
Tropic of Cancer
Montréal
Toronto
Detroit
Chicago
Pittsburgh
St. Louis
New York
Philadelphia
Baltimore
Los Angeles
New Orleans
Houston
60
160
140
120
100
80
60
40
60
40
20
80

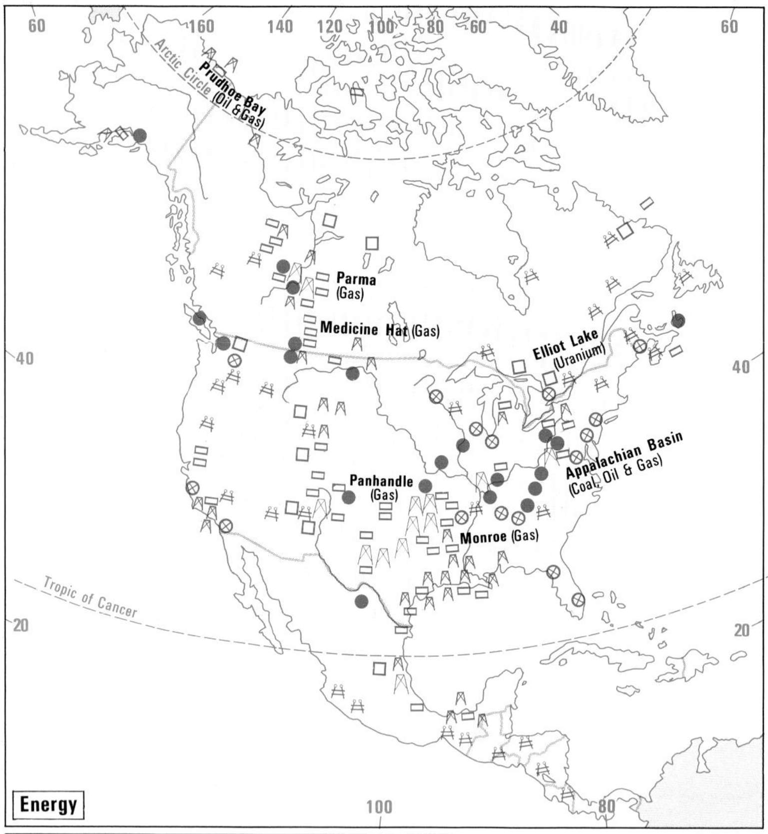

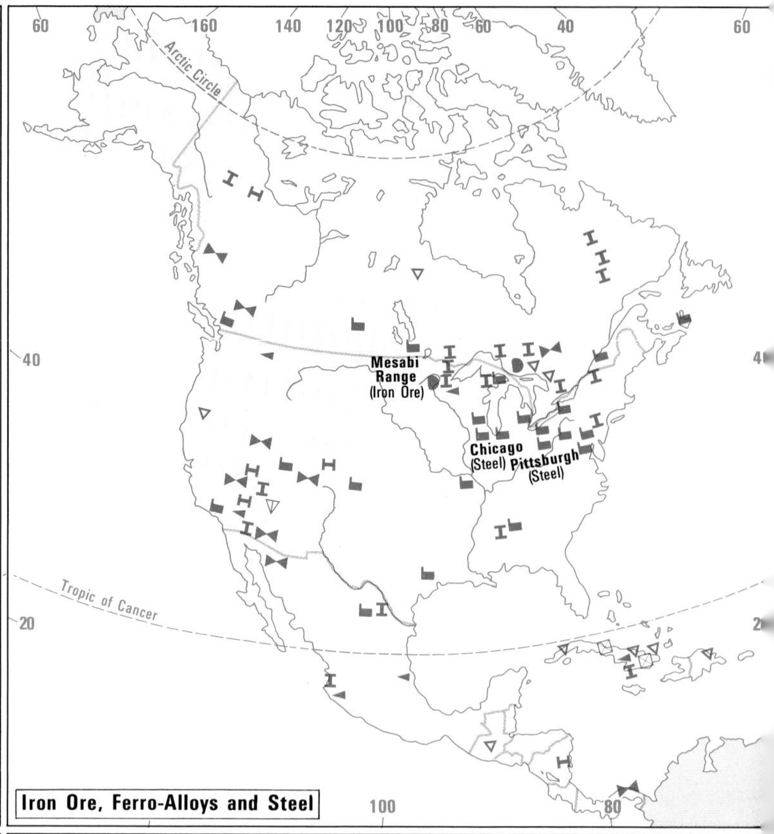

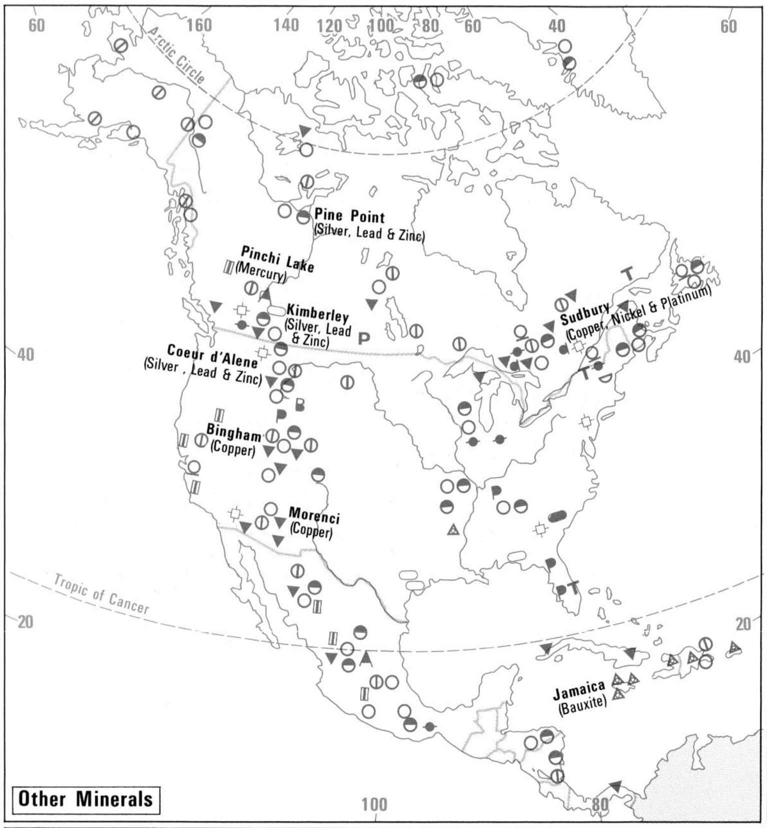

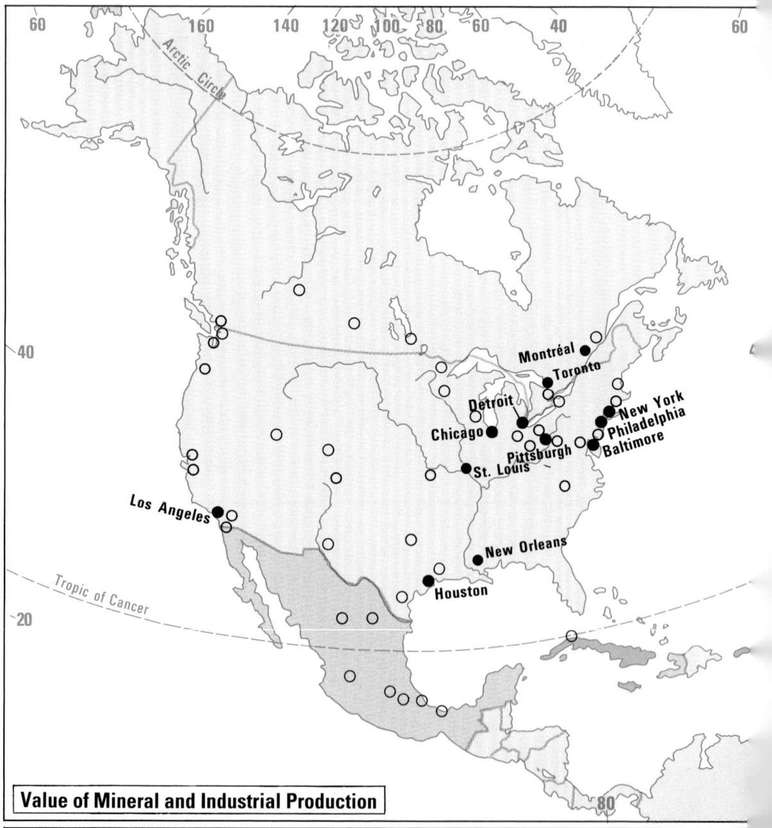

Other Minerals:
- Antimony
- Asbestos
- Bauxite
- Beryllium
- Copper
- Gold
- Lead and zinc
- Lithium
- Mercury
- Mica
- Phosphates
- Platinum
- Potash
- Pyrites
- Silver
- Sulphur
- Titanium

Mineral Production and Industrial Activity as a percentage of G.D.P.

- 40% – 49%
- 30 – 39%
- 20% – 29%
- 10% – 19%
- No data available

- Major industrial centre
- Other industrial centre

Latest available statistics

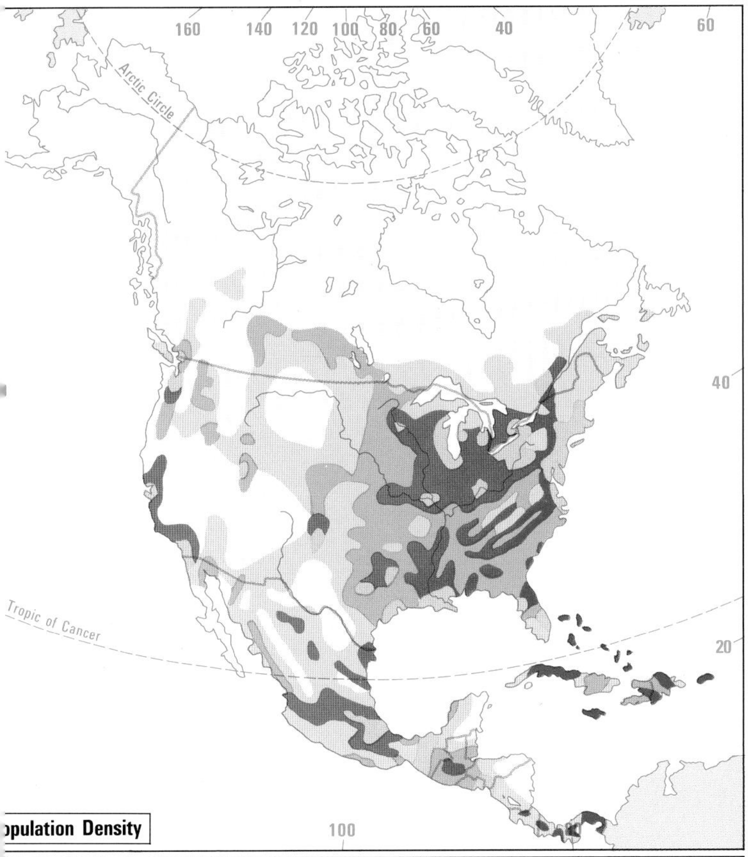

Population Density

Map labels: 160, 140, 120, 100, 80, 60, 60, 40, 40, 20, 20, 100
Arctic Circle
Tropic of Cancer

Density (persons per sq. km)

Over 100		1–10	
50–100		Under 1	
10–50			

1000   2000 kilometres

Urban Population

Map city labels:
Vancouver, Seattle, Montreal, Boston, Toronto, New York, Sacramento, Chicago, Philadelphia, San Francisco, Denver, St Louis, Los Angeles, Phoenix, Dallas, Atlanta, San Antonio, Houston, New Orleans, Miami, Monterrey, Havana, Guadalajara, Mexico City

Map labels: 60, 160, 140, 120, 100, 80, 60, 40, 60, 40, 20, 20, 100, 80

Arctic Circle
Tropic of Cancer

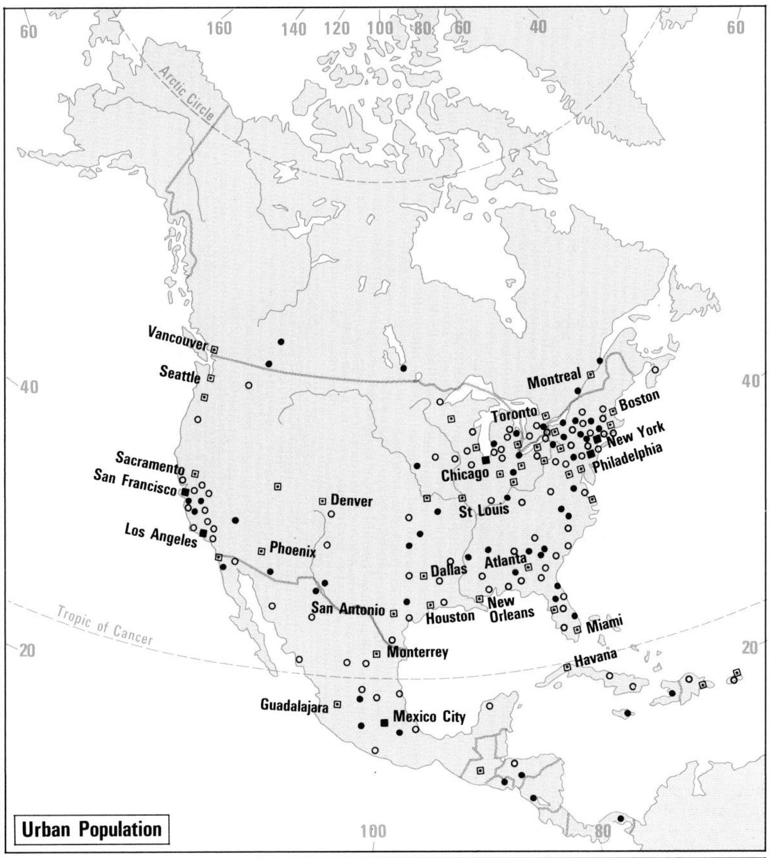

Population of Cities

- ■ Over 5 million
- ⊡ 1–5 million
- ● 500 000–1 million
- ○ 250 000–500 000

0   1000   2000 kilometres

Population by Selected Country

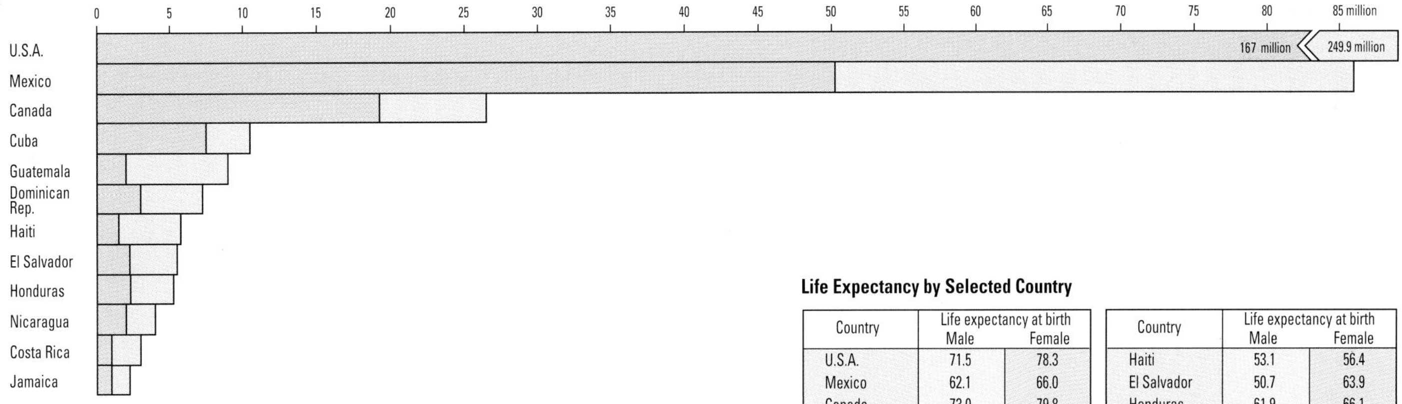

Scale: 0, 5, 10, 15, 20, 25, 30, 35, 40, 45, 50, 55, 60, 65, 70, 75, 80, 85 million

- U.S.A. 167 million 249.9 million
- Mexico
- Canada
- Cuba
- Guatemala
- Dominican Rep.
- Haiti
- El Salvador
- Honduras
- Nicaragua
- Costa Rica
- Jamaica

Urban population as a proportion of total population

Source: U.N. Statistics 1990 (estimates)

Life Expectancy by Selected Country

Country	Life expectancy at birth Male	Female	Country	Life expectancy at birth Male	Female
U.S.A.	71.5	78.3	Haiti	53.1	56.4
Mexico	62.1	66.0	El Salvador	50.7	63.9
Canada	73.0	79.8	Honduras	61.9	66.1
Cuba	72.6	76.1	Nicaragua	62.0	64.6
Guatemala	55.1	59.4	Costa Rica	72.4	77.0
Dominican Rep.	63.9	68.1	Jamaica	70.4	74.8

Percentage Population Breakdown by Age and Sex

Source: U.N. Demographic Yearbook 1990

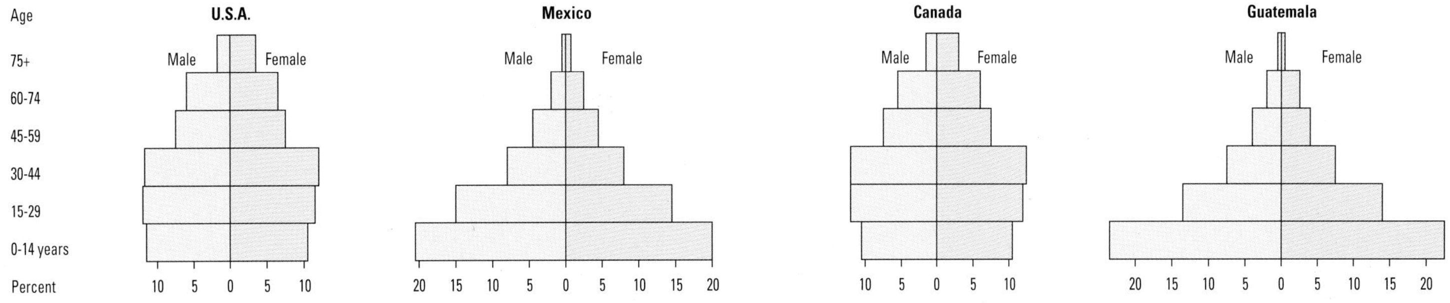

Age brackets: 75+, 60-74, 45-59, 30-44, 15-29, 0-14 years

U.S.A. — Male / Female — Percent: 10, 5, 0, 5, 10

Mexico — Male / Female — Percent: 20, 15, 10, 5, 0, 5, 10, 15, 20

Canada — Male / Female — Percent: 10, 5, 0, 5, 10

Guatemala — Male / Female — Percent: 20, 15, 10, 5, 0, 5, 10, 15, 20

CANADA – AGRICULTURE, FISHING AND FORESTRY

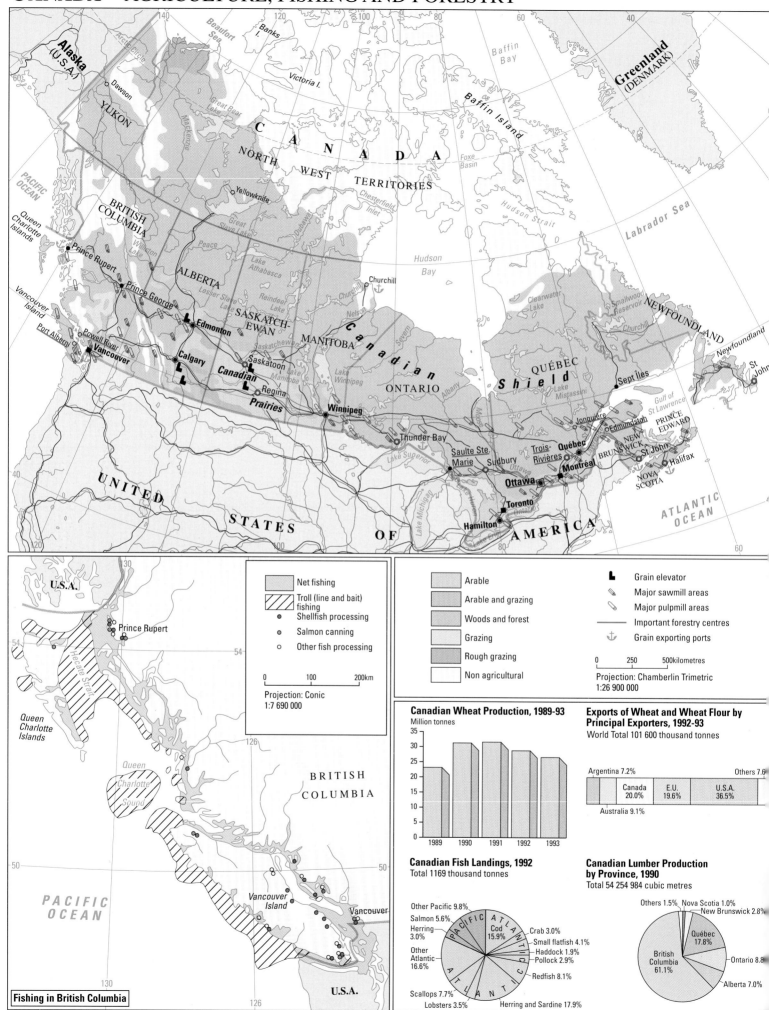

Legend

Fishing (British Columbia inset):
- Net fishing
- Troll (line and bait) fishing
- Shellfish processing
- Salmon canning
- Other fish processing

Projection: Conic
1:7 690 000

Agriculture:
- Arable
- Arable and grazing
- Woods and forest
- Grazing
- Rough grazing
- Non agricultural

Forestry:
- Grain elevator
- Major sawmill areas
- Major pulpmill areas
- Important forestry centres
- Grain exporting ports

0   250   500kilometres

Projection: Chamberlin Trimetric
1:26 900 000

Canadian Wheat Production, 1989-93

Million tonnes

1989	1990	1991	1992	1993

Exports of Wheat and Wheat Flour by Principal Exporters, 1992-93

World Total 101 600 thousand tonnes

| Argentina 7.2% | Canada 20.0% | E.U. 19.6% | U.S.A. 36.5% | Others 7.6 |

Australia 9.1%

Canadian Fish Landings, 1992

Total 1169 thousand tonnes

- Other Pacific 9.8%
- Salmon 5.6%
- Herring 3.0%
- Other Atlantic 16.6%
- Scallops 7.7%
- Lobsters 3.5%
- Herring and Sardine 17.9%
- Redfish 8.1%
- Pollock 2.9%
- Haddock 1.9%
- Small flatfish 4.1%
- Crab 3.0%
- Cod 15.9%

Canadian Lumber Production by Province, 1990

Total 54 254 984 cubic metres

- Others 1.5%
- Nova Scotia 1.0%
- New Brunswick 2.8%
- Québec 17.8%
- Ontario 8.8
- Alberta 7.0%
- British Columbia 61.1%

Fishing in British Columbia

USA – PHYSICAL AND POLITICAL

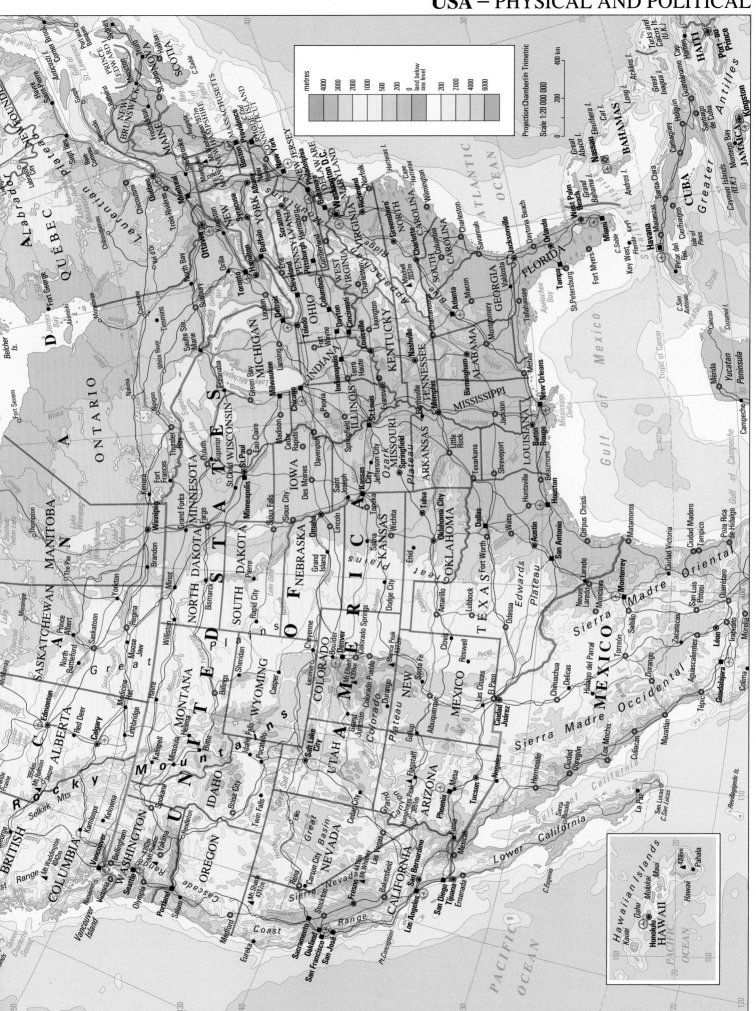

Projection: Chamberlin Trimetric

Scale 1:20 000 000

USA – SOIL EROSION, AGRICULTURAL REGIONS AND CONSERVATION AREAS

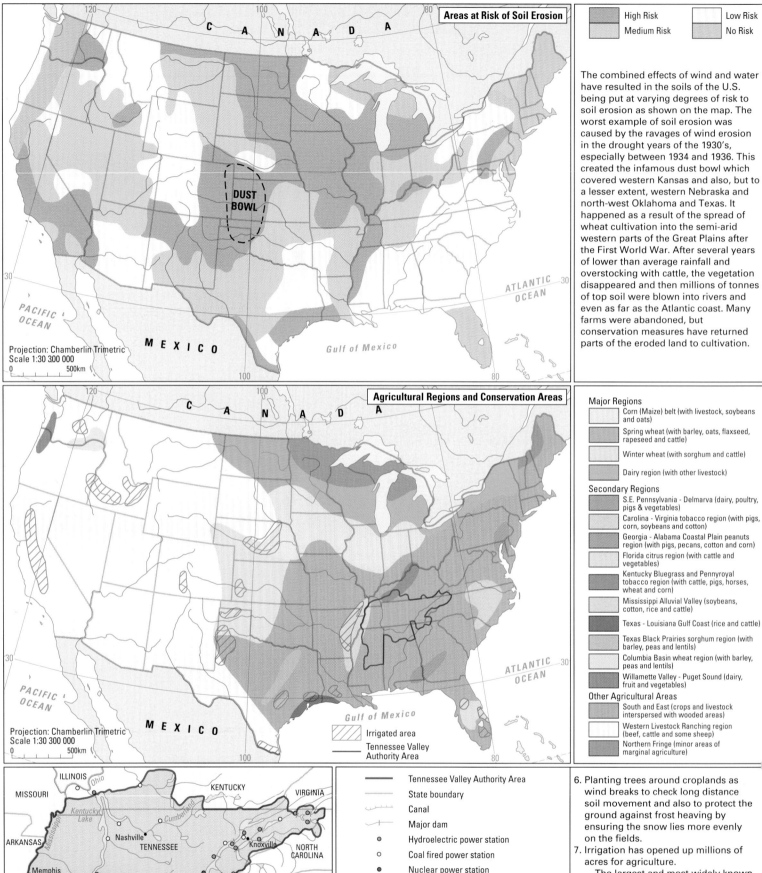

Areas at Risk of Soil Erosion

High Risk
Medium Risk
Low Risk
No Risk

The combined effects of wind and water have resulted in the soils of the U.S. being put at varying degrees of risk to soil erosion as shown on the map. The worst example of soil erosion was caused by the ravages of wind erosion in the drought years of the 1930's, especially between 1934 and 1936. This created the infamous dust bowl which covered western Kansas and also, but to a lesser extent, western Nebraska and north-west Oklahoma and Texas. It happened as a result of the spread of wheat cultivation into the semi-arid western parts of the Great Plains after the First World War. After several years of lower than average rainfall and overstocking with cattle, the vegetation disappeared and then millions of tonnes of top soil were blown into rivers and even as far as the Atlantic coast. Many farms were abandoned, but conservation measures have returned parts of the eroded land to cultivation.

Projection: Chamberlin Trimetric
Scale 1:30 300 000
0   500km

Agricultural Regions and Conservation Areas

Major Regions
- Corn (Maize) belt (with livestock, soybeans and oats)
- Spring wheat (with barley, oats, flaxseed, rapeseed and cattle)
- Winter wheat (with sorghum and cattle)
- Dairy region (with other livestock)

Secondary Regions
- S.E. Pennsylvania - Delmarva (dairy, poultry, pigs & vegetables)
- Carolina - Virginia tobacco region (with pigs, corn, soybeans and cotton)
- Georgia - Alabama Coastal Plain peanuts region (with pigs, pecans, cotton and corn)
- Florida citrus region (with cattle and vegetables)
- Kentucky Bluegrass and Pennyroyal tobacco region (with cattle, pigs, horses, wheat and corn)
- Mississippi Alluvial Valley (soybeans, cotton, rice and cattle)
- Texas - Louisiana Gulf Coast (rice and cattle)
- Texas Black Prairies sorghum region (with barley, peas and lentils)
- Columbia Basin wheat region (with barley, peas and lentils)
- Willamette Valley - Puget Sound (dairy, fruit and vegetables)

Other Agricultural Areas
- South and East (crops and livestock interspersed with wooded areas)
- Western Livestock Ranching region (beef, cattle and some sheep)
- Northern Fringe (minor areas of marginal agriculture)

Projection: Chamberlin Trimetric
Scale 1:30 300 000
0   500km

/// Irrigated area
— Tennessee Valley Authority Area

Tennessee Valley Authority

— Tennessee Valley Authority Area
— State boundary
— Canal
— Major dam
○ Hydroelectric power station
○ Coal fired power station
● Nuclear power station

Scale 1:9 100 000
0   100km

Techniques used to prevent soil erosion

1. Adoption of trash farming, whereby straw and trash are laid on the soil to retain moisture.
2. Replacement of row crops like wheat with grass.
3. Contour ploughing and strip cropping.
4. Using improved pasture grasses and more drought resistant wheat strains.
5. Combining arable with livestock farming.
6. Planting trees around croplands as wind breaks to check long distance soil movement and also to protect the ground against frost heaving by ensuring the snow lies more evenly on the fields.
7. Irrigation has opened up millions of acres for agriculture.

The largest and most widely known conservation scheme is the Tennessee Valley Authority. Managing the 47 dams is a complex balance of ensuring there is enough capacity in the system to absorb a flood, while at the same time providing enough water for the 30 hydroelectric power stations; cooling water for the coal fired and nuclear power stations; full reservoirs for sports and enough water the rivers for barges.

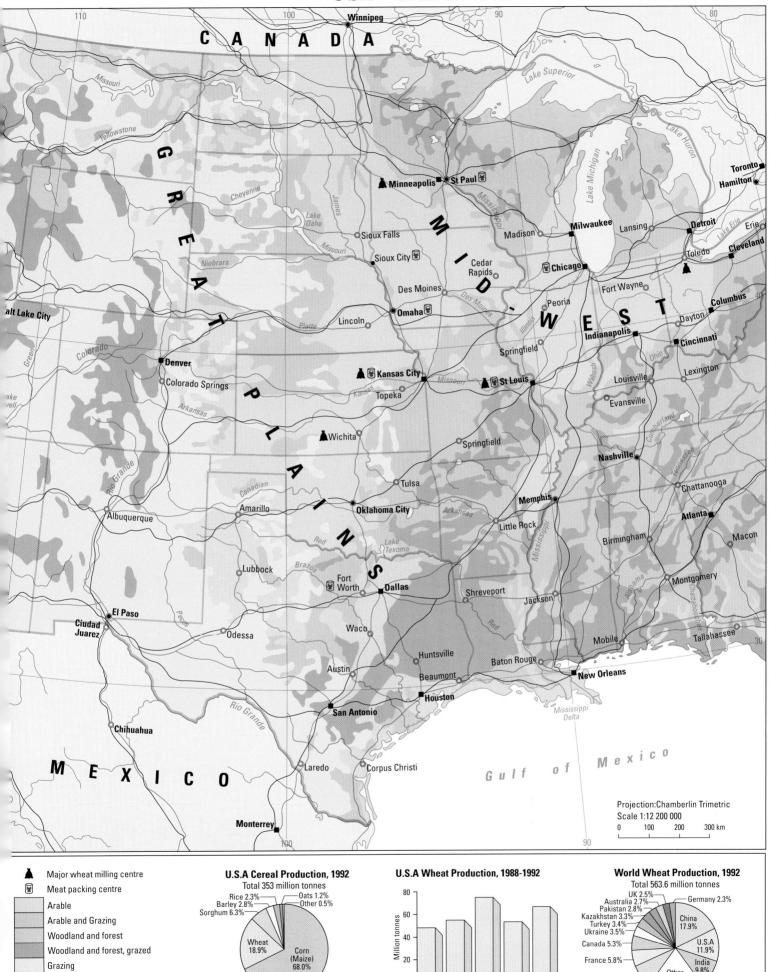

Projection:Chamberlin Trimetric
Scale 1:12 200 000

0   100   200   300 km

Legend:

▲ Major wheat milling centre

⬧ Meat packing centre

Arable

Arable and Grazing

Woodland and forest

Woodland and forest, grazed

Grazing

Swamp and marsh

U.S.A Cereal Production, 1992
Total 353 million tonnes

Rice 2.3%
Sorghum 6.3%
Barley 2.8%
Oats 1.2%
Other 0.5%
Wheat 18.9%
Corn (Maize) 68.0%

U.S.A Wheat Production, 1988-1992

Million tonnes

80
60
40
20
0

1988   1989   1990   1991   1992

World Wheat Production, 1992
Total 563.6 million tonnes

UK 2.5%
Australia 2.7%
Pakistan 2.8%
Kazakhstan 3.3%
Turkey 3.4%
Ukraine 3.5%
Canada 5.3%
France 5.8%
Russia 8.2%
Other 20.6%
Germany 2.3%
China 17.9%
U.S.A 11.9%
India 9.8%

NORTH EAST USA – ECONOMIC

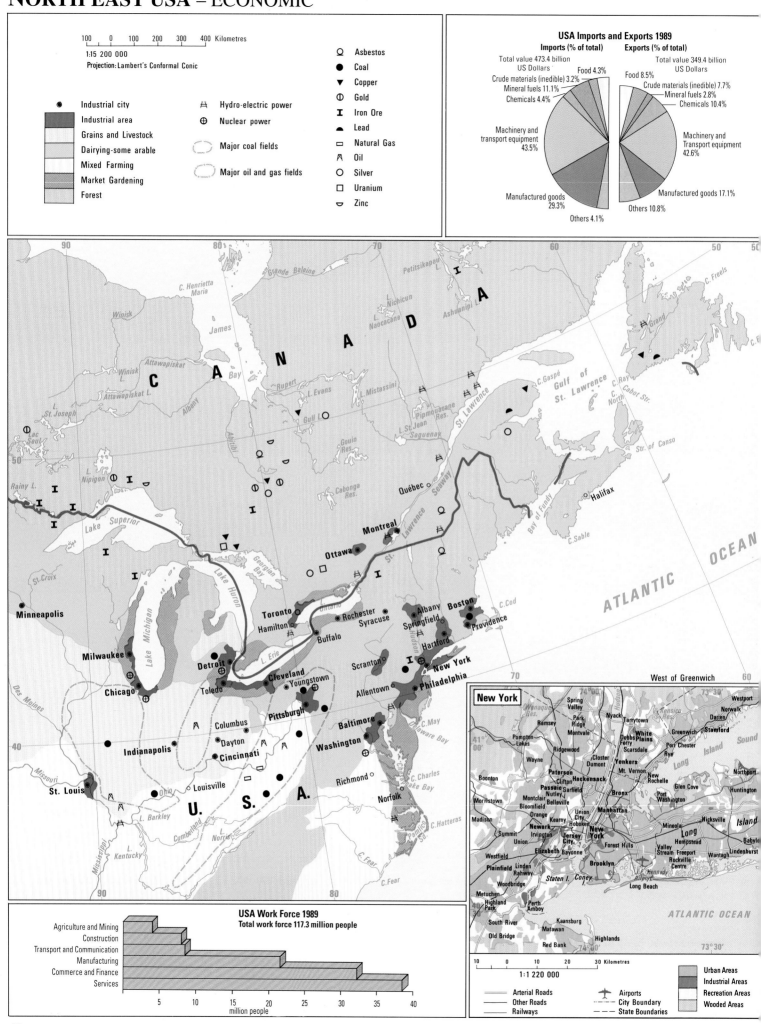

Scale
100 0 100 200 300 400 Kilometres
1:15 200 000
Projection: Lambert's Conformal Conic

Legend
- Industrial city
- Industrial area
- Grains and Livestock
- Dairying-some arable
- Mixed Farming
- Market Gardening
- Forest

- ⋈ Hydro-electric power
- ⊕ Nuclear power
- Major coal fields
- Major oil and gas fields

- Ọ Asbestos
- ● Coal
- ▼ Copper
- ◐ Gold
- I Iron Ore
- ▲ Lead
- ▱ Natural Gas
- Ⱥ Oil
- ○ Silver
- ▢ Uranium
- ◡ Zinc

USA Imports and Exports 1989

Imports (% of total)
Total value 473.4 billion US Dollars
- Food 4.3%
- Crude materials (inedible) 3.2%
- Mineral fuels 11.1%
- Chemicals 4.4%
- Machinery and transport equipment 43.5%
- Manufactured goods 29.3%
- Others 4.1%

Exports (% of total)
Total value 349.4 billion US Dollars
- Food 8.5%
- Crude materials (inedible) 7.7%
- Mineral fuels 2.8%
- Chemicals 10.4%
- Machinery and Transport equipment 42.6%
- Manufactured goods 17.1%
- Others 10.8%

USA Work Force 1989
Total work force 117.3 million people

- Agriculture and Mining
- Construction
- Transport and Communication
- Manufacturing
- Commerce and Finance
- Services

5 10 15 20 25 30 35 40
million people

New York (inset)
Scale: 10 0 10 20 30 Kilometres
1:1 220 000

- Arterial Roads
- Other Roads
- Railways
- Airports
- City Boundary
- State Boundaries

- Urban Areas
- Industrial Areas
- Recreation Areas
- Wooded Areas

West of Greenwich

SOUTH AMERICA – PHYSICAL AND POLITICAL

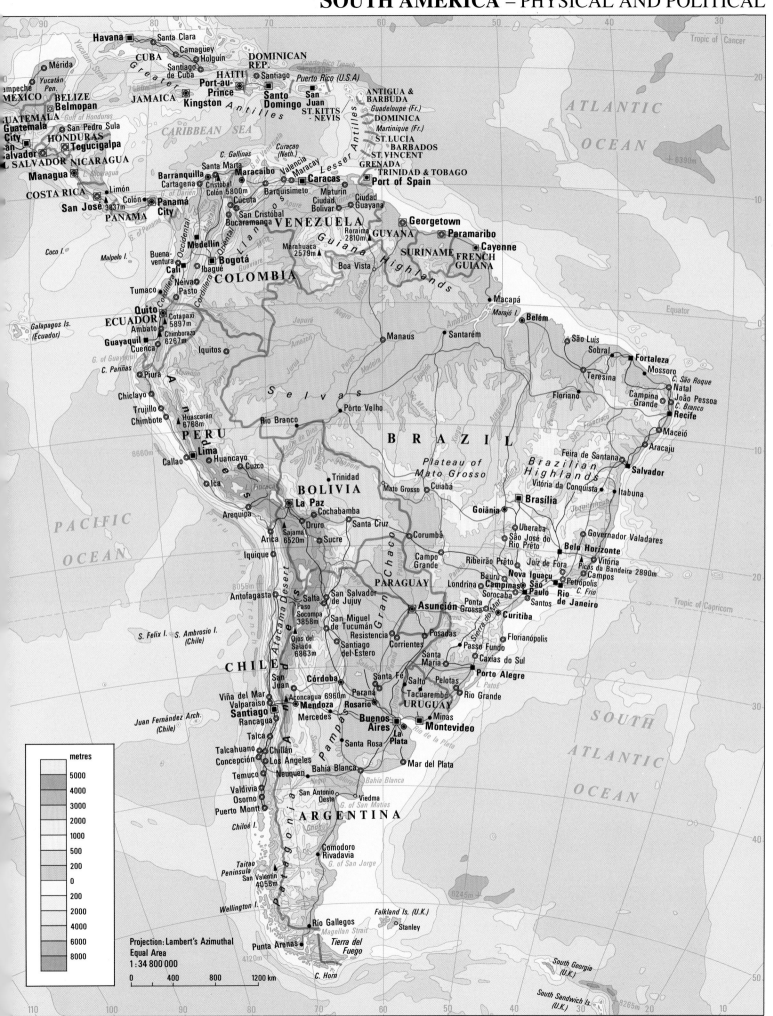

Projection: Lambert's Azimuthal
Equal Area
1 : 34 800 000

0   400   800   1200 km

metres
5000
4000
3000
2000
1000
500
200
0
200
2000
4000
6000
8000

SOUTH AMERICA – CLIMATE

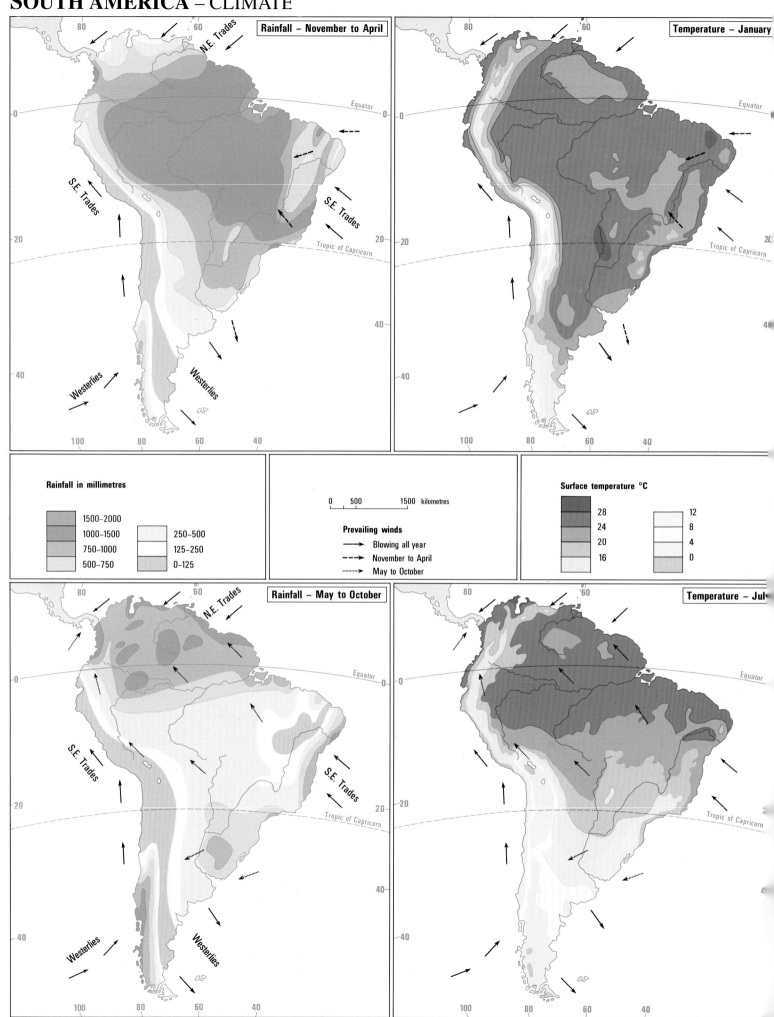

Rainfall – November to April

N.E. Trades
S.E. Trades
S.E. Trades
Westerlies
Westerlies
Equator
Tropic of Capricorn

Temperature – January

Equator
Tropic of Capricorn

Rainfall in millimetres

- 1500–2000
- 1000–1500
- 750–1000
- 500–750
- 250–500
- 125–250
- 0–125

0 500 1500 kilometres

Prevailing winds
→ Blowing all year
⇢ November to April
⋯⋯> May to October

Surface temperature °C

- 28
- 24
- 20
- 16
- 12
- 8
- 4
- 0

Rainfall – May to October

N.E. Trades
S.E. Trades
S.E. Trades
Westerlies
Westerlies
Equator
Tropic of Capricorn

Temperature – July

Equator
Tropic of Capricorn

Caribbean Sea

ATLANTIC OCEAN

Trinidad and Tobago

G. of Panama

Cordillera Occidental

Cordillera Oriental

Llanos

Orinoco

Guiana

Pakaraima Mts.

Highlands

Equator

Purumayo

Japura

Negro

Amazon

S e l v a s

Jurua

Amazon

Ucayali

Purus

Madeira

Tapajos

Xingu

Tocantins

São Francisco

A n d e s

Plateau of Mato Grosso

L. Titicaca

Bolivian

Plateau

Atacama Desert

Gran Chaco

Paraguay

Brazilian Highlands

Serra da Mantiqueira

Tropic of Capricorn

PACIFIC

OCEAN

Pilcomayo

Bermejo

Parana

Uruguay

Entre Rios

Pampas

Salado

Colorado

Negro

La Plata

ATLANTIC

Chonos Archipelago

Patagonia

G. of San Jorge

OCEAN

Falkland Is.

South Georgia

Tierra del Fuego

C. Horn

Land cover maps show a combination of natural vegetation and land use, ie how humans have affected the natural environment with their farming techniques. See also the World Natural Vegetation Map on page 122.

Projection: Lambert's Azimuthal Equal Area
1 : 34 800 000
0   400   800   1200 km

Cultivated land	Forest and woodland
Cultivated land and grassland	Grassland
Swamp and marsh	Barren land (including permanent ice)
Scrub and sparse grassland	

SOUTH AMERICA – AGRICULTURE

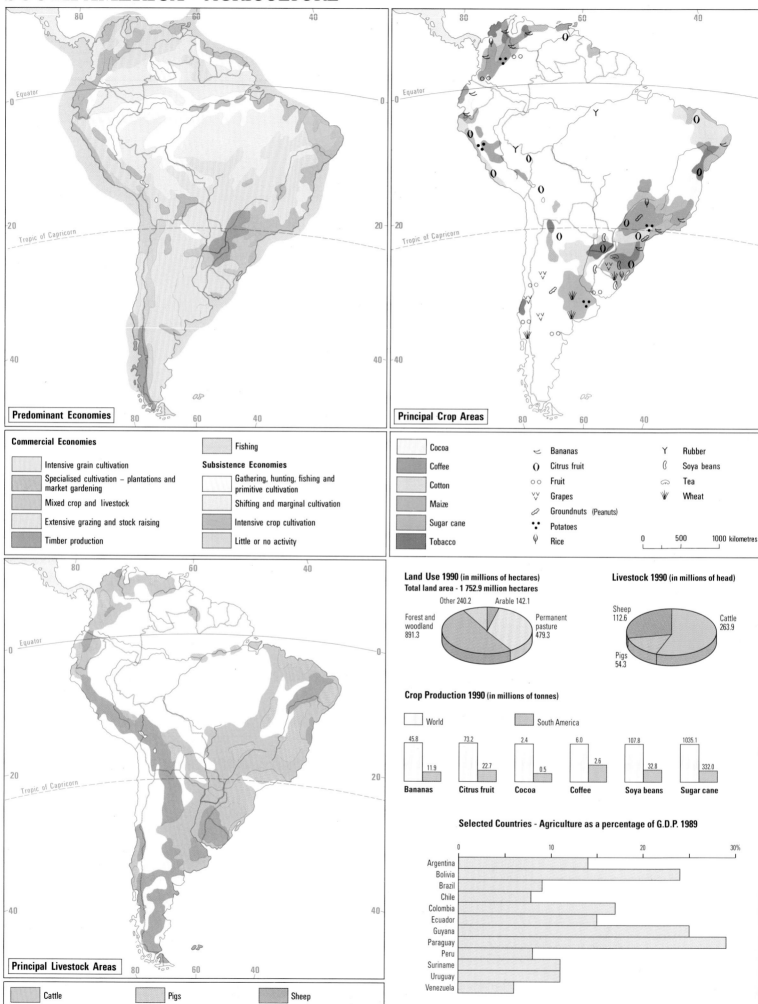

Predominant Economies

Commercial Economies

- Intensive grain cultivation
- Specialised cultivation – plantations and market gardening
- Mixed crop and livestock
- Extensive grazing and stock raising
- Timber production
- Fishing

Subsistence Economies

- Gathering, hunting, fishing and primitive cultivation
- Shifting and marginal cultivation
- Intensive crop cultivation
- Little or no activity

Principal Crop Areas

- Cocoa
- Coffee
- Cotton
- Maize
- Sugar cane
- Tobacco
- ⌒ Bananas
- O Citrus fruit
- o o Fruit
- v v Grapes
- ⌀ Groundnuts (Peanuts)
- ⦂ Potatoes
- Ψ Rice
- Y Rubber
- ∫ Soya beans
- ⌒ Tea
- Ψ Wheat

0   500   1000 kilometres

Principal Livestock Areas

- Cattle
- Pigs
- Sheep

Land Use 1990 (in millions of hectares)
Total land area - 1 752.9 million hectares

- Other 240.2
- Arable 142.1
- Forest and woodland 891.3
- Permanent pasture 479.3

Livestock 1990 (in millions of head)

- Sheep 112.6
- Cattle 263.9
- Pigs 54.3

Crop Production 1990 (in millions of tonnes)

- World
- South America

Crop	World	South America
Bananas	45.8	11.9
Citrus fruit	73.2	22.7
Cocoa	2.4	0.5
Coffee	6.0	2.6
Soya beans	107.8	32.8
Sugar cane	1035.1	332.0

Selected Countries - Agriculture as a percentage of G.D.P. 1989

0   10   20   30%

- Argentina
- Bolivia
- Brazil
- Chile
- Colombia
- Ecuador
- Guyana
- Paraguay
- Peru
- Suriname
- Uruguay
- Venezuela

64

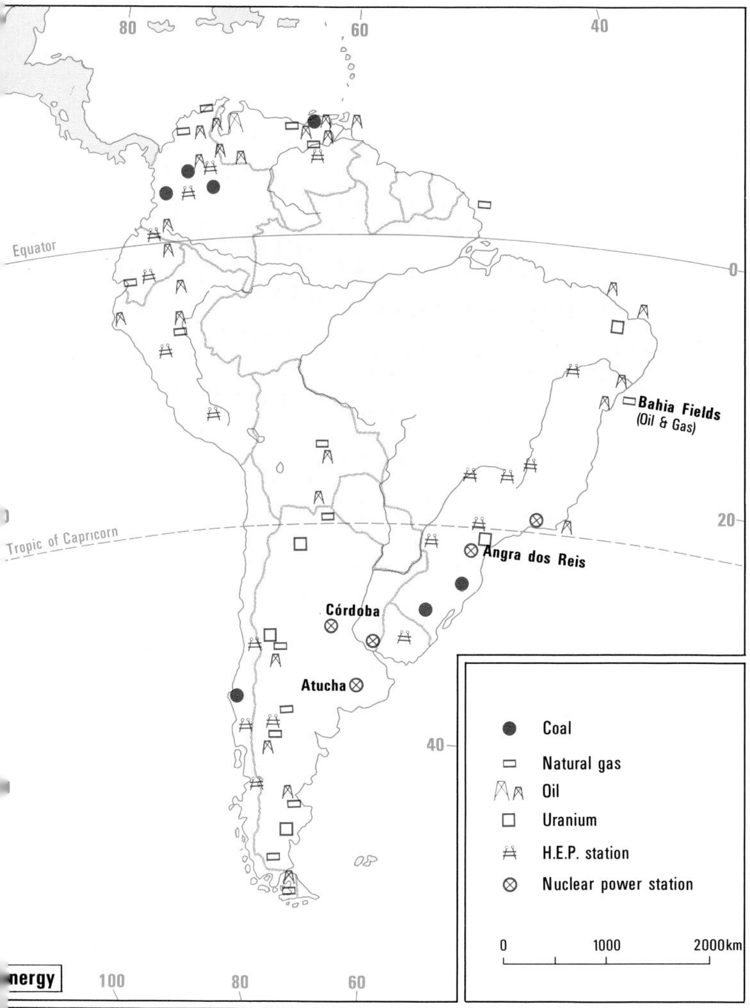
Bahia Fields
(Oil & Gas)
Angra dos Reis
Córdoba
Atucha
Equator
Tropic of Capricorn
Coal
Natural gas
Oil
Uranium
H.E.P. station
Nuclear power station
0
1000
2000km
Energy

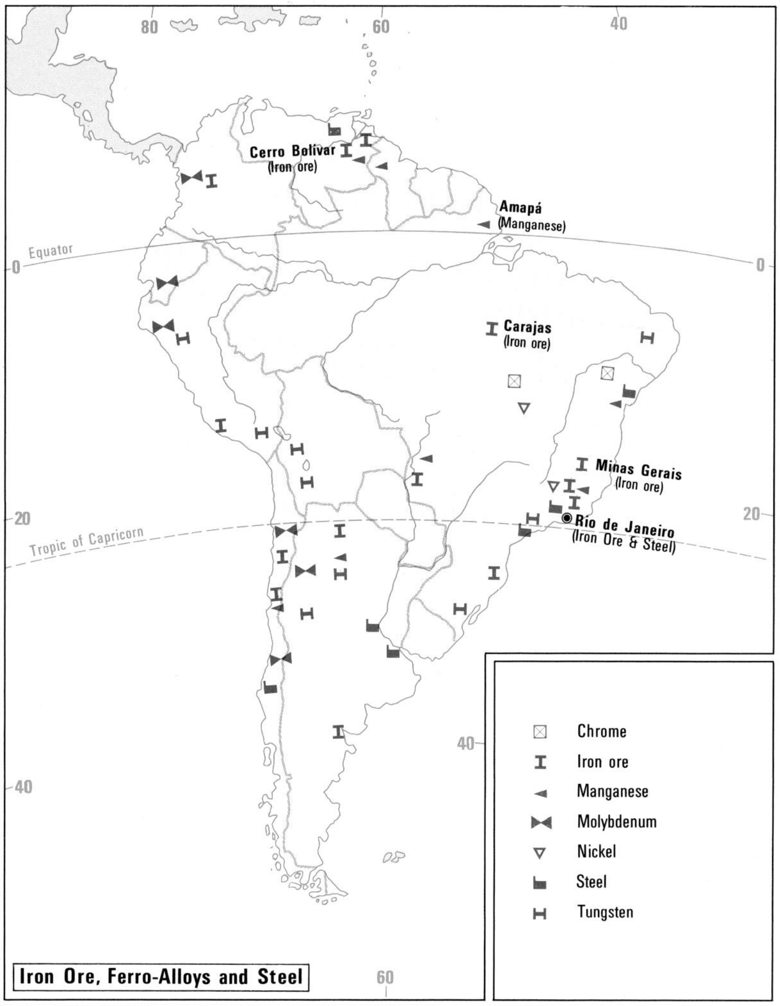
Cerro Bolivar
(Iron ore)
Amapá
(Manganese)
Carajas
(Iron ore)
Minas Gerais
(Iron ore)
Rio de Janeiro
(Iron Ore & Steel)
Equator
Tropic of Capricorn
Chrome
Iron ore
Manganese
Molybdenum
Nickel
Steel
Tungsten
Iron Ore, Ferro-Alloys and Steel

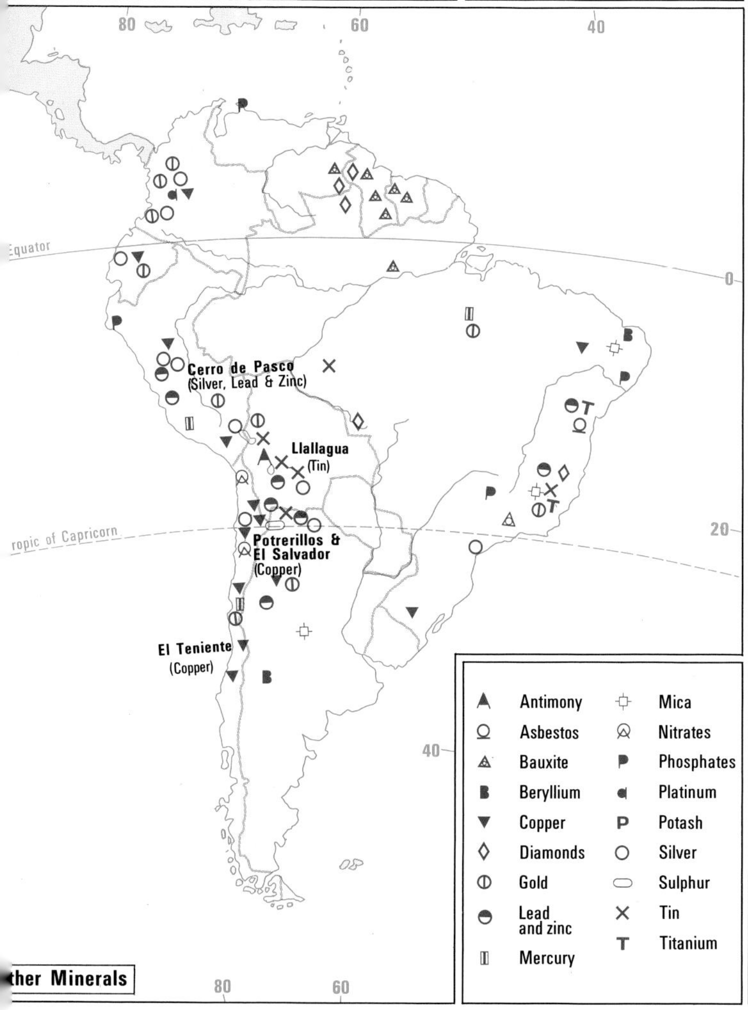
Cerro de Pasco
(Silver, Lead & Zinc)
Llallagua
(Tin)
Potrerillos &
El Salvador
(Copper)
El Teniente
(Copper)
Equator
Tropic of Capricorn
Antimony
Asbestos
Bauxite
Beryllium
Copper
Diamonds
Gold
Lead and zinc
Mercury
Mica
Nitrates
Phosphates
Platinum
Potash
Silver
Sulphur
Tin
Titanium
Other Minerals

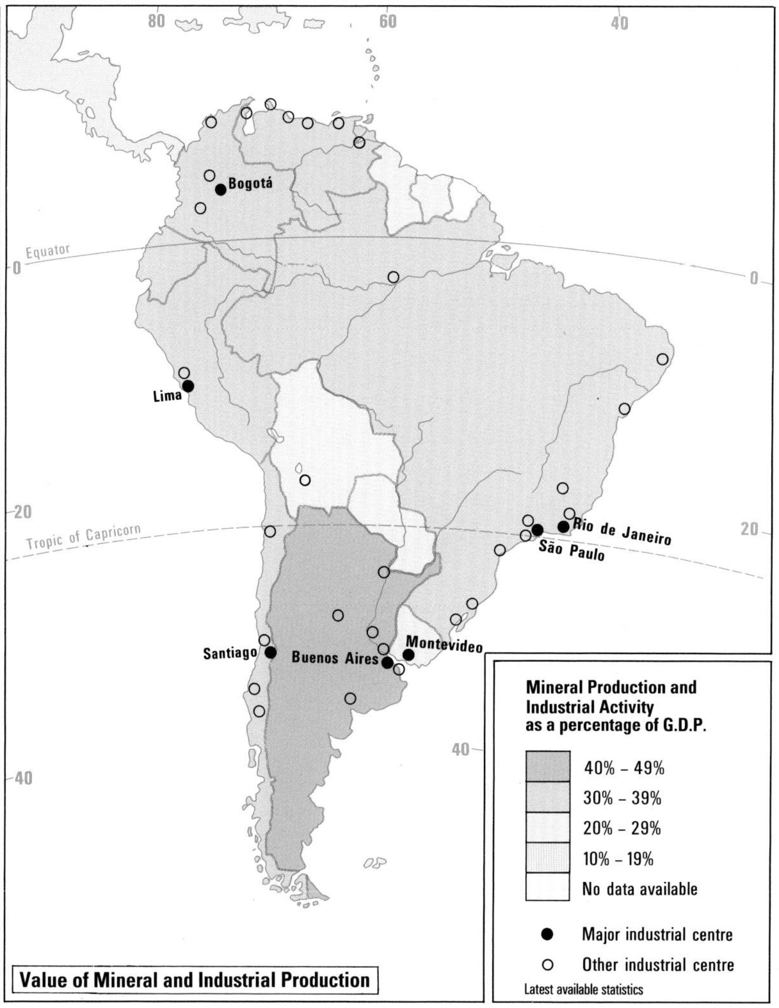
Bogotá
Lima
Rio de Janeiro
São Paulo
Santiago
Buenos Aires
Montevideo
Equator
Tropic of Capricorn
Mineral Production and Industrial Activity as a percentage of G.D.P.
40% – 49%
30% – 39%
20% – 29%
10% – 19%
No data available
Major industrial centre
Other industrial centre
Latest available statistics
Value of Mineral and Industrial Production

Population Density

Density (persons per sq. km)

	Over 100
	50–100
	10–50
	1–10
	Under 1

0   500   1000 km

Urban Population

Caracas
Medellín
Cali Bogotá
Quito
Guayaquil
Lima
Recife
Salvador
Nova Belo Horizonte
Iguaçu
Rio de Janeiro
São Paulo
Porto Alegre
Santiago
Buenos Aires Montevideo

Equator
Tropic of Capricorn

Population of Cities

- ■ Over 5 million
- ⊞ 1–5 million
- ● 500 000–1 million
- ○ 250 000–500 000

0   500   1000 km

Population by Selected Country

Brazil
Colombia
Argentina
Peru
Venezuela
Chile
Ecuador
Bolivia
Paraguay
Uruguay
Guyana
Suriname

Scale: 0 5 10 15 20 25 30 35 40 | 105 110 115 120 125 130 135 140 145 150 milli

Urban population as a proportion of total population

Source: U.N. Statistics 1990 (estimates)

Life Expectancy by Selected Country

Country	Life expectancy at birth Male	Female	Country	Life expectancy at birth Male	Female
Brazil	62.3	67.6	Ecuador	63.4	67.6
Colombia	63.4	69.2	Bolivia	50.9	55.4
Argentina	65.5	72.7	Paraguay	64.4	68.5
Peru	56.8	66.5	Uruguay	68.4	74.9
Venezuela	66.7	72.8	Guyana	60.4	66.1
Chile	68.0	75.0	Suriname	66.4	71.3

Percentage Population Breakdown by Age and Sex

Source: U.N. Demographic Yearbook 1990

Age			
75+			
60–74			
45–59			
30–44			
15–29			
0–14 years			

Brazil — Male / Female
Argentina — Male / Female
Colombia — Male / Female

Percent: 15 10 5 0 5 10 15

PERU – PHYSICAL, POLITICAL AND ECONOMIC ACTIVITY

Key

Metres

- Over 4000
- 2000-4000
- 1000-2000
- 500-1000
- 200-500
- 0-200

▲ Mountain Peak
— International Boundary
⋯ Department Boundary
— Main Road
— Railway
⊕ International Airport
■ Capital City
● Important Town
○ Other Town

0 100 200 300 400km

Total area: 1 280 000 sq. km.
Total population: 22 453 861 (1992)
Population density: 18 people per sq. km.
Capital city: Lima
Capital population: 6 414 500
Birth rate: 31 per 1000 (1992)
Death rate: 9 per 1000 (1992)

The most important sector of the Peruvian economy is manufacturing. The major industries, most of which are located in the Lima/Callao area, include textiles, footwear, paper products, food processing and metals. Agriculture and fishing employed 33% of the working population in 1992. Fishmeal is the second most valuable export, while coffee, sugar cane and cotton are important cash crops. Peru is rich in mineral wealth, with significant deposits of silver, lead, zinc, iron ore and petroleum. The most important mineral though, is copper which accounted for over 23% of export earnings in 1992. Since the 1940's, the town of Callao has been combined with Lima to form Greater Lima, the sixth largest city in Latin America, with a population of over 6.4 million people.

Domestic Exports, 1992
Total Value U.S. $ 3 484m

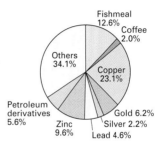

- Fishmeal 12.6%
- Coffee 2.0%
- Copper 23.1%
- Gold 6.2%
- Silver 2.2%
- Lead 4.6%
- Zinc 9.6%
- Petroleum derivatives 5.6%
- Others 34.1%

Economic Activity

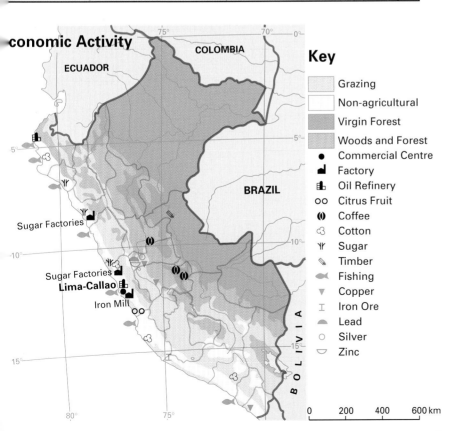

Key

- Grazing
- Non-agricultural
- Virgin Forest
- Woods and Forest
- ● Commercial Centre
- Factory
- Oil Refinery
- ○○ Citrus Fruit
- ◐ Coffee
- ◌ Cotton
- ⋎ Sugar
- ◁ Timber
- Fishing
- ▼ Copper
- I Iron Ore
- Lead
- ○ Silver
- ▽ Zinc

Annual Rainfall

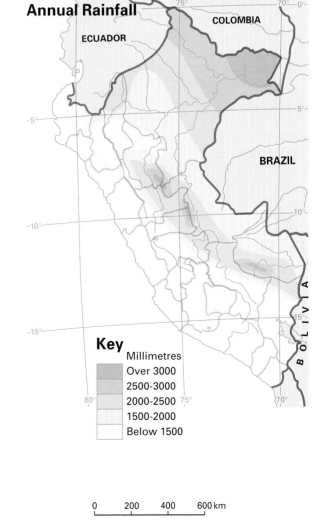

Key

Millimetres

- Over 3000
- 2500-3000
- 2000-2500
- 1500-2000
- Below 1500

0 200 400 600 km

BRAZIL – PHYSICAL, POLITICAL AND ECONOMIC ACTIVITY

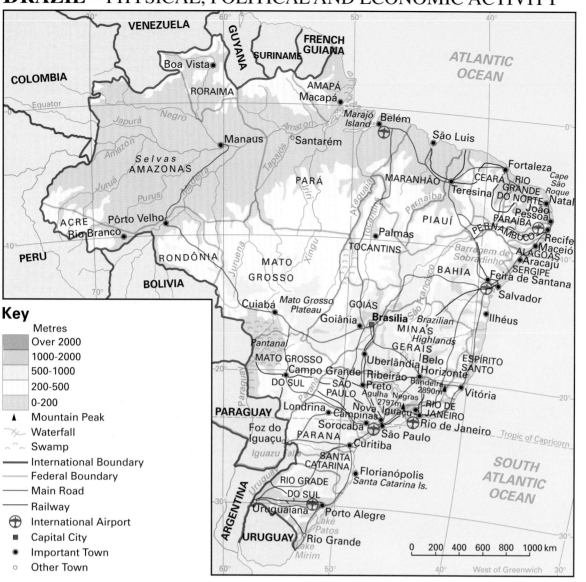

Key

Metres
- Over 2000
- 1000-2000
- 500-1000
- 200-500
- 0-200

- ▲ Mountain Peak
- ✕ Waterfall
- ∿ Swamp
- ▬ International Boundary
- ─ Federal Boundary
- ─ Main Road
- ─ Railway
- ⊕ International Airport
- ■ Capital City
- ● Important Town
- ○ Other Town

Total area: 8 511 996 sq. km.
Total population: 156 275 397 (1992)
Population density: 18 people per sq. km.
Population of main towns:
Brasília, (the capital), 1.6 million
São Paulo 9.5 million, Rio de Janeiro 5.3 million
Birth rate: 26 per 1000 (1992)
Death rate: 7 per 1000 (1992)

Agriculture is a very important part of the Brazilian economy with soya beans being the principal cash crop and accounting for 8% of export earnings in 1993. Brazil is rich in mineral deposits, with iron ore and tin being the major exports. Manufacturing is the most valuable sector of the economy, with the most important industries being food processing, machinery and transport equipment, chemicals, textiles and steel. Brasília replaced Rio de Janeiro as the capital city in 1956. This new town was built to encourage people to move away from the overcrowded south-east industrial region.

Gross Domestic Product by Economic Activity, 1991

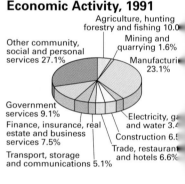

- Agriculture, hunting forestry and fishing 10.0
- Mining and quarrying 1.6%
- Manufacturi 23.1%
- Electricity, ga and water 3.4
- Construction 6.5
- Trade, restaurant and hotels 6.6%
- Transport, storage and communications 5.1%
- Finance, insurance, real estate and business services 7.5%
- Government services 9.1%
- Other community, social and personal services 27.1%

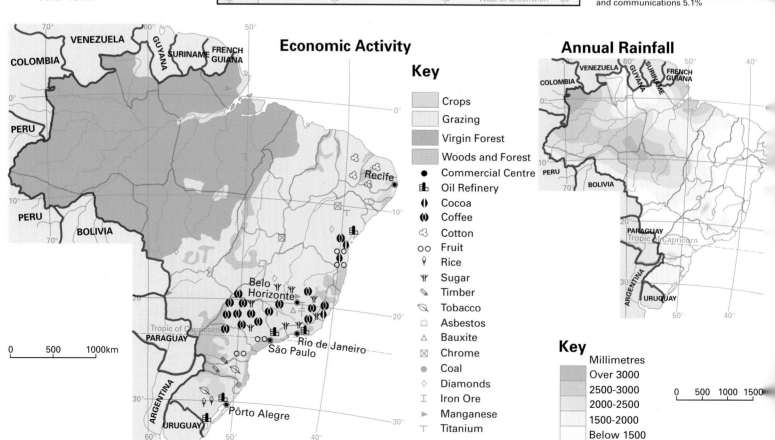

Economic Activity

Key
- Crops
- Grazing
- Virgin Forest
- Woods and Forest
- ● Commercial Centre
- ⛫ Oil Refinery
- ◖ Cocoa
- ◕ Coffee
- ☘ Cotton
- ∞ Fruit
- ⸸ Rice
- ⅄ Sugar
- ✎ Timber
- ✑ Tobacco
- Ω Asbestos
- △ Bauxite
- ⊠ Chrome
- ● Coal
- ◇ Diamonds
- ⊥ Iron Ore
- ▶ Manganese
- ⊤ Titanium

Annual Rainfall

Key
Millimetres
- Over 3000
- 2500-3000
- 2000-2500
- 1500-2000
- Below 1500

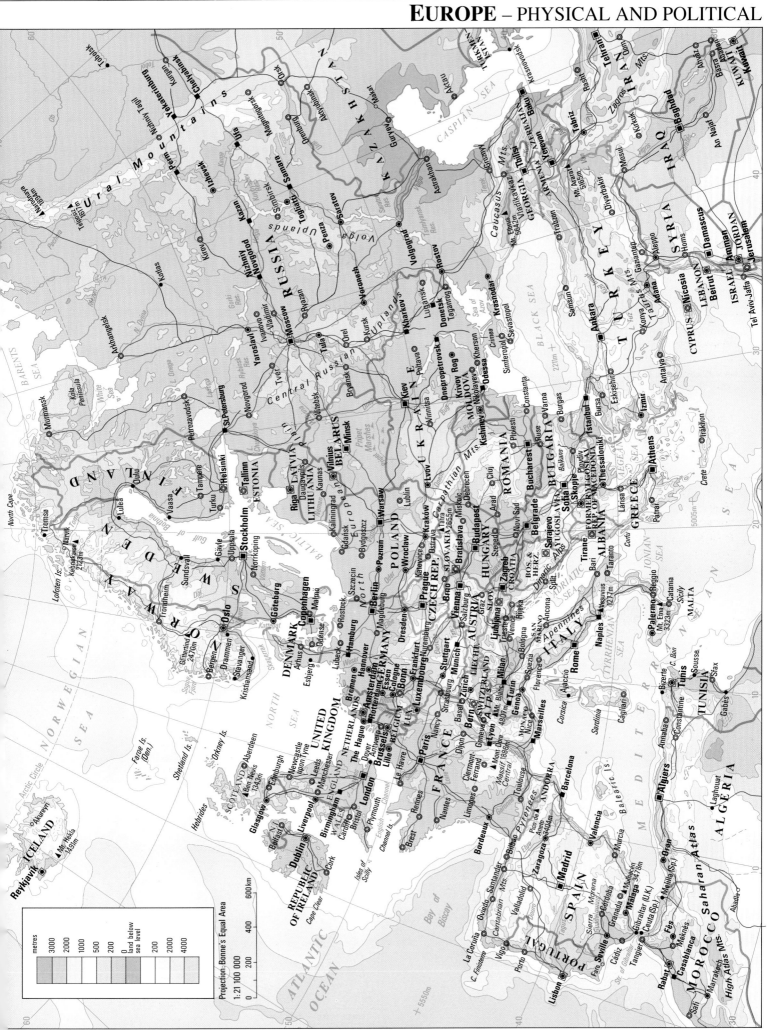

Projection: Bonne's Equal Area

1:21 100 000

metres							
3000	2000	1000	500	200	0 land below sea level	200	2000	4000

0   200   400   600 km

EUROPE – CLIMATE

Rainfall – November to April

Temperature – January

Rainfall in millimetres

1000–1500
750–1000
500–750
250–500
125–250
0–125

0   500   1000   1500   kilometres

Prevailing winds

– – – ▶ November to April

·······▶ May to October

Surface temperature °C

28
24
20
16
12
8
4
0
−4
−8
−12
−16
below −20

Rainfall – May to October

Temperature – July

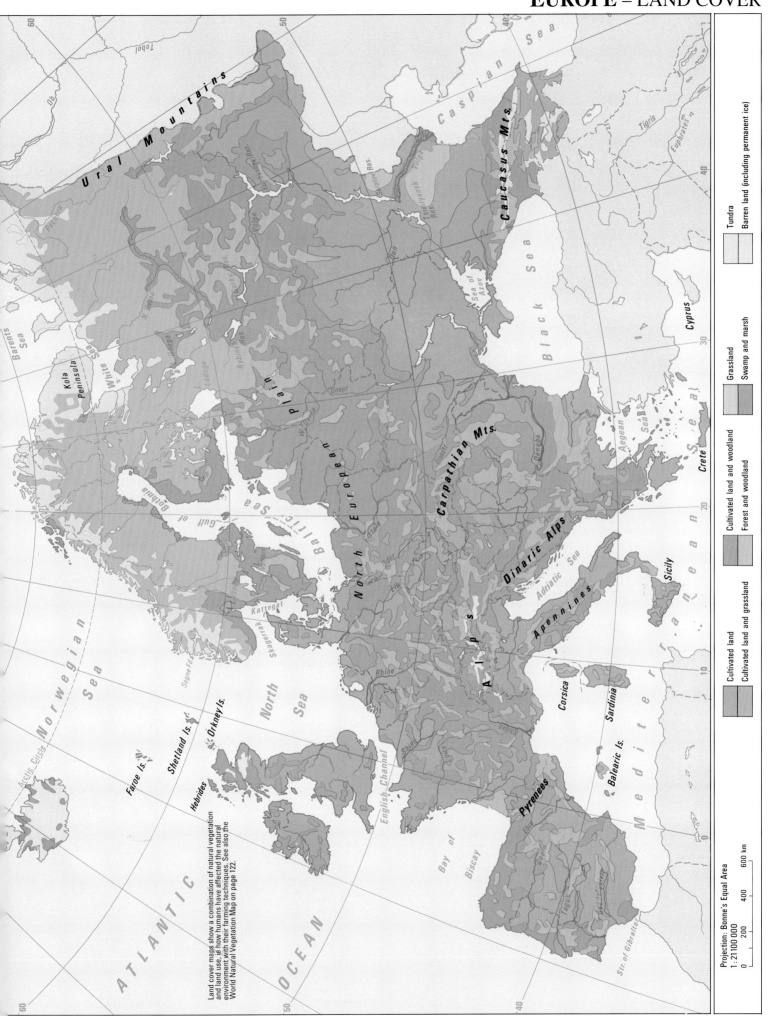

Tundra

Barren land (including permanent ice)

Grassland

Swamp and marsh

Cultivated land and woodland

Forest and woodland

Cultivated land

Cultivated land and grassland

Ural Mountains

Caspian Sea

Caucasus Mts.

Black Sea

Cyprus

Sea of Azov

Tigris

Euphrates

North European Plain

Carpathian Mts.

Dinaric Alps

Apennines

Alps

Sicily

Adriatic Sea

Aegean Sea

Crete

Mediterranean Sea

Corsica

Sardinia

Balearic Is.

Pyrenees

Bay of Biscay

Str. of Gibraltar

English Channel

North Sea

Norwegian Sea

ATLANTIC OCEAN

Barents Sea

White Sea

Kola Peninsula

Gulf of Bothnia

Baltic Sea

Kattegat

Skagerrak

Sognefjord

Faroe Is.

Shetland Is.

Orkney Is.

Hebrides

Arctic Circle

Ob

Tobol

Pechora

N. Dvina

Onega

Ladoga

Volga

Don

Dnepr

W. Dvina

Vistula

Oder

Elbe

Rhine

Ebro

Tagus

Douro

Guadalquivir

Tsimlyansk Res.

Rybinsk Res.

Stalingrad Res.

Danube

Land cover maps show a combination of natural vegetation
and land use, ie how humans have affected the natural
environment with their farming techniques. See also the
World Natural Vegetation Map on page 122.

Projection: Bonne's Equal Area
1 : 21 100 000

0   200   400   600 km

71

EUROPE – AGRICULTURE

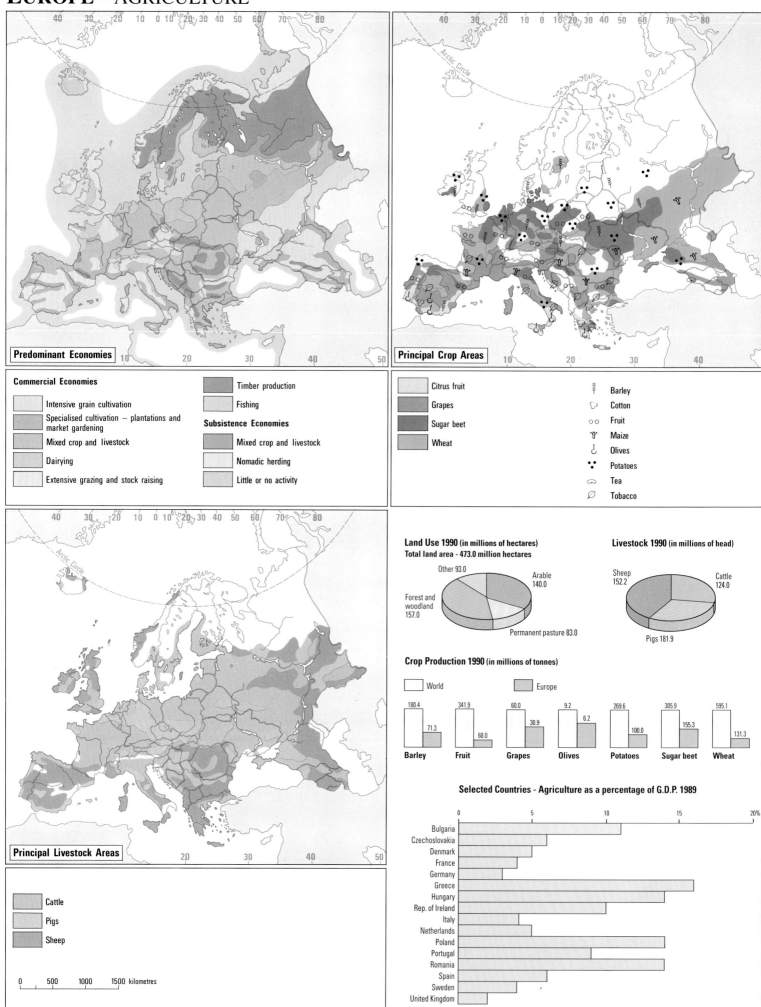

Predominant Economies

Commercial Economies

- Intensive grain cultivation
- Specialised cultivation – plantations and market gardening
- Mixed crop and livestock
- Dairying
- Extensive grazing and stock raising
- Timber production
- Fishing

Subsistence Economies

- Mixed crop and livestock
- Nomadic herding
- Little or no activity

Principal Crop Areas

- Citrus fruit
- Grapes
- Sugar beet
- Wheat
- Barley
- Cotton
- Fruit
- Maize
- Olives
- Potatoes
- Tea
- Tobacco

Principal Livestock Areas

- Cattle
- Pigs
- Sheep

0 500 1000 1500 kilometres

Land Use 1990 (in millions of hectares)
Total land area - 473.0 million hectares

Other 93.0
Arable 140.0
Forest and woodland 157.0
Permanent pasture 83.0

Livestock 1990 (in millions of head)

Sheep 152.2
Cattle 124.0
Pigs 181.9

Crop Production 1990 (in millions of tonnes)

World | Europe

Crop	World	Europe
Barley	180.4	71.3
Fruit	341.9	68.0
Grapes	60.0	30.9
Olives	9.2	6.2
Potatoes	269.6	100.0
Sugar beet	305.9	155.3
Wheat	595.1	131.3

Selected Countries - Agriculture as a percentage of G.D.P. 1989

0   5   10   15   20%

- Bulgaria
- Czechoslovakia
- Denmark
- France
- Germany
- Greece
- Hungary
- Rep. of Ireland
- Italy
- Netherlands
- Poland
- Portugal
- Romania
- Spain
- Sweden
- United Kingdom

72

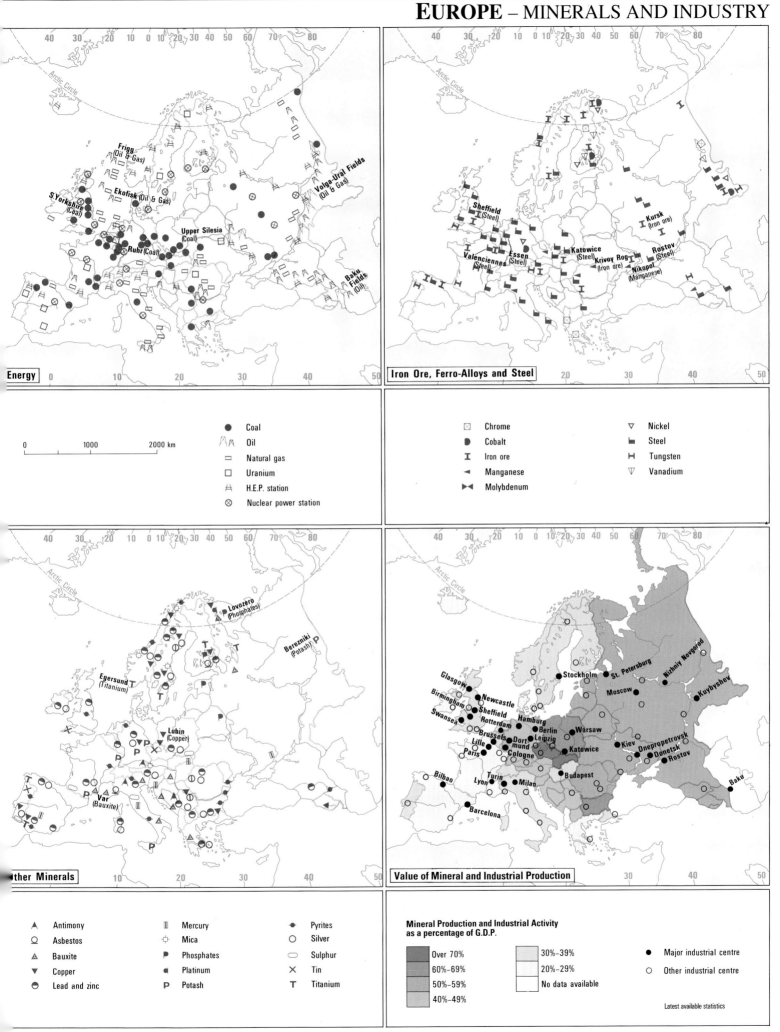

Energy

Frigg (Oil & Gas)
Ekofisk (Oil & Gas)
S Yorkshire (Coal)
Ruhr (Coal)
Upper Silesia (Coal)
Volga-Ural Fields (Oil & Gas)
Baku Fields (Oil)

●	Coal
∧∧	Oil
⊐	Natural gas
☐	Uranium
⚏	H.E.P. station
⊗	Nuclear power station

0 1000 2000 km

Iron Ore, Ferro-Alloys and Steel

Sheffield (Steel)
Valenciennes (Steel)
Essen (Steel)
Katowice (Steel)
Krivoy Rog (Iron ore)
Kursk (Iron ore)
Rostov (Steel)
Nikopol (Manganese)

⊠	Chrome	▽	Nickel
◗	Cobalt	⊨	Steel
I	Iron ore	⋈	Tungsten
◀	Manganese	▽	Vanadium
▶◀	Molybdenum		

Other Minerals

Lovozero (Phosphates)
Egersund (Titanium)
Berezniki (Potash)
Lubin (Copper)
Var (Bauxite)

▲	Antimony	⌶	Mercury	✦	Pyrites
⊖	Asbestos	✛	Mica	○	Silver
△	Bauxite	⊵	Phosphates	⬭	Sulphur
▼	Copper	◖	Platinum	✕	Tin
⊖	Lead and zinc	P	Potash	T	Titanium

Value of Mineral and Industrial Production

Glasgow
Birmingham
Swansea
Newcastle
Sheffield
Rotterdam
Brussels
Lille
Paris
Hamburg
Dortmund
Berlin
Cologne
Leipzig
Warsaw
Katowice
Kiev
Dnepropetrovsk
Donetsk
Rostov
Bilbao
Lyon
Turin
Milan
Budapest
Barcelona
Stockholm
St. Petersburg
Moscow
Nizhniy Novgorod
Kuybyshev
Baku

Mineral Production and Industrial Activity as a percentage of G.D.P.

▨	Over 70%
	60%–69%
	50%–59%
	40%–49%
	30%–39%
	20%–29%
	No data available

● Major industrial centre
○ Other industrial centre

Latest available statistics

EUROPE – POPULATION

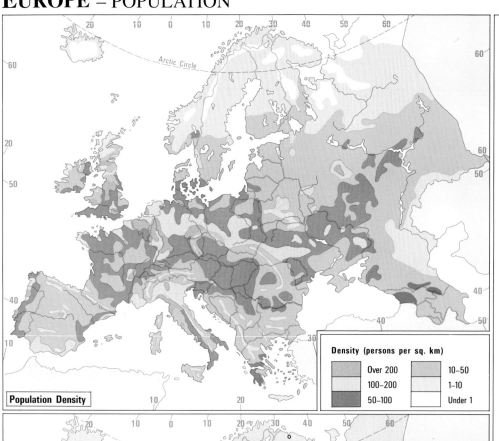

Population Density

Density (persons per sq. km)

Over 200	10–50
100–200	1–10
50–100	Under 1

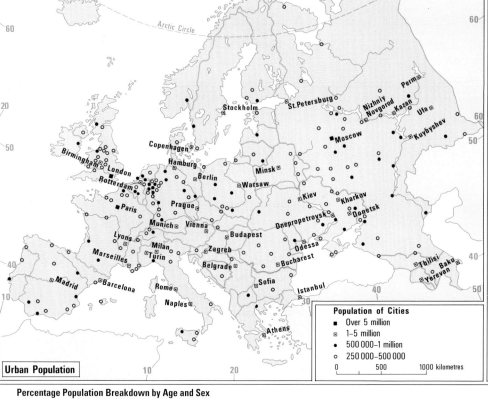

Urban Population

Population of Cities
- ■ Over 5 million
- ⊡ 1–5 million
- ● 500 000–1 million
- ○ 250 000–500 000

0   500   1000 kilometres

Life Expectancy by Selected Country

Country	Life Expectancy at birth Male	Female
Germany	71.8	78.4
Italy	72.0	78.6
United Kingdom	72.1	77.9
France	72.3	80.5
Spain	72.5	78.6
Poland	67.1	75.7
Romania	66.5	72.4
Austria	72.3	79.3
Netherlands	73.6	80.2
Hungary	65.4	73.8
Portugal	68.3	75.2
Greece	72.1	76.3
Belgium	70.0	76.8
Bulgaria	68.3	74.7

Population by Selected Country

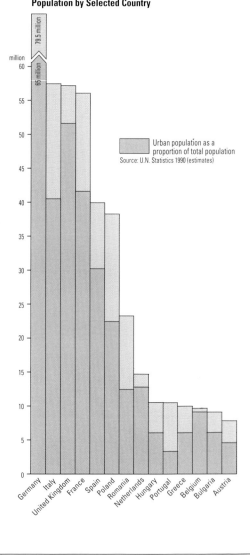

Urban population as a proportion of total population
Source: U.N. Statistics 1990 (estimates)

Percentage Population Breakdown by Age and Sex
Source: U.N. Demographic Yearbook 1990

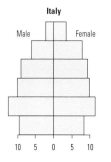

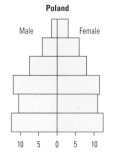

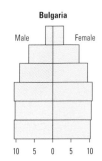

74

© COPYRIGHT MACMILLAN EDUCATION LTD

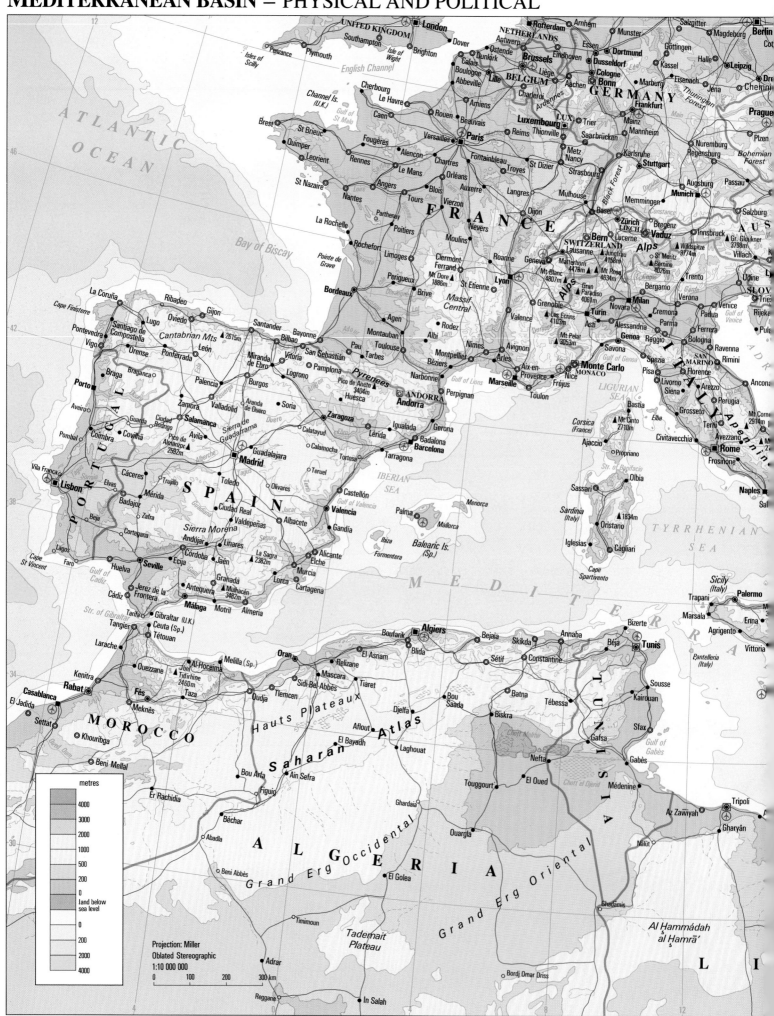

ATLANTIC OCEAN

UNITED KINGDOM
London
Penzance
Plymouth
Southampton
Isle of Wight
Brighton
Dover
Isles of Scilly
English Channel
Cherbourg
Channel Is. (U.K.)
Le Havre
Brest
St Brieuc
Quimper
Caen
Gulf of St Malo
Fougères
Rouen
Beauvais
Amiens
Abbeville
Charleroi
Ardennes
Boulogne
Calais
Dunkirk
Ostende
Lille
Antwerp
Brussels
BELGIUM
Liège
Aachen
Eindhoven
NETHERLANDS
Rotterdam
Arnhem
Munster
Essen
Dortmund
Dusseldorf
Cologne
Bonn
Marburg
Salzgitter
Magdeburg
Berlin
Cot
GERMANY
Göttingen
Kassel
Halle
Leipzig
Dre
Chemni
Eisenach
Jena
Thuringian Forest
Marburg
Frankfurt
Mainz
Prague
Plzen
Bohemian Forest
Mannheim
Saarbrücken
Karlsruhe
Nuremburg
Regensburg
Passau
Stuttgart
Augsburg
Munich
Salzburg
Memmingen
Basel
Constance
AUS
Villach
Gr. Glockner 3798m
Innsbruck
Wildspitze 3774m
Bern
Bregenz
Vaduz
LIECH.
Zürich
SWITZERLAND
Lausanne
Lucerne
Geneva
Matterhorn 4478m
Jungfrau 4158m
St Moritz
Bernina 4026m
Mt Rosa 4634m
Mt Blanc 4807m
Alps
Gran Paradiso 4061m
Trento
Udine
SLOV
Tries
Pula
ADR
France
Paris
Versailles
Chartres
Fontainebleau
Orléans
St Dizier
Troyes
Reims
Thionville
Metz
Nancy
Strasbourg
Mulhouse
Black Forest
Dijon
Nevers
Moulins
Roanne
Langres
Luxembourg
LUX
Trier
Alencon
Le Mans
Angers
Rennes
St Nazaire
Nantes
Blois
Vierzon
Tours
Parthenay
Auxerre
Poitiers
La Rochelle
Rochefort
Limoges
Périgueux
Brive
Clermont-Ferrand
Mt Dore 1886m
St Étienne
Lyon
Valence
Grenoble
Les Ecrins 4103m
Mt Pelat 3053m
Geneva
Massif Central
Agen
Montauban
Rodez
Albi
Tarn
Nîmes
Avignon
Arles
Aix-en-Provence
Marseille
Gulf of Lions
Monte Carlo
MONACO
Nice
Fréjus
Toulon
Durance
Turin
Milan
Novara
Cremona
Verona
Bergamo
Asti
Alessandria
Parma
Genoa
Reggio
Savona
Spezia
Padua
Venice
Gulf of Venice
Rijeka
Ferrera
Bologna
Ravenna
Rimini
LIGURIAN SEA
Bastia
Corsica (France)
Mt Cinto 2710m
Ajaccio
Propriano
Pisa
Livorno
Siena
Florence
Arezzo
Perugia
Grosseto
Terni
Mt Corno 2914m
Ancona
ITALY
Apennin
SAN MARINO
Pico de Almanzor 2592m
Pau
Tarbes
Toulouse
Béziers
Montpellier
Narbonne
Perpignan
ANDORRA
Andorra
Huesca
Pico de Aneto 3404m
Pyrenees
Bayonne
St Jean
Bordeaux
Pointe de Grave
La Coruña
Cape Finisterre
Santiago de Compostela
Pontevedra
Vigo
Lugo
Orense
Oviedo
Gijón
Ribadeo
León
Ponferrada
Cantabrian Mts
2615m
Santander
Bilbao
Miranda de Ebro
Vitoria
San Sebastián
Pamplona
Logroño
Aranda de Duero
Soria
Calatayud
Zaragoza
Lérida
Igualada
Barcelona
Badalona
Gerona
Tarragona
Tortosa
Teruel
Calamocha
Zamora
Valladolid
Palencia
Burgos
Braga
Bragança
Porto
Aveiro
Pombal
Guarda
Ciudad Rodrigo
Salamanca
Ávila
Sierra de Guadarrama
Madrid
Guadalajara
Coimbra
Covilhã
Vila Franca
Lisbon
Elvas
Cáceres
Trujillo
Toledo
Olivares
Mérida
Badajoz
Zafra
Beja
Lagos
Cortegana
PORTUGAL
SPAIN
Sierra Morena
Ciudad Real
Valdepeñas
Albacete
Alcázar
La Sagra 2382m
Murcia
Lorca
Cartagena
Alicante
Elche
Gandía
Valencia
Gulf of Valencia
Castellón
IBERIAN SEA
Palma
Ibiza
Formentera
Mallorca
Menorca
Balearic Is. (Sp.)
Huelva
Seville
Écija
Córdoba
Jaén
Linares
Andújar
Antequera
Granada
Mulhacén 3482m
Motril
Almería
Málaga
Gibraltar (U.K.)
Str. of Gibraltar
Tarifa
Ceuta (Sp.)
Tétouan
Tangier
Larache
Kenitra
Rabat
Casablanca
El Jadida
Settat
Khouribga
Beni Mellal
MOROCCO
Ouezzane
Melilla (Sp.)
Al-Hoceima
Jbel Tidirhine 2460m
Fès
Meknès
Taza
Oujda
Tlemcen
Sidi-Bel-Abbès
Mascara
Tiaret
Oran
Relizane
El Asnam
Mostaganem
Boufarik
Blida
Algiers
Bejaia
Skikda
Annaba
Béja
Bizerte
Tunis
TUNISIA
Sousse
Kairouan
Sfax
Gulf of Gabès
Gabès
Médenine
Nefta
Gafsa
Tébessa
Batna
Biskra
Constantine
Sétif
Bou Saâda
Djelfa
Aflout
Laghouat
El Bayadh
Atlas
Saharan
Hauts Plateaux
Bou Arfa
Ain Sefra
Figuig
Er Rachidia
Béchar
Abadla
Beni Abbès
Timimoun
Adrar
Reggane
In Salah
Tademaït Plateau
ALGERIA
Grand Erg Occidental
Grand Erg Oriental
El Golea
Ghardaia
Ouargla
Touggourt
El Oued
Nefta
Chott el Djerid
Chott Melrhir
Nalūt
Ghadamis
Az Zawiyah
Tripoli
Gharyān
Al Hammādah al Hamrā'
LI
MEDITERRANEAN
TYRRHENIAN SEA
Sardinia (Italy)
1834m
Oristano
Iglesias
Cagliari
Sassari
Olbia
Str. of Bonifacio
Civitavecchia
Rome
Frosinone
Avezzano
Naples
Sal
Cape Spartivento
Sicily (Italy)
Palermo
Trapani
Marsala
Enna
Agrigento
Vittoria
Pantelleria (Italy)

© COPYRIGHT MACMILLAN EDUCATION LTD

77

RHINE BASIN – ECONOMIC

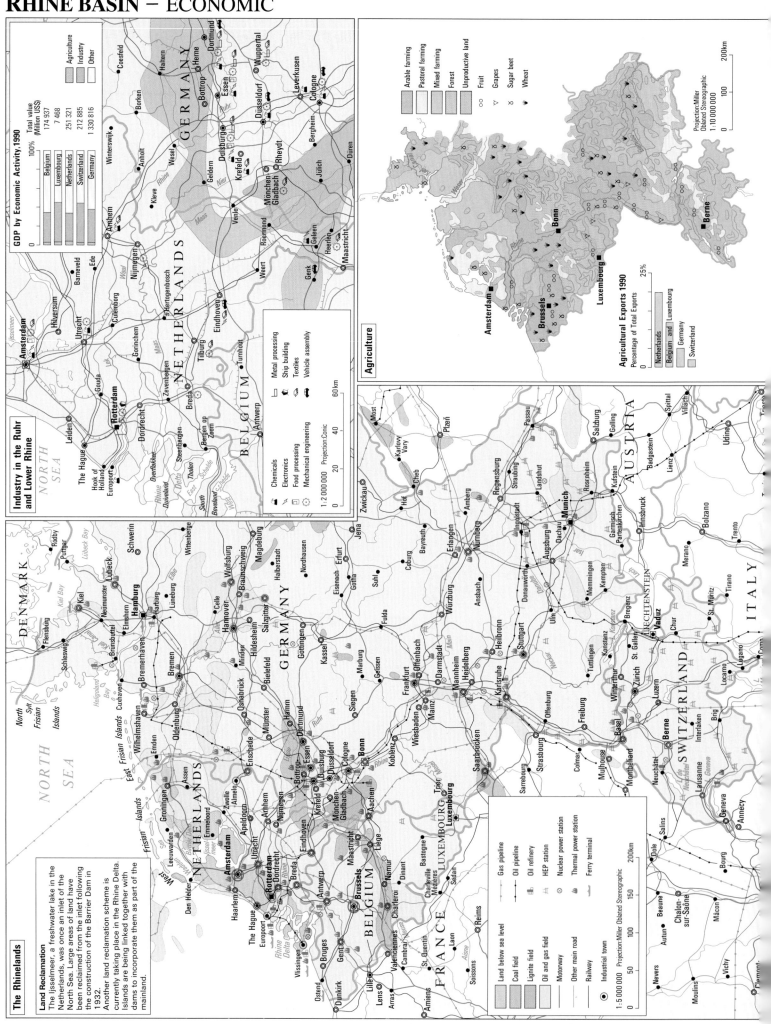

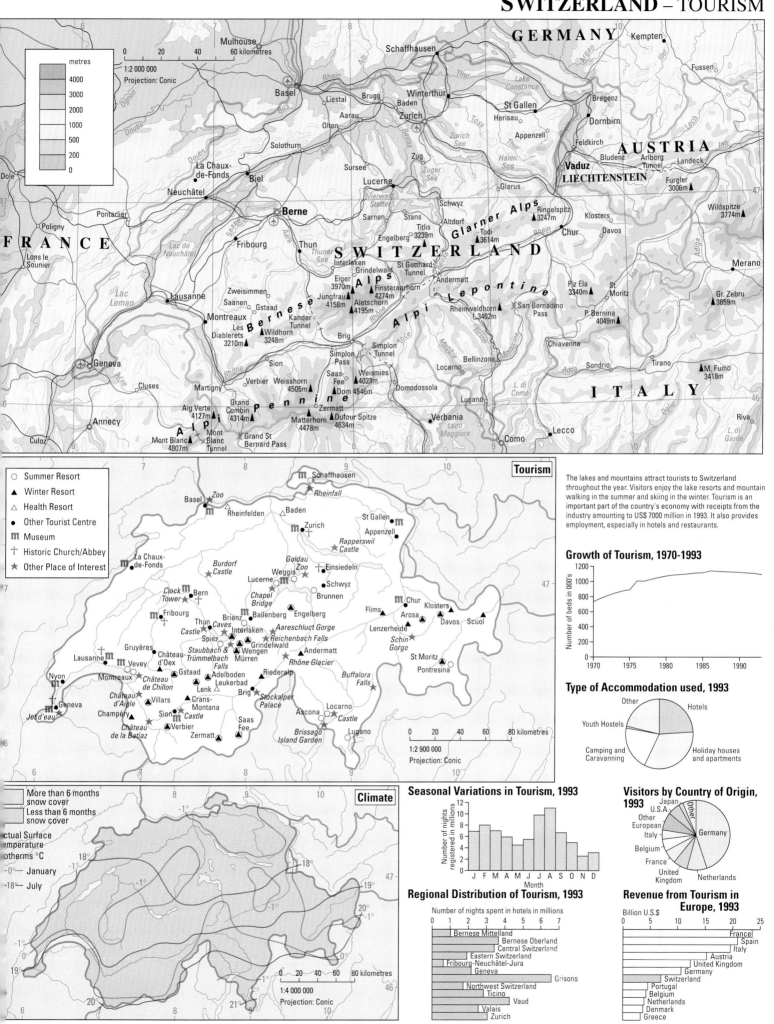

The lakes and mountains attract tourists to Switzerland throughout the year. Visitors enjoy the lake resorts and mountain walking in the summer and skiing in the winter. Tourism is an important part of the country's economy with receipts from the industry amounting to US$ 7000 million in 1993. It also provides employment, especially in hotels and restaurants.

BRITISH ISLES – PHYSICAL AND POLITICAL

Projection: Transverse Mercator
1:4 500 000

Metres
1000
500
200
0
Land below sea level
200

0   40   80   120   160 km

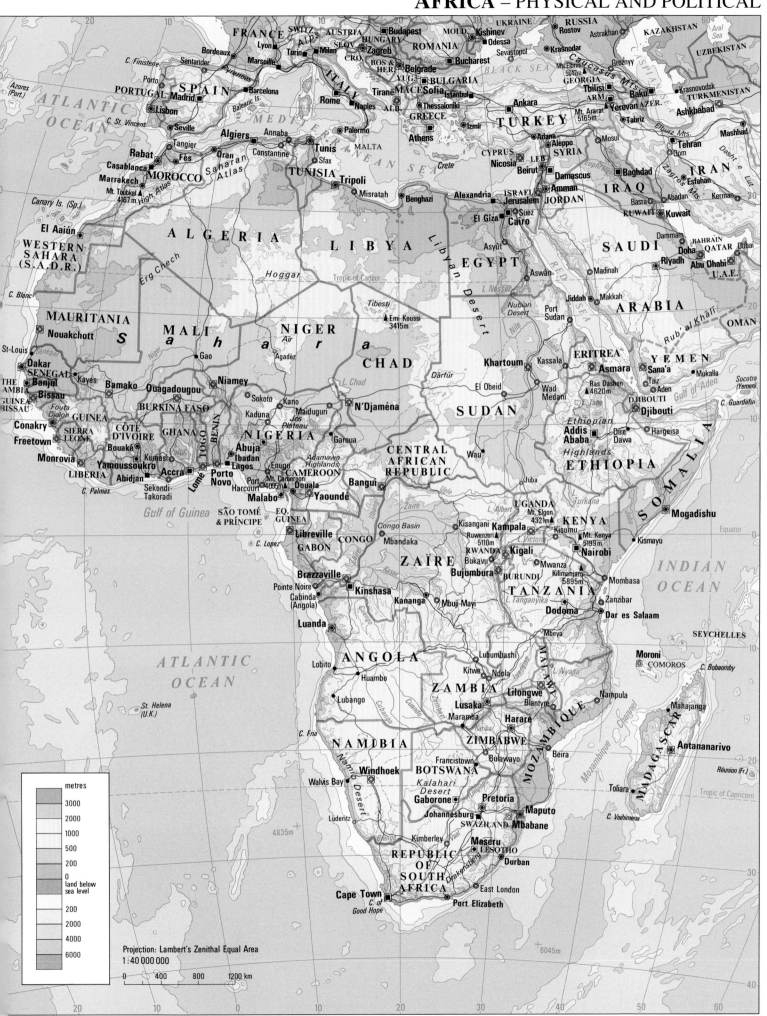

AFRICA – CLIMATE

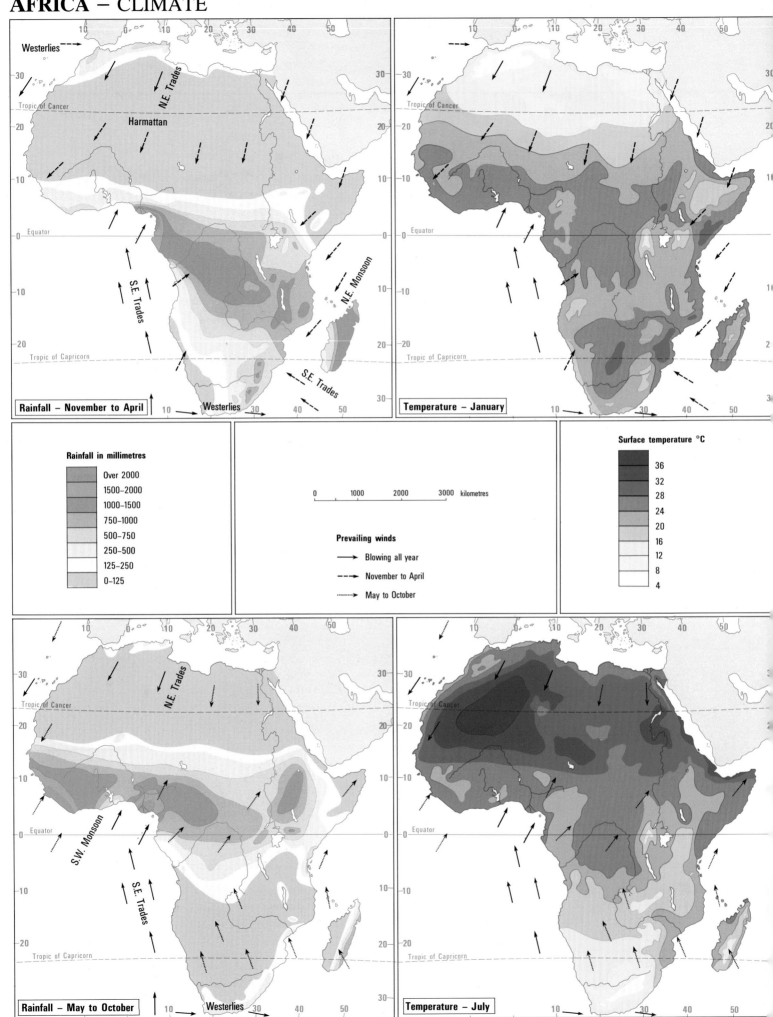

Westerlies

N.E. Trades

Harmattan

Tropic of Cancer

S.E. Trades

N.E. Monsoon

Equator

Tropic of Capricorn

S.E. Trades

Rainfall – November to April

Westerlies

Temperature – January

Rainfall in millimetres

	Over 2000
	1500–2000
	1000–1500
	750–1000
	500–750
	250–500
	125–250
	0–125

0   1000   2000   3000 kilometres

Prevailing winds

→ Blowing all year

--→ November to April

····→ May to October

Surface temperature °C

	36
	32
	28
	24
	20
	16
	12
	8
	4

N.E. Trades

Tropic of Cancer

S.W. Monsoon

Equator

S.E. Trades

Tropic of Capricorn

Rainfall – May to October

Westerlies

N.E. Trades

Tropic of Cancer

Equator

Tropic of Capricorn

Temperature – July

MEDITERRANEAN SEA

Str. of Gibraltar
Tell Atlas
Saharan Atlas
High Atlas
Canary Is.
G. of Gabes
G. of Sirte
Libyan Desert
Eastern Desert
RED SEA
Nubian Desert
Tropic of Cancer
Vert
Senégal
S a h a r a
Niger
L. Chad
Fouta Djalon
Jos Plateau
Benue
Volta
Adamawa Highlands
Bight of Benin
C. Palmas
Gulf of Guinea
Nile
White Nile
L. Tana
Ethiopian Highlands
Gulf of Aden
Somali Peninsula
L. Turkana
Uele
Congo Basin
Zaire
Rift Valley
Equator
ATLANTIC OCEAN
INDIAN OCEAN
Tanganyika
Bié Plateau
Nyasa
Comoro Is.
Namib Desert
Kalahari Desert
Zambezi
Mozambique Channel
Madagascar
Limpopo
Tropic of Capricorn
Orange
Vaal
Drakensberg
Great Karoo
C. of Good Hope

- Cultivated land
- Cultivated land and grazing land
- Grassland and grazing land
- Forest and woodland
- Swamp and marsh
- Semi-desert and desert

Projection: Lambert's Zenithal Equal Area
1 : 40 000 000

0   400   800   1200 km

The above map shows the present day natural environment of the African continent. This map differs from the vegetation map on page 122 in that it shows how man has modified the natural landscape through intensive agriculture, grazing and urban development.
However, vast areas of the continent's desert and tropical rain forest environment remain relatively unaffected by man. The table on the right indicates the percentage distribution of land use in Africa, divided into four main categories.

Land Use	1964–1966	1981–1983
Cultivated land	5%	6%
Grassland and grazing land	26%	26%
Forest and woodland	25%	23%
Other land	43%	44%

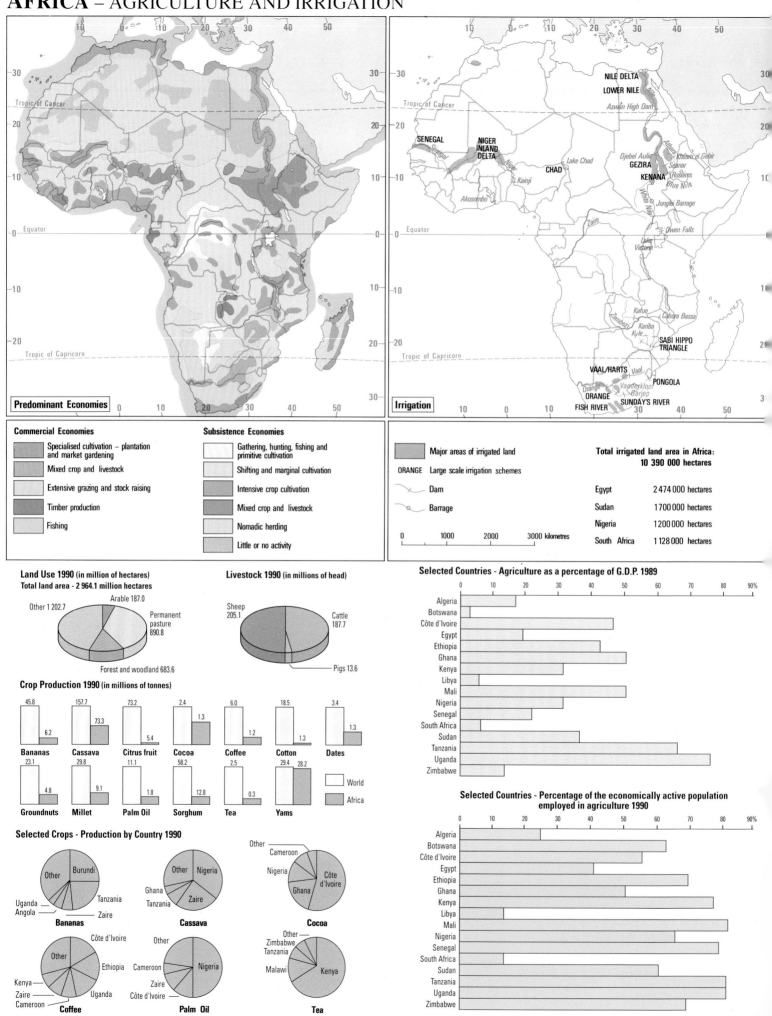

Predominant Economies

Commercial Economies
- Specialised cultivation – plantation and market gardening
- Mixed crop and livestock
- Extensive grazing and stock raising
- Timber production
- Fishing

Subsistence Economies
- Gathering, hunting, fishing and primitive cultivation
- Shifting and marginal cultivation
- Intensive crop cultivation
- Mixed crop and livestock
- Nomadic herding
- Little or no activity

Irrigation

- Major areas of irrigated land
- ORANGE Large scale irrigation schemes
- Dam
- Barrage

0   1000   2000   3000 kilometres

Total irrigated land area in Africa:
10 390 000 hectares

Egypt	2 474 000 hectares
Sudan	1 700 000 hectares
Nigeria	1 200 000 hectares
South Africa	1 128 000 hectares

Land Use 1990 (in million of hectares)
Total land area - 2 964.1 million hectares

Other 1 202.7
Arable 187.0
Permanent pasture 890.8
Forest and woodland 683.6

Livestock 1990 (in millions of head)

Sheep 205.1
Cattle 187.7
Pigs 13.6

Crop Production 1990 (in millions of tonnes)

Crop	World	Africa
Bananas	45.8	6.2
Cassava	157.7	73.3
Citrus fruit	73.2	5.4
Cocoa	2.4	1.3
Coffee	6.0	1.2
Cotton	18.5	1.3
Dates	3.4	1.3
Groundnuts	23.1	4.8
Millet	29.8	9.1
Palm Oil	11.1	1.8
Sorghum	58.2	12.8
Tea	2.5	0.3
Yams	29.4	28.2

World / Africa

Selected Crops - Production by Country 1990

Bananas — Other, Burundi, Tanzania, Zaire, Angola, Uganda

Cassava — Other, Nigeria, Zaire, Tanzania, Ghana

Cocoa — Other, Cameroon, Nigeria, Côte d'Ivoire, Ghana

Coffee — Other, Côte d'Ivoire, Ethiopia, Uganda, Cameroon, Zaire, Kenya

Palm Oil — Other, Nigeria, Zaire, Côte d'Ivoire, Cameroon

Tea — Other, Zimbabwe, Tanzania, Kenya, Malawi

Selected Countries - Agriculture as a percentage of G.D.P. 1989

Algeria, Botswana, Côte d'Ivoire, Egypt, Ethiopia, Ghana, Kenya, Libya, Mali, Nigeria, Senegal, South Africa, Sudan, Tanzania, Uganda, Zimbabwe

Selected Countries - Percentage of the economically active population employed in agriculture 1990

Algeria, Botswana, Côte d'Ivoire, Egypt, Ethiopia, Ghana, Kenya, Libya, Mali, Nigeria, Senegal, South Africa, Sudan, Tanzania, Uganda, Zimbabwe

AFRICA – DESERTIFICATION AND ENVIRONMENTAL PROBLEMS

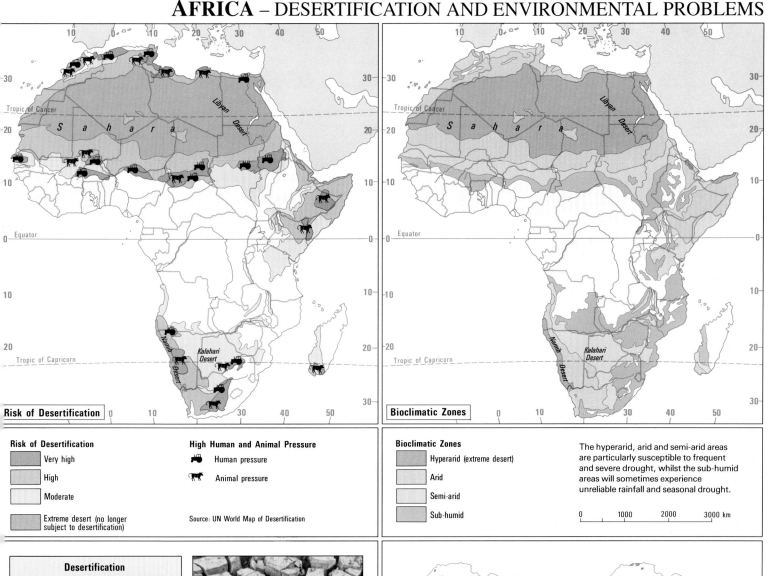

Risk of Desertification

Bioclimatic Zones

Risk of Desertification

- Very high
- High
- Moderate
- Extreme desert (no longer subject to desertification)

High Human and Animal Pressure

- 🚜 Human pressure
- 🐂 Animal pressure

Source: UN World Map of Desertification

Bioclimatic Zones

- Hyperarid (extreme desert)
- Arid
- Semi-arid
- Sub-humid

The hyperarid, arid and semi-arid areas are particularly susceptible to frequent and severe drought, whilst the sub-humid areas will sometimes experience unreliable rainfall and seasonal drought.

0   1000   2000   3000 km

Desertification

Desertification is the extension of desert conditions to the arid and semi-arid zones bordering extreme deserts. It is becoming more commonly accepted that the major causes of desertification are a combination of increasing human and animal pressure on the land, in conjunction with occasional periods of severe drought. Man's activities of overcultivation, overgrazing and large scale destruction of woodland for fuel in these vulnerable areas has led to the removal of the natural vegetation cover. Surface run-off and the resultant soil erosion has become an increasing problem leading to the inability of the environment to support ever increasing population levels.

During the dry season the ground becomes hard, developing wide cracks, and cannot hold enough moisture to permit plant growth. The unreliability of the rainfall can lead to severe droughts causing famine and starvation.

Deforestation

Deforestation is the term used to describe the removal and clearance of forested areas, by man. It is estimated that some 12 million hectares of forest are being removed annually throughout the world, and consequently such severe deforestation is having an extremely serious effect on the environment. In Africa, both tropical forest and open woodland are being rapidly depleted to provide the expanding population with fuelwood, timber and additional land for cultivation. The poor tropical soils left after forest clearance are generally unsuitable for cultivation, only remaining fertile for a short period of time, and they are particularly susceptible to soil erosion.

Deforestation

- Tropical forest
- —— Areas of forest undergoing rapid removal

0   2000   4000 km

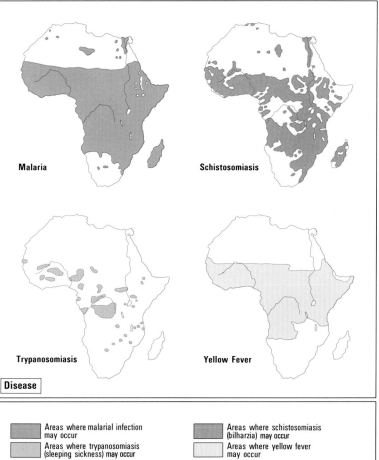

Malaria

Schistosomiasis

Trypanosomiasis

Yellow Fever

Disease

- Areas where malarial infection may occur
- Areas where trypanosomiasis (sleeping sickness) may occur
- Areas where schistosomiasis (bilharzia) may occur
- Areas where yellow fever may occur

AFRICA – MINERALS AND ENERGY

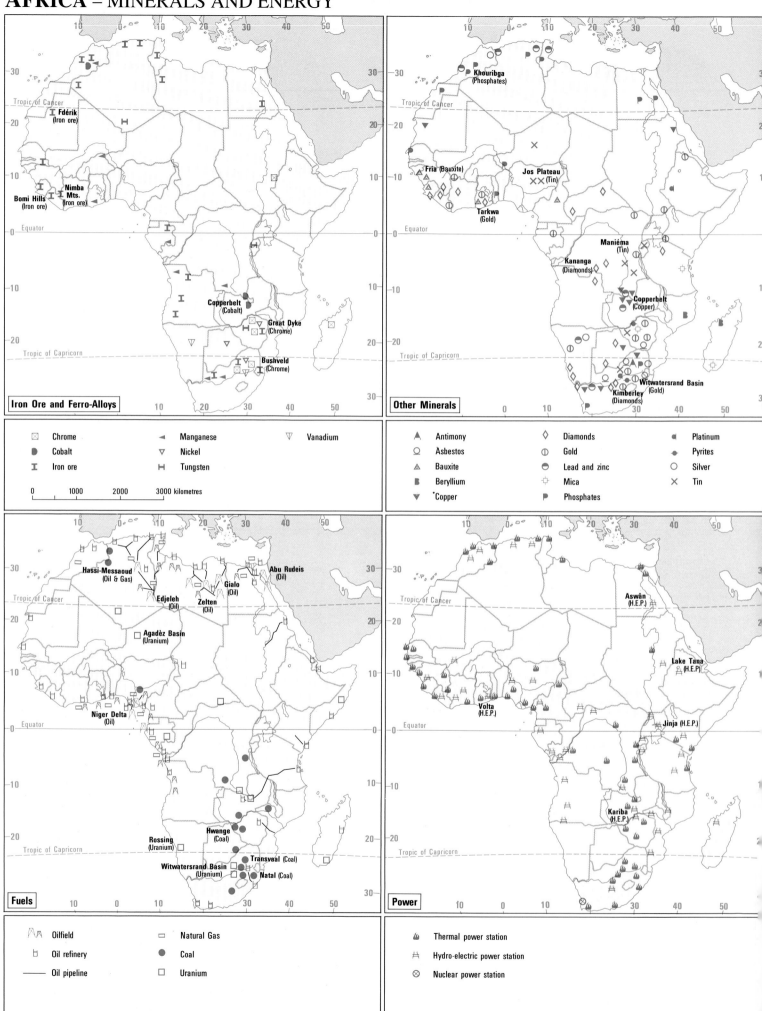

Iron Ore and Ferro-Alloys

Fdérik (Iron ore)
Bomi Hills (Iron ore)
Nimba Mts. (Iron ore)
Copperbelt (Cobalt)
Great Dyke (Chrome)
Bushveld (Chrome)

⊠ Chrome	◄ Manganese	▽ Vanadium
◖ Cobalt	▽ Nickel	
I Iron ore	⊢ Tungsten	

0   1000   2000   3000 kilometres

Other Minerals

Khouribga (Phosphates)
Fria (Bauxite)
Jos Plateau (Tin)
Tarkwa (Gold)
Maniéma (Tin)
Kananga (Diamonds)
Copperbelt (Copper)
Witwatersrand Basin (Gold)
Kimberley (Diamonds)

▲ Antimony	◇ Diamonds	◧ Platinum
◔ Asbestos	◍ Gold	◆ Pyrites
△ Bauxite	⊖ Lead and zinc	○ Silver
⬕ Beryllium	⊕ Mica	✕ Tin
▼ *Copper	℗ Phosphates	

Fuels

Hassi-Messaoud (Oil & Gas)
Edjeleh (Oil)
Gialo (Oil)
Zelten (Oil)
Abu Rudeis (Oil)
Agadèz Basin (Uranium)
Niger Delta (Oil)
Rossing (Uranium)
Hwange (Coal)
Transvaal (Coal)
Witwatersrand Basin (Uranium)
Natal (Coal)

⋀⋀ Oilfield	▯ Natural Gas
♭ Oil refinery	● Coal
— Oil pipeline	▢ Uranium

Power

Aswân (H.E.P.)
Lake Tana (H.E.P.)
Volta (H.E.P.)
Jinja (H.E.P.)
Kariba (H.E.P.)

♨ Thermal power station
⌗ Hydro-electric power station
⊗ Nuclear power station

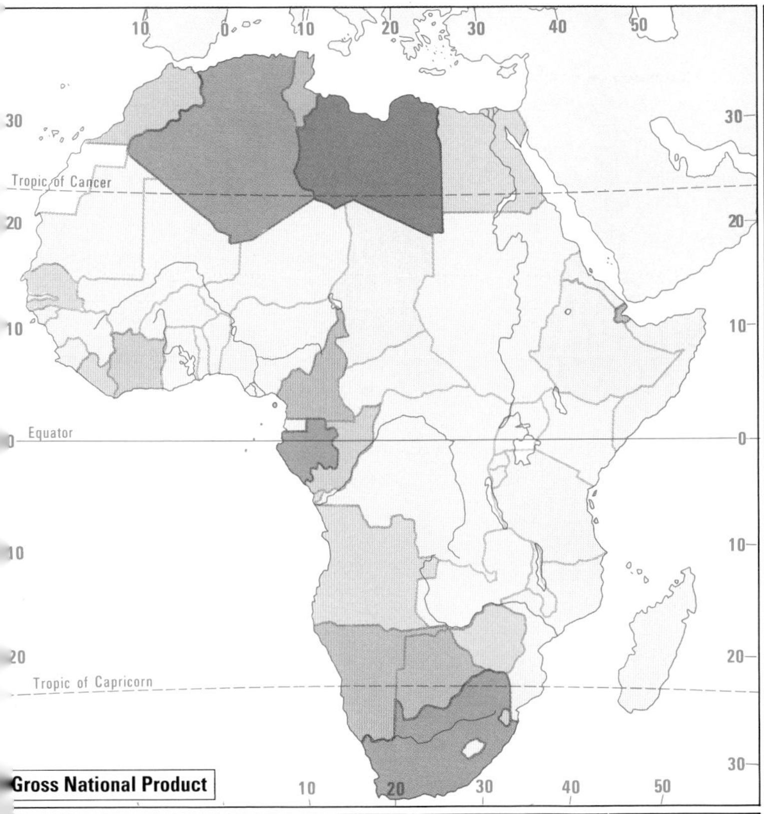

Tropic of Cancer
Equator
Tropic of Capricorn

Gross National Product

G.N.P. per capita 1989 (U.S. dollars)

- More than 5000
- 2000–4999
- 1000–1999
- 750–999
- 500–749
- 250–499
- 0–249
- No data available

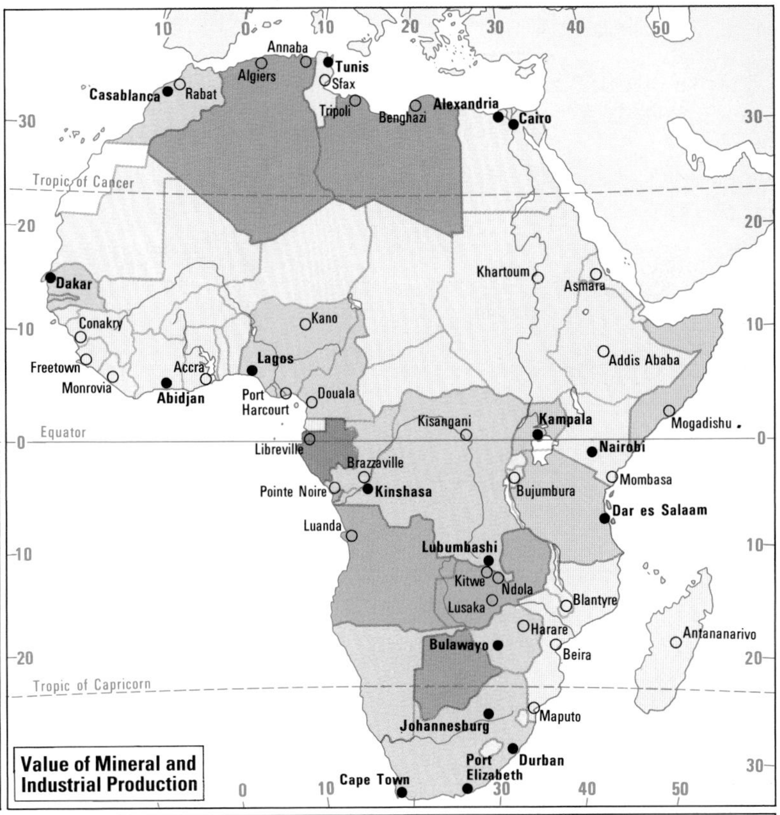

Annaba
Tunis
Algiers
Sfax
Casablanca
Rabat
Tripoli
Benghazi
Alexandria
Cairo
Khartoum
Asmara
Dakar
Kano
Conakry
Addis Ababa
Freetown
Accra
Lagos
Monrovia
Abidjan
Port Harcourt
Douala
Kisangani
Kampala
Mogadishu
Libreville
Nairobi
Brazzaville
Mombasa
Pointe Noire
Kinshasa
Bujumbura
Dar es Salaam
Luanda
Lubumbashi
Kitwe
Ndola
Blantyre
Lusaka
Harare
Antananarivo
Bulawayo
Beira
Maputo
Johannesburg
Durban
Port Elizabeth
Cape Town
Tropic of Cancer
Equator
Tropic of Capricorn

Value of Mineral and Industrial Production

Mineral Production and Industrial Activity as a percentage of G.D.P.

- More than 60%
- 50%–59%
- 40%–49%
- 30%–39%
- 20%–29%
- 10%–19%
- 0%–9%
- No data available
- ● Major industrial centre
- ○ Other industrial centre

Latest available statistics

Annaba
Tunis
Algiers
Sfax
Casablanca
Rabat
Tripoli
Benghazi
Alexandria
Cairo
Dakar
Khartoum
Asmara
Conakry
Kano
Freetown
Accra
Lagos
Addis Ababa
Monrovia
Abidjan
Port Harcourt
Douala
Kampala
Mogadishu
Kisangani
Libreville
Nairobi
Brazzaville
Mombasa
Bujumbura
Pointe Noire
Kinshasa
Dar es Salaam
Luanda
Lubumbashi
Kitwe
Ndola
Blantyre
Lusaka
Harare
Antananarivo
Bulawayo
Beira
Tropic of Capricorn
Johannesburg
Maputo
Cape Town
Port Elizabeth
Durban

Industry

- Iron and steel
- Engineering
- Ship building
- Vehicles
- Chemicals
- Textiles
- Timber and paper
- Food processing

0 1000 2000 3000 kilometres

Exports by Commodity Group for Selected Countries 1990 (or latest available statistics)

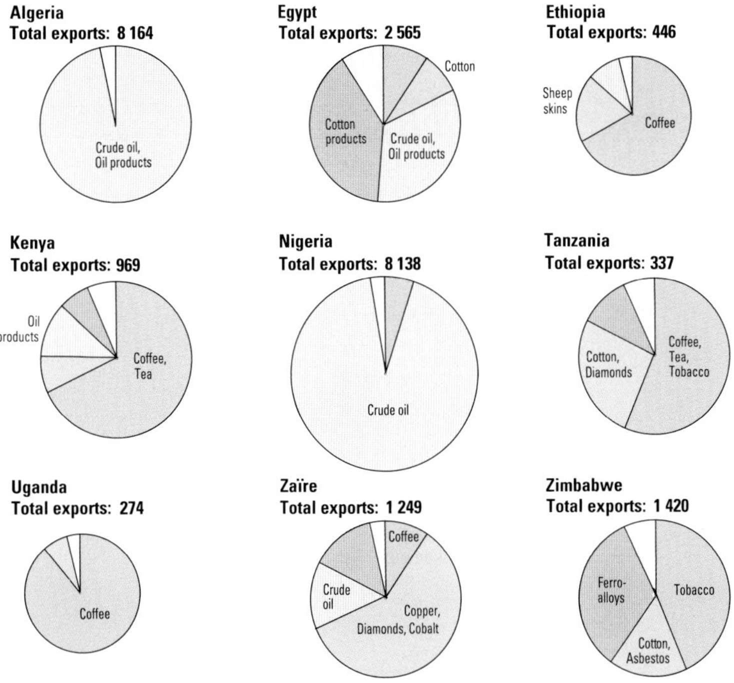

Algeria
Total exports: 8 164
Crude oil, Oil products
Egypt
Total exports: 2 565
Cotton
Cotton products
Crude oil, Oil products
Ethiopia
Total exports: 446
Sheep skins
Coffee
Kenya
Total exports: 969
Oil products
Coffee, Tea
Nigeria
Total exports: 8 138
Crude oil
Tanzania
Total exports: 337
Cotton, Diamonds
Coffee, Tea, Tobacco
Uganda
Total exports: 274
Coffee
Zaïre
Total exports: 1 249
Coffee
Crude oil
Copper, Diamonds, Cobalt
Zimbabwe
Total exports: 1 420
Ferro-alloys
Tobacco
Cotton, Asbestos

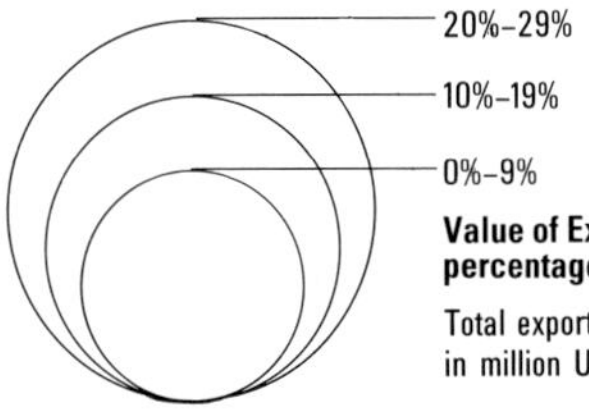

20%–29%
10%–19%
0%–9%

Value of Exports as a percentage of G.N.P.

Total export figures in million US dollars

Commodity Groups

- Food, beverages and tobacco
- Raw materials, excluding fuels
- Crude oil and petroleum
- Machinery and manufactured goods
- Others (may include above categories where these are small)
- Tea, Coffee — Major export goods

© COPYRIGHT MACMILLAN EDUCATION LTD

AFRICA – POPULATION

Population Density

Population Density

Urban Population

Casablanca · Algiers · Alexandria · Cairo · El Giza · Addis Ababa · Abidjan · Accra · Lagos · Nairobi · Kinshasa · Johannesburg · Cape Town

Urban Population

Density (persons per sq. km)
- Over 100
- 50–100
- 25–50
- 5–25
- Under 5

0 1000 2000 3000 kilometres

Population of Cities
- ■ Over 5 million
- ⊡ 1–5 million
- ● 500 000 – 1 million
- ○ 250 000 – 500 000

0 1000 2000 3000 kilometres

Population by Selected Country

Nigeria — 108.5 million
Egypt
Ethiopia
Zaire
South Africa
Tanzania
Sudan
Morocco
Algeria
Kenya
Uganda
Mozambique
Ghana
Côte d'Ivoire

Urban population as a proportion of total population

Source: U.N. Statistics 1990 (estimates)

Life Expectancy by Selected Country

Country	Life expectancy at birth Male	Female	Country	Life expectancy at birth Male	Female
Nigeria	48.8	52.2	Morocco	59.1	62.5
Egypt	57.8	60.3	Algeria	61.6	63.3
Ethiopia	42.4	45.6	Kenya	56.5	60.5
Zaire	50.3	53.7	Uganda	49.4	52.7
South Africa	57.5	63.5	Mozambique	44.9	48.1
Tanzania	51.3	54.7	Ghana	52.2	55.8
Sudan	48.6	51.0	Côte d'Ivoire	50.8	54.2

Percentage Population Breakdown by Age and Sex

Source: U.N. Demographic Yearbook 1990

Egypt · Ethiopia · Zaire

Age: 75+ · 60-74 · 45-59 · 30-44 · 15-29 · 0-14 years

Male / Female

Percent

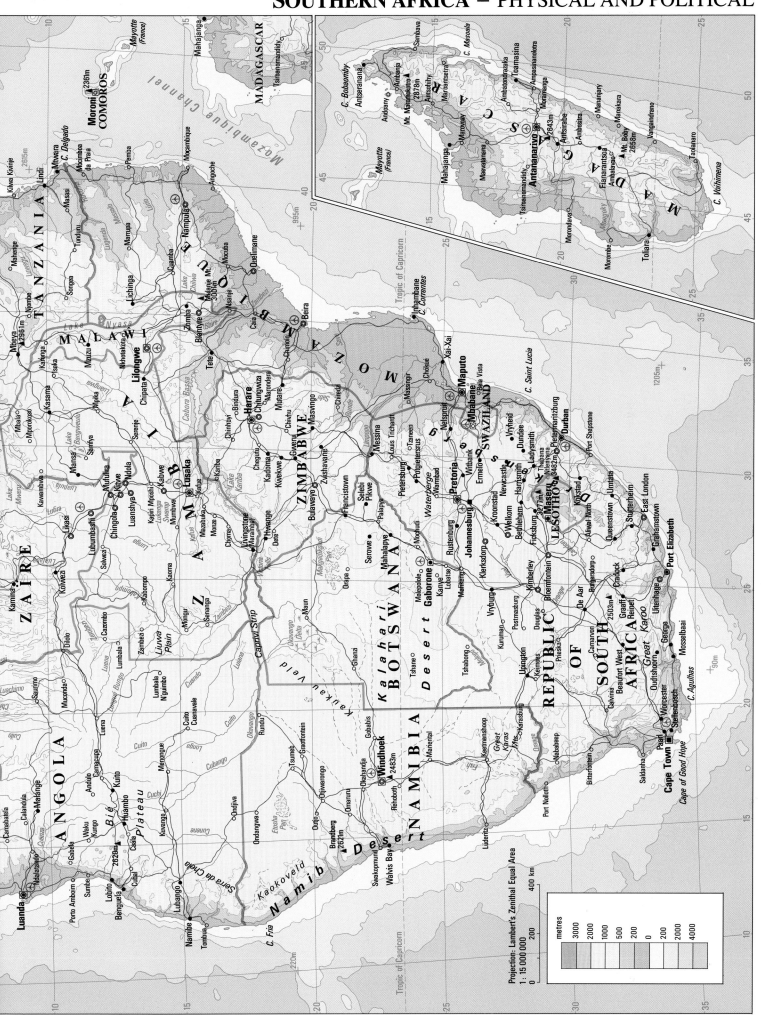

Projection: Lambert's Zenithal Equal Area
1 : 15 000 000
0   200   400 km

SOUTHERN AFRICA – ECONOMIC

Minerals and Industry (map)

Major industrial centre
Secondary industrial centre
Minor industrial centre

U Uranium
Oilfield
Oil pipeline

Lead and zinc
Manganese
Natural gas
Phosphates

Platinum
Salt
Silver
Tin

Copper
Diamonds
Gold
Iron ore

Asbestos
Chrome
Coal
Cobalt

Minerals and Industry

Map labels (Minerals and Industry):
Comoro Is., Mahajanga, Antananarivo, Toamasina, Antananarivo, Mahajanga, Toamasina, Antananarivo
Nacala, Mozambique, Blantyre, Lilongwe, L. Nyasa, Beira, Inhambane, Lubumbashi, Ndola, Chipata, Kolwezi, Kitwe, Lusaka, Kafue, Huambo, Livingstone, Harare, Mutare, Louis Trichard, Maputo, Pietermaritzburg, Durban, Kwekwe, Bulawayo, Johannesburg, Pretoria, Selebi Pikwe, Gaborone, Bloemfontein, East London, Kimberley, Port Elizabeth, Mosselbaai, Windhoek, Saldanha, Cape Town, C. of Good Hope, Walvis Bay, Lüderitz, Lobito, Namibe, C. Fria

SADC (map)

SADC (Southern African Development Community) aims to establish common economic, political and social values and systems; and strengthened regional solidarity, peace and security. Each member country is responsible for co-ordinating specific development areas, as outlined below.

Member of SADC
Landlocked member of SADC

Country	Area of Responsibility *
ANGOLA	Energy
BOTSWANA	Control of Livestock Disease and Agricultural Research
LESOTHO	Tourism, Land Use and Conservation
MALAŴI	Fisheries, Wildlife and Forestry
MOZAMBIQUE	Transport and Communications
SWAZILAND	Manpower Development and
TANZANIA	Industrial Development and Trade
ZAMBIA	Mining
ZIMBABWE	Food Security

Map labels (SADC): Mombasa, Dar es Salaam, Nacala, Nampula, Mombiquez Channel, Tropic of Capricorn, MADAGASCAR, KENYA, Nairobi, Kampala, UGANDA, RWANDA, Kigali, BURUNDI, Bujumbura, ZAÏRE, Kinshasa, Brazzaville, CONGO, GABON, CABINDA (Angola), Luanda, ANGOLA, Huambo, Lobito, Lubango, Kananga, Kasai, Ilebo, Lubumbashi, Kalemie, Kasama, L. Tanganyika, Mwanza, Arusha, Dodoma, TANZANIA, Mbeya, Kigoma, L. Nyasa, MALAŴI, Lilongwe, Blantyre, Tete, Lindi, MOZAMBIQUE, Beira, Nampula, ZAMBIA, Lusaka, Ndola, Livingstone, ZIMBABWE, Harare, Bulawayo, Francistown, BOTSWANA, Gaborone, NAMIBIA, Windhoek, Walvis Bay, Maun, SOUTH AFRICA, Johannesburg, Pretoria, SWAZILAND, Mbabane, Maputo, LESOTHO, Maseru, Durban, Port Elizabeth, Cape Town, Cape of Good Hope

(Namibia's Area of Responsibility to be decided)
(S. Africa's Area of Responsibility to be decided)

1:40 000 000
0   500   1000 km

Agriculture (map)

Agriculture

Commercial farming – e.g. cereals, citrus fruit, groundnuts, tea
Irrigated farming – e.g. cotton, sugar cane
Subsistence farming – e.g. maize, millet, goats, sheep
Non-intensive livestock rearing – e.g. cattle, goats, sheep
Desert – some nomadic herding
Lake and sea fishing
Forest

Projection: Lambert's Zenithal Equal Area
1:32 000 000
0   400   800   1200 km

Map labels (Agriculture): Comoro Is., Mozambique Channel, Antananarivo, Lilongwe, Lusaka, Harare, Maputo, Pretoria, Gaborone, Windhoek, Cape Town, C. of Good Hope, C. Fria, Tropic of Capricorn

Conservation and Tourism (map)

Conservation and Tourism

Forest
National park
National reserve/

Historic site
Recreational fishing
Place of interest
Game park
Beach
Fort
Prehistoric site

Projection: Lambert's Zenithal Equal Area
1:32 000 000
0   400   800 km

Map labels (Conservation and Tourism): Comoro Is., Mozambique Channel, Mahajanga, Antananarivo, Antseranana, Nosy-Be, L. Tritiva, Lac Sacré, ISALO, L. Evata, Taolagnaro, L. Nyasa, Livingstonia, Zumba, Mt. Mulanje, Salima, NORTH LUANGWA, SOUTH LUANGWA, Cabana, Cabora Bassa, Pungwe Gorge, GORONGOSA, Beira, Inhassoro, Vilanculos, Livingstone Memorial, Kariba Falls, Mundalila Falls, Wonder, Gorge, Katue Bge, Kariba Dam, Mutare, Great Zimbabwe, GONAREZHOU, Banhine, Echo Caves, Nossa Senhora de Conceicao, Maputo, LUIWA PLAIN, SIOMA NGWEZI, Lukulu, KAFUE, CHOBE, Maun, CENTRAL KALAHARI, HWANGE, Kgwanda Hills, Palapye, KRUGER, Sudwala Caves, Pretoria, Johannesburg, Port Shepstone, Port St. Johns, Durban, East London, Port Elizabeth, Mosselbaai, Kimberley, Gariep Dam, Bloemhof Dam, Vaal Dam, Cango Caves, GEMSBOK, Gaborone, QUICAMA, LUANDO, CAMEIA, BIKAUR, MUPA, ETOSHA, IONA, SKELETON COAST, KAUDOM, Hobo Meteorite, Burnt Mountain, Quedas do Ruadana, Tundavala, Mukurob, Kokerboom Wood, Fish River Canyon, Augrabies Falls, Bidouw Valley, NAMIB NAUKLUFT, Walvis Bay, Windhoek, Namibe, C. Fria, Tropic of Capricorn, Cape Town, C. of Good Hope

NIGERIA – MINERALS, INDUSTRY AND OIL

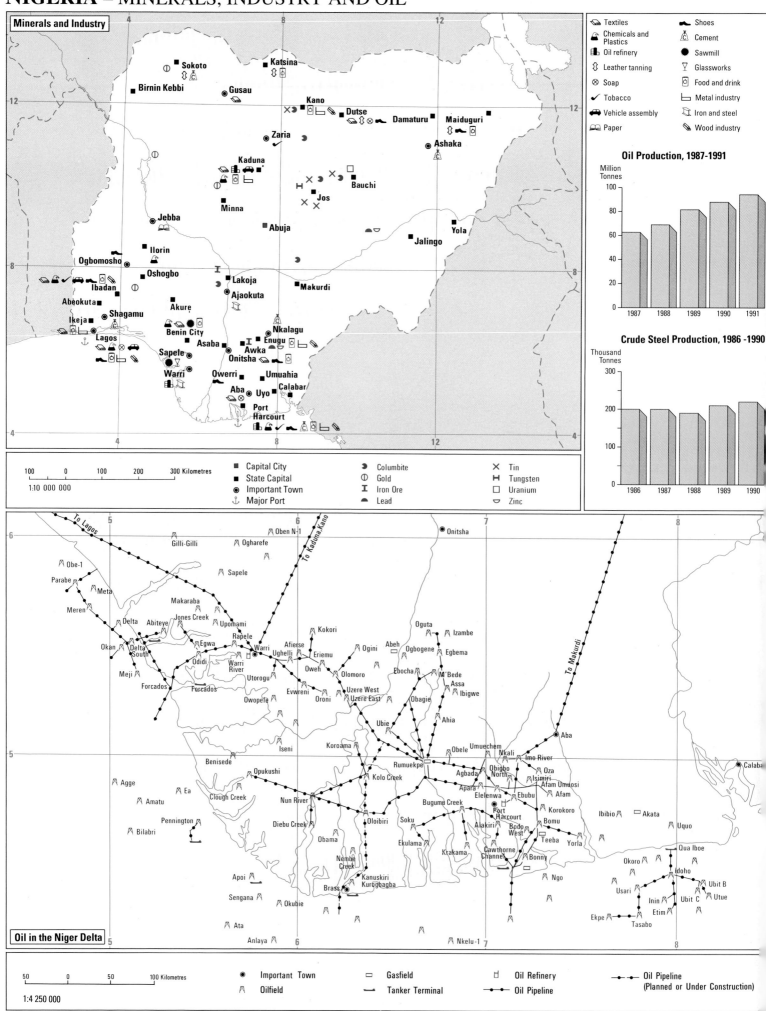

Minerals and Industry

Legend (Industry symbols):

Textiles		Shoes	
Chemicals and Plastics		Cement	
Oil refinery		Sawmill	
Leather tanning		Glassworks	
Soap		Food and drink	
Tobacco		Metal industry	
Vehicle assembly		Iron and steel	
Paper		Wood industry	

Map labels: Sokoto, Katsina, Birnin Kebbi, Gusau, Kano, Dutse, Damaturu, Maiduguri, Zaria, Ashaka, Kaduna, Bauchi, Jos, Minna, Abuja, Jalingo, Yola, Jebba, Ilorin, Ogbomosho, Oshogbo, Lakoja, Makurdi, Ibadan, Ajaokuta, Abeokuta, Akure, Ikeja, Shagamu, Nkalagu, Benin City, Lagos, Asaba, Enugu, Awka, Sapele, Onitsha, Warri, Owerri, Umuahia, Aba, Uyo, Calabar, Port Harcourt

Oil Production, 1987-1991

Million Tonnes

1987	1988	1989	1990	1991

(bar chart, values approx. 60, 70, 80, 90, 95)

Crude Steel Production, 1986 -1990

Thousand Tonnes

1986	1987	1988	1989	1990

(bar chart, values approx. 200, 200, 190, 210, 220)

Scale: 100 0 100 200 300 Kilometres   1:10 000 000

Map legend:

Capital City		Columbite		Tin	
State Capital		Gold		Tungsten	
Important Town		Iron Ore		Uranium	
Major Port		Lead		Zinc	

Oil in the Niger Delta

Map labels: To Lagos, Oben N-1, Gilli-Gilli, Ogharefe, To Kaduna, Kano, Onitsha, Obe-1, Sapele, Parabe, Meta, Makaraba, Meren, Jones Creek, Upomami, Kokori, Oguta, Izambe, Delta, Abiteye, Rapele, Afierse, Ogini, Abeh, Ogbogene, Egbema, Okan, Delta South, Egwa, Warri, Ughelli, Eriemu, Ebocha, M'Bede, Assa, Ibigwe, Odidi, Warri River, Oweh, Olomoro, To Makurdi, Meji, Utorogu, Evwreni, Uzere West, Obagie, Ahia, Forcados, Owopele, Oroni, Uzere East, Ubie, Aba, Iseni, Koroama, Obele, Umuechem, Nkali, Benisede, Rumuekpe, Calabar, Opukushi, Kolo Creek, Agbada, Oza, Agge, Isimiri, Afam Umuosi, Ea, Apara, Afam, Ibibio, Akata, Amatu, Clough Creek, Nun River, Bugumu Creek, Elelenwa, Ebubu, Uquo, Pennington, Diebu Creek, Soku, Port Harcourt, Korokoro, Bilabri, Oloibiri, Alakiri, Bomu, Okoro, Idoho, Obama, Ekulama, Krakama, Bodo West, Teeba, Yorla, Usari, Ubit B, Nembe Creek, Cawthorne Channel, Bonny, Ngo, Inin, Ubit C, Utue, Apoi, Kanuskiri, Kurogbagba, Ekpe, Etim, Tasabo, Sengana, Okubie, Qua Iboe, Ata, Brass, Anlaya, Nkelu-1

Scale: 50 0 50 100 Kilometres   1:4 250 000

Map legend:

Important Town	Gasfield	Oil Refinery	Oil Pipeline
Oilfield	Tanker Terminal	Oil Pipeline	Oil Pipeline (Planned or Under Construction)

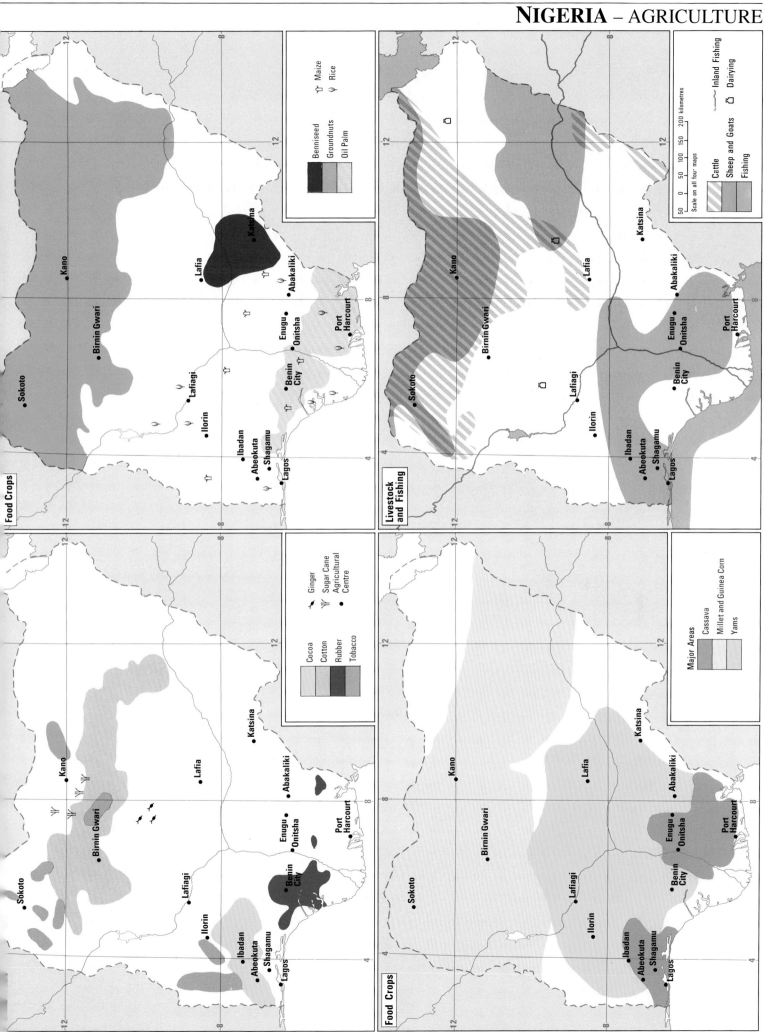

Food Crops

Maize
Rice

Benniseed
Groundnuts
Oil Palm

Katsina
Kano
Lafia
Abakaliki
Birnin Gwari
Enugu
Onitsha
Port Harcourt
Sokoto
Benin City
Lafiagi
Ilorin
Ibadan
Abeokuta
Shagamu
Lagos

Livestock and Fishing

Inland Fishing
Dairying

Cattle
Sheep and Goats
Fishing

200 kilometres
150
100
50
0
50
Scale on all four maps

Kano
Katsina
Birnin Gwari
Lafia
Abakaliki
Sokoto
Enugu
Onitsha
Port Harcourt
Lafiagi
Benin City
Ilorin
Ibadan
Abeokuta
Shagamu
Lagos

Food Crops

Ginger
Sugar Cane
Agricultural Centre

Cocoa
Cotton
Rubber
Tobacco

Katsina
Kano
Lafia
Abakaliki
Birnin Gwari
Enugu
Onitsha
Port Harcourt
Sokoto
Benin City
Lafiagi
Ilorin
Ibadan
Abeokuta
Shagamu
Lagos

Food Crops

Major Areas
Cassava
Millet and Guinea Corn
Yams

Katsina
Kano
Lafia
Abakaliki
Birnin Gwari
Enugu
Onitsha
Port Harcourt
Sokoto
Benin City
Lafiagi
Ilorin
Ibadan
Abeokuta
Shagamu
Lagos

Projection: Lambert's Azimuthal Equal Area
1 : 40 000 000

0   500   1000   1500 km

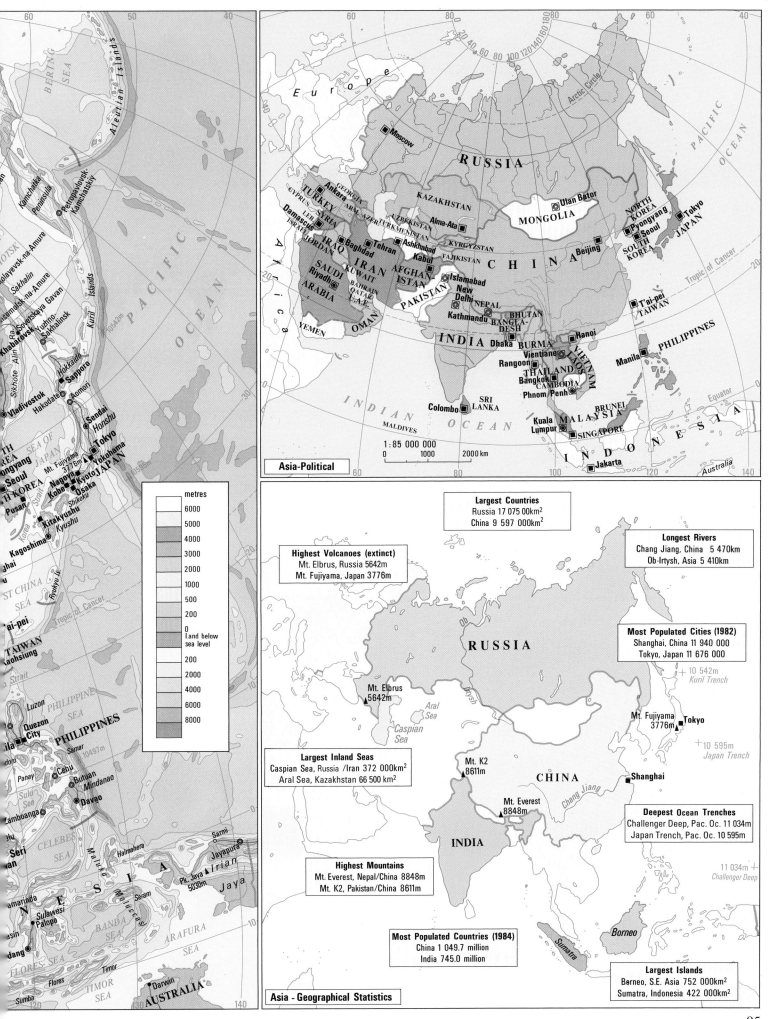

Asia-Political

1:85 000 000
0   1000   2000 km

metres
6000
5000
4000
3000
2000
1000
500
200
0
Land below sea level
200
2000
4000
6000
8000

Asia - Geographical Statistics

Largest Countries
Russia 17 075 00km²
China 9 597 000km²

Longest Rivers
Chang Jiang, China 5 470km
Ob-Irtysh, Asia 5 410km

Highest Volcanoes (extinct)
Mt. Elbrus, Russia 5642m
Mt. Fujiyama, Japan 3776m

Most Populated Cities (1982)
Shanghai, China 11 940 000
Tokyo, Japan 11 676 000

Largest Inland Seas
Caspian Sea, Russia /Iran 372 000km²
Aral Sea, Kazakhstan 66 500 km²

Deepest Ocean Trenches
Challenger Deep, Pac. Oc. 11 034m
Japan Trench, Pac. Oc. 10 595m

Highest Mountains
Mt. Everest, Nepal/China 8848m
Mt. K2, Pakistan/China 8611m

Most Populated Countries (1984)
China 1 049.7 million
India 745.0 million

Largest Islands
Berneo, S.E. Asia 752 000km²
Sumatra, Indonesia 422 000km²

+ 10 542m
Kuril Trench

+ 10 595m
Japan Trench

11 034m +
Challenger Deep

Mt. Elbrus 5642m
Mt. K2 8611m
Mt. Everest 8848m
Mt. Fujiyama 3776m — Tokyo
Shanghai

RUSSIA
CHINA
INDIA
Borneo
Sumatra
Aral Sea
Caspian Sea
Ob
Irtysh
Chang Jiang

ASIA – CLIMATE

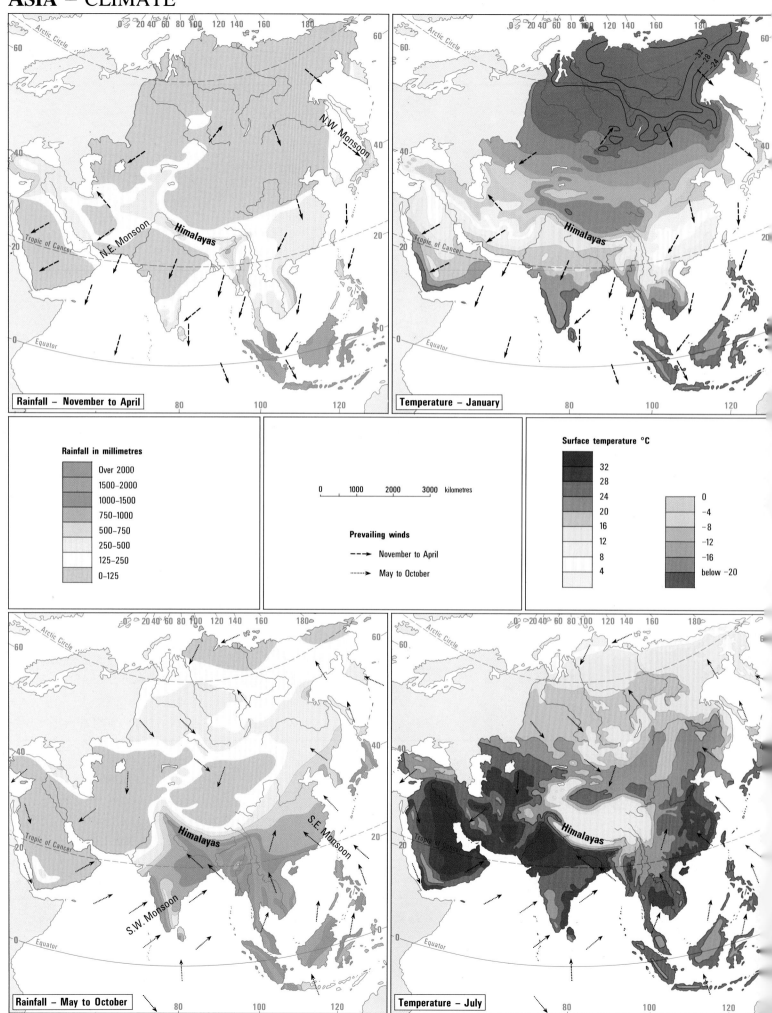

Rainfall – November to April

N.W. Monsoon

N.E. Monsoon

Himalayas

Temperature – January

Himalayas

Rainfall in millimetres

- Over 2000
- 1500–2000
- 1000–1500
- 750–1000
- 500–750
- 250–500
- 125–250
- 0–125

0   1000   2000   3000   kilometres

Prevailing winds

- – – –▶   November to April
- ·······▶   May to October

Surface temperature °C

32	0
28	−4
24	−8
20	−12
16	−16
12	below −20
8	
4	

Rainfall – May to October

Himalayas

S.E. Monsoon

S.W. Monsoon

Temperature – July

Himalayas

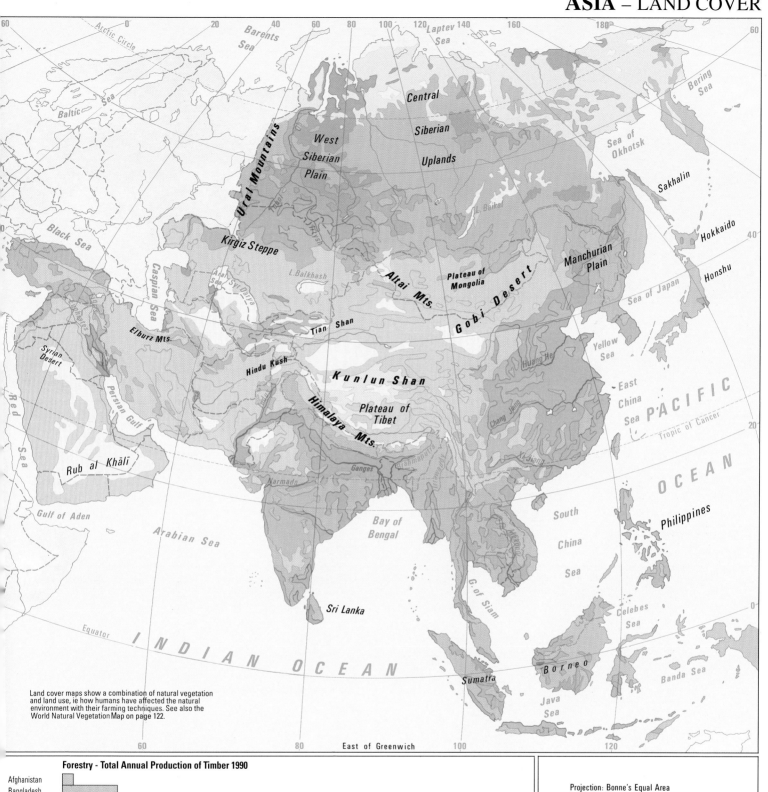

60 Arctic Circle 0 Barents 20 40 60 80 100 120 Laptev 140 160 180 60
Baltic Sea Sea Sea of Bering
Sea Okhotsk Sea
Central
West Siberian
Ural Mountains Siberian Uplands Sakhalin
Plain
L.Baikal Hokkaido
Black Sea Kirgiz Steppe 40 Honshu
Caspian Sea Manchurian
Aral Sea Syr Darya Plateau of Plain
L.Balkhash Altai Mts. Mongolia Sea of Japan
Elburz Mts. Gobi Desert
Syrian Tian Shan Huang He Yellow
Desert Hindu Kush Kunlun Shan Sea
Red Persian Himalaya Mts. Plateau of Chang Jiang East PACIFIC
Sea Gulf Rub al Khālī Tibet China
Bahrametra Sea Tropic of Cancer 20
Ganges Xi Jiang
Gulf of Aden Narmada South
Arabian Bay of China OCEAN
Sea Bengal Sea Philippines
Equator Sri Lanka G. of Siam Celebes
INDIAN OCEAN Sea
Sumatra Borneo Banda Sea
Land cover maps show a combination of natural vegetation Java
and land use, ie how humans have affected the natural Sea
environment with their farming techniques. See also the
World Natural Vegetation Map on page 122.
60 80 East of Greenwich 100 120

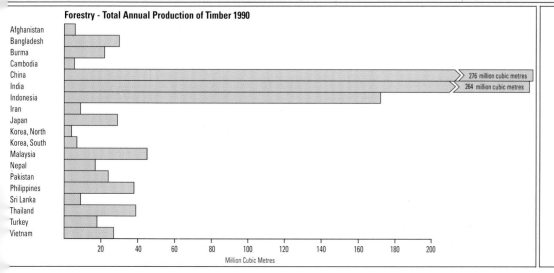

Forestry - Total Annual Production of Timber 1990

Afghanistan	
Bangladesh	
Burma	
Cambodia	
China	276 million cubic metres
India	264 million cubic metres
Indonesia	
Iran	
Japan	
Korea, North	
Korea, South	
Malaysia	
Nepal	
Pakistan	
Philippines	
Sri Lanka	
Thailand	
Turkey	
Vietnam	

20 40 60 80 100 120 140 160 180 200
Million Cubic Metres

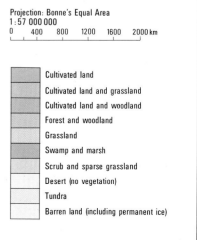

Projection: Bonne's Equal Area
1:57 000 000

0 400 800 1200 1600 2000 km

Cultivated land
Cultivated land and grassland
Cultivated land and woodland
Forest and woodland
Grassland
Swamp and marsh
Scrub and sparse grassland
Desert (no vegetation)
Tundra
Barren land (including permanent ice)

ASIA – AGRICULTURE

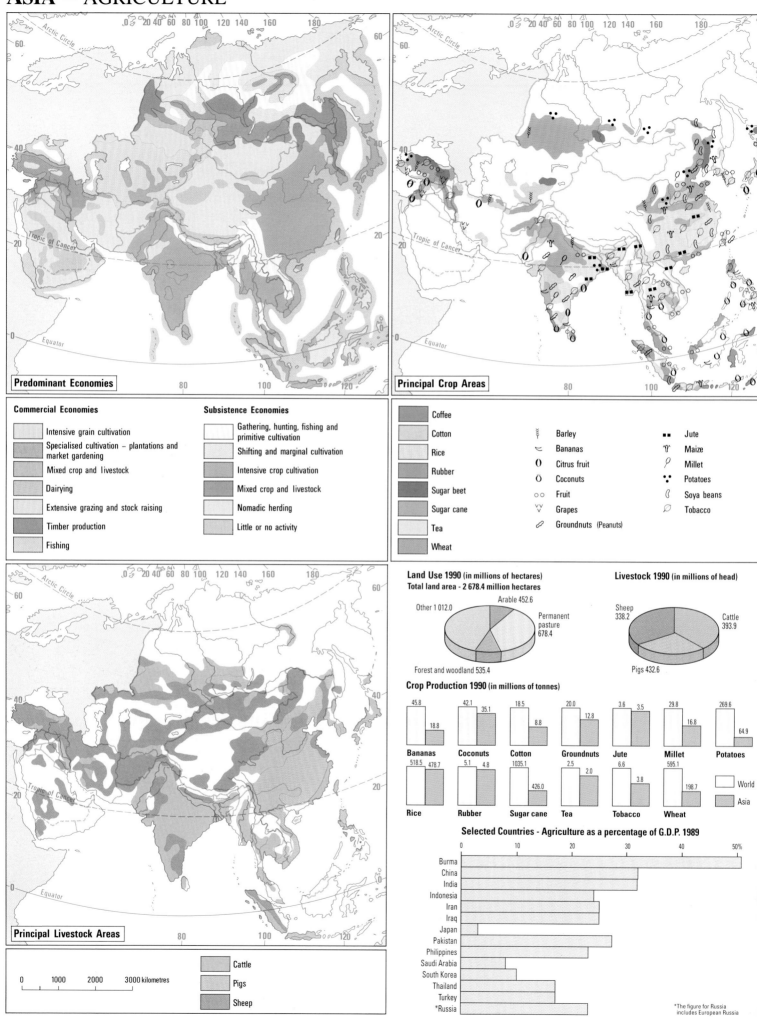

Predominant Economies

Commercial Economies
- Intensive grain cultivation
- Specialised cultivation – plantations and market gardening
- Mixed crop and livestock
- Dairying
- Extensive grazing and stock raising
- Timber production
- Fishing

Subsistence Economies
- Gathering, hunting, fishing and primitive cultivation
- Shifting and marginal cultivation
- Intensive crop cultivation
- Mixed crop and livestock
- Nomadic herding
- Little or no activity

Principal Crop Areas

- Coffee
- Cotton
- Rice
- Rubber
- Sugar beet
- Sugar cane
- Tea
- Wheat

- ⅄ Barley
- ⌇ Bananas
- 0 Citrus fruit
- Ö Coconuts
- ○○ Fruit
- ᴠᴠ Grapes
- ⟋ Groundnuts (Peanuts)

- ▪▪ Jute
- ↑ Maize
- ⌀ Millet
- ⋰ Potatoes
- (Soya beans
- ⟋ Tobacco

Principal Livestock Areas

| 0 | 1000 | 2000 | 3000 kilometres |

- Cattle
- Pigs
- Sheep

Land Use 1990 (in millions of hectares)
Total land area - 2 678.4 million hectares

- Other 1 012.0
- Arable 452.6
- Permanent pasture 678.4
- Forest and woodland 535.4

Livestock 1990 (in millions of head)

- Sheep 338.2
- Cattle 393.9
- Pigs 432.6

Crop Production 1990 (in millions of tonnes)

Crop	World	Asia
Bananas	45.8	18.8
Coconuts	42.1	35.1
Cotton	18.5	8.8
Groundnuts	20.0	12.8
Jute	3.6	3.5
Millet	29.8	16.8
Potatoes	269.6	64.9
Rice	518.5	478.7
Rubber	5.1	4.8
Sugar cane	1035.1	426.0
Tea	2.5	2.0
Tobacco	6.6	3.8
Wheat	595.1	198.7

☐ World
▨ Asia

Selected Countries - Agriculture as a percentage of G.D.P. 1989

0   10   20   30   40   50%

- Burma
- China
- India
- Indonesia
- Iran
- Iraq
- Japan
- Pakistan
- Philippines
- Saudi Arabia
- South Korea
- Thailand
- Turkey
- *Russia

*The figure for Russia includes European Russia

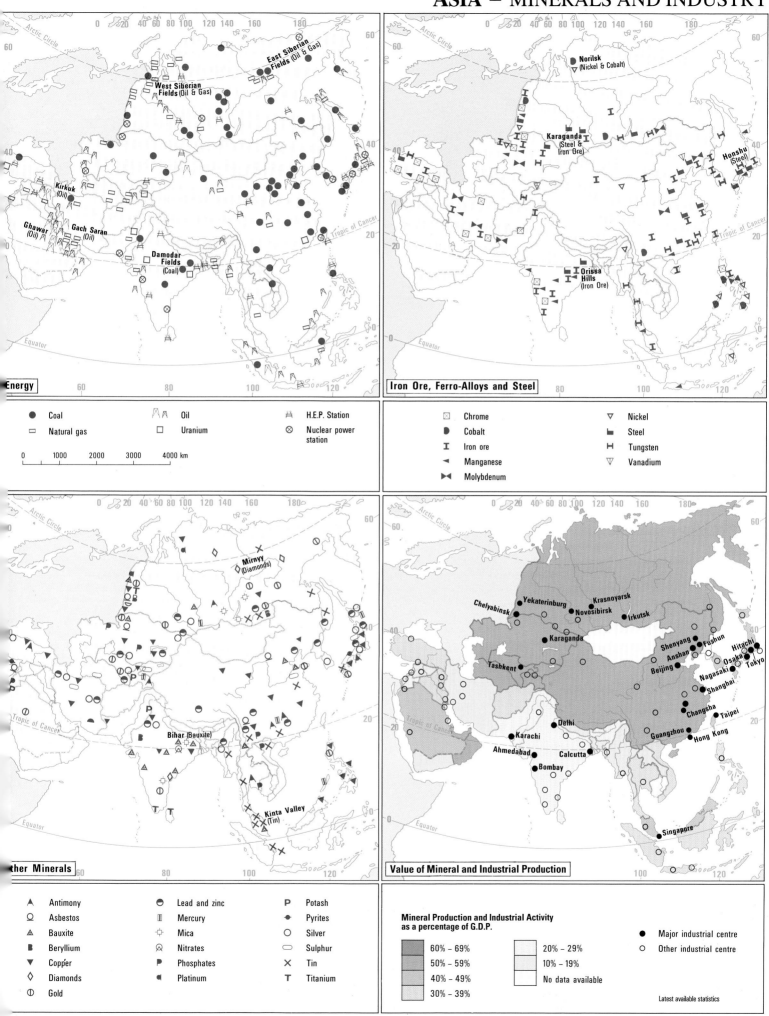

Energy

● Coal	⋏⋏ Oil	⚹ H.E.P. Station
⊟ Natural gas	☐ Uranium	⊗ Nuclear power station

0 1000 2000 3000 4000 km

Labels on Energy map: West Siberian Fields (Oil & Gas); East Siberian Fields (Oil & Gas); Kirkuk (Oil); Ghawar (Oil); Gach Saran (Oil); Damodar Fields (Coal)

Iron Ore, Ferro-Alloys and Steel

⊠ Chrome		▽ Nickel
◗ Cobalt		⊾ Steel
I Iron ore		⊢ Tungsten
◀ Manganese		▽ Vanadium
►◄ Molybdenum		

Labels on Iron Ore map: Norilsk (Nickel & Cobalt); Karaganda (Steel & Iron Ore); Honshu (Steel); Orissa Hills (Iron Ore)

Other Minerals

⋏ Antimony	⊖ Lead and zinc	P Potash
Ω Asbestos	▯ Mercury	◆ Pyrites
△ Bauxite	⊹ Mica	○ Silver
B Beryllium	⊠ Nitrates	⊟ Sulphur
▼ Copper	P Phosphates	✕ Tin
◇ Diamonds	◄ Platinum	T Titanium
⊕ Gold		

Labels on Other Minerals map: Mirnyy (Diamonds); Bihar (Bauxite); Kinta Valley (Tin)

Value of Mineral and Industrial Production

Mineral Production and Industrial Activity as a percentage of G.D.P.

60% – 69%	20% – 29%
50% – 59%	10% – 19%
40% – 49%	No data available
30% – 39%	

● Major industrial centre
○ Other industrial centre

Latest available statistics

Labels on Value map: Chelyabinsk; Yekaterinburg; Krasnoyarsk; Novosibirsk; Irkutsk; Karaganda; Tashkent; Shenyang; Fushun; Anshan; Hitachi; Osaka; Tokyo; Beijing; Nagasaki; Shanghai; Changsha; Taipei; Delhi; Guangzhou; Hong Kong; Karachi; Ahmedabad; Calcutta; Bombay; Singapore

ASIA – POPULATION

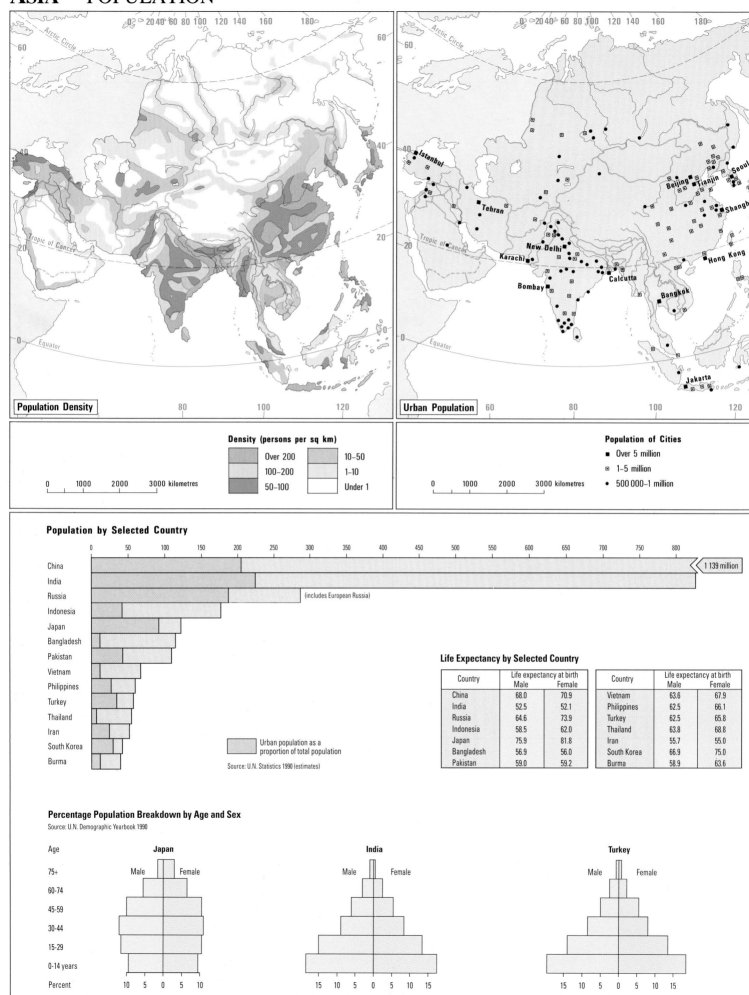

Population Density

Density (persons per sq km)

Over 200	10–50
100–200	1–10
50–100	Under 1

0   1000   2000   3000 kilometres

Urban Population

Population of Cities

■ Over 5 million
⊡ 1–5 million
• 500 000–1 million

0   1000   2000   3000 kilometres

Population by Selected Country

China — 1 139 million
India
Russia (includes European Russia)
Indonesia
Japan
Bangladesh
Pakistan
Vietnam
Philippines
Turkey
Thailand
Iran
South Korea
Burma

Urban population as a proportion of total population

Source: U.N. Statistics 1990 (estimates)

Life Expectancy by Selected Country

Country	Life expectancy at birth Male	Female	Country	Life expectancy at birth Male	Female
China	68.0	70.9	Vietnam	63.6	67.9
India	52.5	52.1	Philippines	62.5	66.1
Russia	64.6	73.9	Turkey	62.5	65.8
Indonesia	58.5	62.0	Thailand	63.8	68.8
Japan	75.9	81.8	Iran	55.7	55.0
Bangladesh	56.9	56.0	South Korea	66.9	75.0
Pakistan	59.0	59.2	Burma	58.9	63.6

Percentage Population Breakdown by Age and Sex

Source: U.N. Demographic Yearbook 1990

Age: 75+, 60–74, 45–59, 30–44, 15–29, 0–14 years

Japan — Male / Female — Percent 10 5 0 5 10

India — Male / Female — 15 10 5 0 5 10 15

Turkey — Male / Female — 15 10 5 0 5 10 15

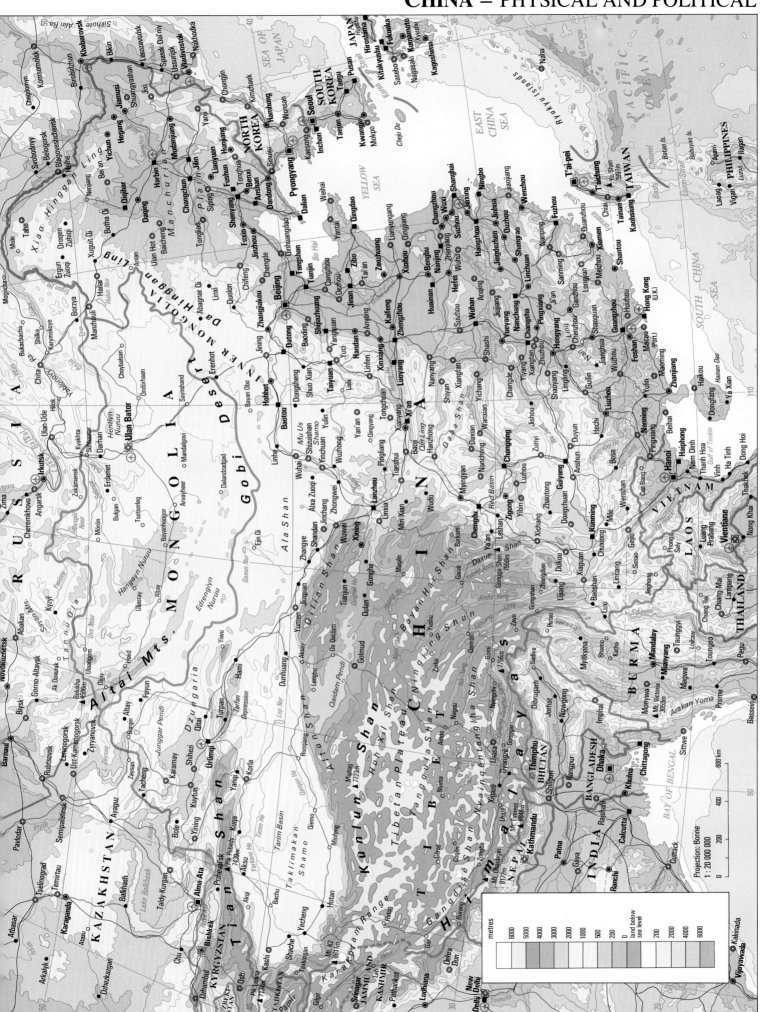

JAPAN – PHYSICAL AND POLITICAL

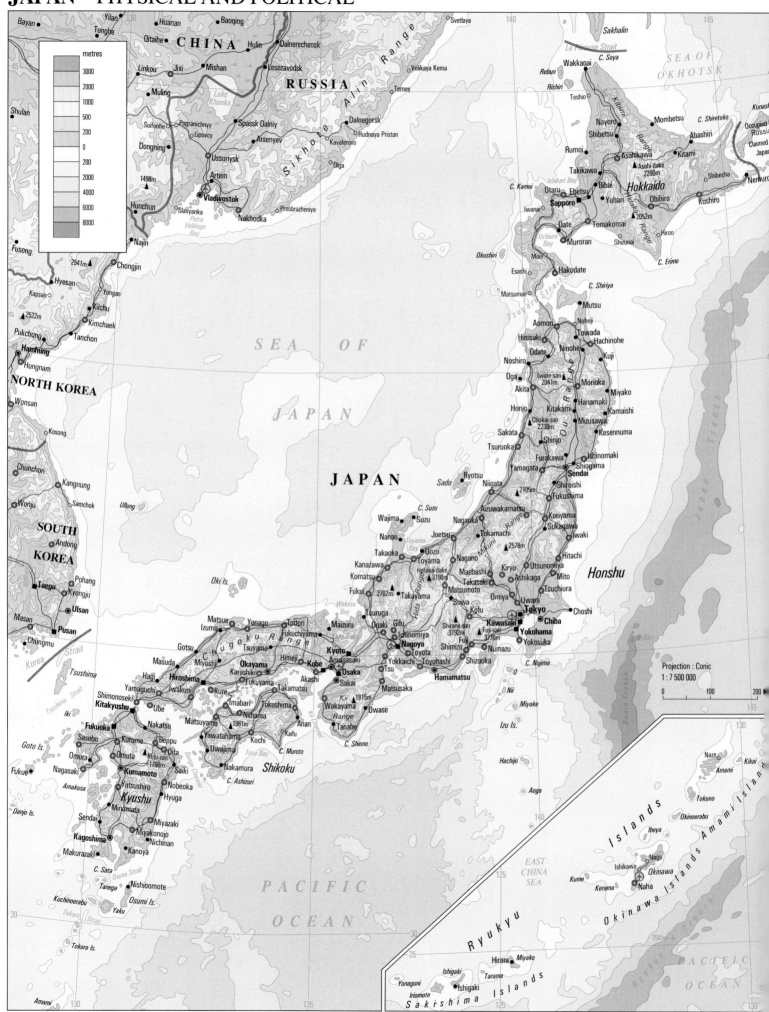

metres
3000
2000
1000
500
200
0
200
2000
4000
6000
8000

CHINA

RUSSIA

Sikhote Alin Range

NORTH KOREA

SOUTH KOREA

SEA OF OKHOTSK

Sakhalin

La Perouse Strait

Hokkaido

Tsugaru Strait

SEA OF JAPAN

JAPAN

Honshu

Japan Trench

Shikoku

Kyushu

Tsushima Strait

Korea Strait

PACIFIC OCEAN

Projection : Conic
1 : 7 500 000
0   100   200

EAST CHINA SEA

Ryukyu Islands

Okinawa Islands

Amami Islands

Sakishima Islands

PACIFIC OCEAN

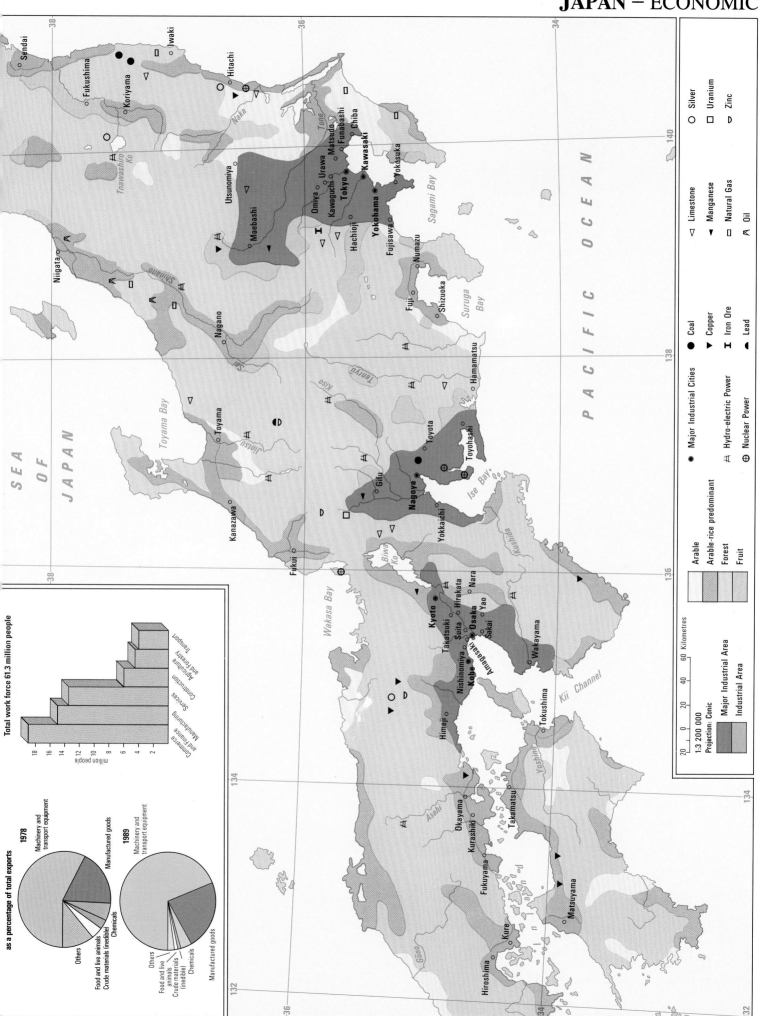

Silver
Uranium
Zinc

Limestone
Manganese
Natural Gas
Oil

Coal
Copper
Iron Ore
Lead

Major Industrial Cities
Hydro-electric Power
Nuclear Power

Arable
Arable-rice predominant
Forest
Fruit

Major Industrial Area
Industrial Area

1:3 200 000
Projection: Conic

20 0 20 40 60 Kilometres

PACIFIC OCEAN

SEA OF JAPAN

Sagami Bay
Suruga Bay
Toyama Bay
Ise Bay
Wakasa Bay
Kii Channel

Sendai
Fukushima
Koriyama
Iwaki
Hitachi
Utsunomiya
Maebashi
Omiya
Urawa
Kawaguchi
Matsudo
Funabashi
Chiba
Tokyo
Kawasaki
Yokosuka
Yokohama
Fujisawa
Hachioji
Numazu
Shizuoka
Fuji
Hamamatsu
Niigata
Nagano
Toyama
Kanazawa
Fukui
Toyota
Toyohashi
Gifu
Nagoya
Yokkaichi
Kyoto
Takatsuki
Hirakata
Nara
Suita
Osaka
Yao
Nishinomiya
Sakai
Kobe
Amagasaki
Wakayama
Himeji
Tokushima
Okayama
Takamatsu
Kurashiki
Fukuyama
Matsuyama
Kure
Hiroshima

Inawashiro Ko
Naka
Tone
Shinano
Sai
Kiso
Tenryu
Jintsu
Biwa Ko
Yoshino
Kino
Asahi
Gono

Total work force 61.3 million people

million people
2 4 6 8 10 12 14 16 18

Commerce and Finance
Manufacturing
Services
Construction
Agriculture and forestry
Transport

as a percentage of total exports

1978
Machinery and transport equipment
Manufactured goods
Chemicals
Crude materials (inedible)
Food and live animals
Others

1989
Machinery and transport equipment
Manufactured goods
Chemicals
Crude materials (inedible)
Food and live animals
Others

INDIA – PHYSICAL AND POLITICAL

metres
6000
5000
4000
3000
2000
1000
500
200
0
200
2000
4000

UZBEKISTAN · Samarkand
KYRGYZSTAN
Karshi · Kashi
Pik Kommunizma ▲7495m
Termez · Kurgan Tyube
TAJIKISTAN ◎ Dushanbe
Pamir
Mazar-e Sharif · Feyzabad · Khorog
Taklimakan Shamo
Shache · Takla Makan
Yecheng · Taxkorgan
Lop Nur · Yumen
Altun Shan
Qaidam Pendi
Da Qaidam
Zhangye
Qilian Shan
Gongh

Baghlan · Hindu Kush
Chitral · Gilgit
Hotan
Mt. Muztag ▲7723m
Kunlun Shan
Golmud
Qiemo

AFGHANISTAN · Ghazni · ▲3787m
Charikar
Jalalabad · Peshawar
Kabul ■
KARAKORAM RANGE
Mt. K2 8611m
Mt. Nanga Parbat ▲8126m
Leh
CHINA
Tibetan Plateau
Amdo
Nagqu

Bannu · Islamabad ◎ Rawalpindi
JAMMU AND KASHMIR
Srinagar
Jammu · Sialkot
Rutog
TIBET
Tanggula Shan
Bomi ▲7756m
Zayu

PAKISTAN
Quetta · Dera Ghazi Khan
Sulaiman Range · Toba Kaka Range
Gujranwala · Lahore ■ · Amritsar
Faisalabad · Okara
Multan · Bahawalpur
Ludhiana · Chandigarh
Jullundur
Sutlej
Himalayas
Mt. Nanda Devi ▲7817m
Lhasa · Xigaze · Gyangze
Mt. Dhaulagiri ▲8172m
Zongba
NEPAL
Kathmandu
Mt. Annapurna 8078m
Mt. Everest ▲8848m
Mt. Kanchenjunga 8598m
Darjiling
Thimphu ◎
BHUTAN
Itanagar · Along · Tezu ▲5881m
Sadiya · Dibrugarh
Jorhat · Patkai Bum

Kirthar Range
Karachi ■ · Hyderabad ■
Sukkur
Thar (Great Indian Desert)
Bikaner · Hisar · Saharanpur
Jaisalmer · Phalodi
Jodhpur · Ajmer
Barmer
Meerut
Delhi ◎ New Delhi
Moradabad
Bareilly
Aligarh
Agra
Jaipur
Gwalior
Lucknow ■
Kanpur ■
Gorakhpur
Darbhanga
Biratnagar
Shiliguri
Dhubri
Rangpur
Khasi Hills
Shillong
Naga Hills ▲3826m Mt. Saramati
Nowgong
Myitkyina
Katha

Gulf of Kachchh · Rann of Kachchh
Kandla · Patan
Jamnagar · Rajkot
Porbander · Bhavnagar ▲643m
Ahmadabad ■
Udaipur
Bhilwara · Kota
Ujjain · Indore
Bhopal
Vindhya Range
Jhansi
Sagar · Murwara
Jabalpur
▲1353m
Allahabad
Varanasi
Ganges
Patna · Gaya
Bhagalpur
Ranchi · Dhanbad
Jamshedpur
Durgapur · Asansol
Rajshahi
Narayanganj
Dhaka ■
BANGLADESH
Barisal
Khulna
Calcutta
Sundarbans
Chittagong
Sylhet · Silchar · Imphal
Agartala
BURMA
Monywa · Mandalay ■
Pakokku · Myingyan
Chin Hills
Mt. Victoria 3053m
Taung

Diu · Surat
Gulf of Khambhat
Vadodara · Dhule
Nasik
Bombay ■ Ulhasnagar
Satpura Range
Tapi
Narmada
Amravati
Nagpur ■
Aurangabad
Nanded
Nizamabad
Raipur · Durg
Bilaspur
Raurkela · Sambalpur
Jagdalpur
Cuttack
Bhubaneshwar
Berhampur
Chilka Lake
INDIA
Deccan
Hirakud Res.
Mouths of the Ganges
Pegu Yoma
Arakan Yoma
Ramree I.
Henzada
Prome
Pegu
Rangoon ■
Bassein
Cape Negrais
Mouths of the Irrawaddy

ARABIAN SEA
Pune ◎
Solapur
Sangli
Kolhapur
Hyderabad ■
Gulbarga
Warangal
Western Ghats
Panaji
Belgaum · Bellary
Dharwad
Kurnool
Eastern Ghats
Rajahmundry
Kakinada
Vijayawada
Guntur · Machilipatnam
Vishakhapatnam
Northern Circars
Coromandel Coast
BAY OF BENGAL

Lakshadweep (Laccadive) Islands (India)
Aminidivi Is.
Kiltan I. · Kadmat I.
Androth I.
Karavati I.
Kalpeni I.
Shimoga ▲1923m
Davangere
Cuddapah
Nellore
Mangalore
Tumkur
Madras
Bangalore ◎
Mysore · Vellore
Pondicherry
Salem ▲2636m
Erode
Coimbatore
Tiruchchirappalli
Calicut
Malabar Coast
Cardamom Hills ▲2695m
Cochin
Madurai
Tuticorin
Tirunelveli
Trivandrum ◎
Jaffna
Palk Strait
Andaman Islands (India)
Middle Andaman I.
North Andaman I.
South Andaman I.
Port Blair
Little Andaman I. ▲4150m
Coco Is. (Burma)
ANDAMAN SEA
Ten Degree Channel
Car Nicobar I.
Teressa I.
Camorta I.
Katchall I.
Nicobar Islands (India)
Little Nicobar I.
Great Nicobar I.

Minicoy I.
Cape Comorin
Gulf of Mannar
Anuradhapura
Trincomalee
Batticaloa
SRI LANKA
Kandy ▲2524m
Badulla
Colombo ■
Galle · Matara
Dondra Head
MALDIVES
INDIAN OCEAN
INDONESIA
Sumatra
Banda Aceh

Projection: Bonne
1:15 000 000
0   200   400km

104

© COPYRIGHT MACMILLAN EDUCATION LTD

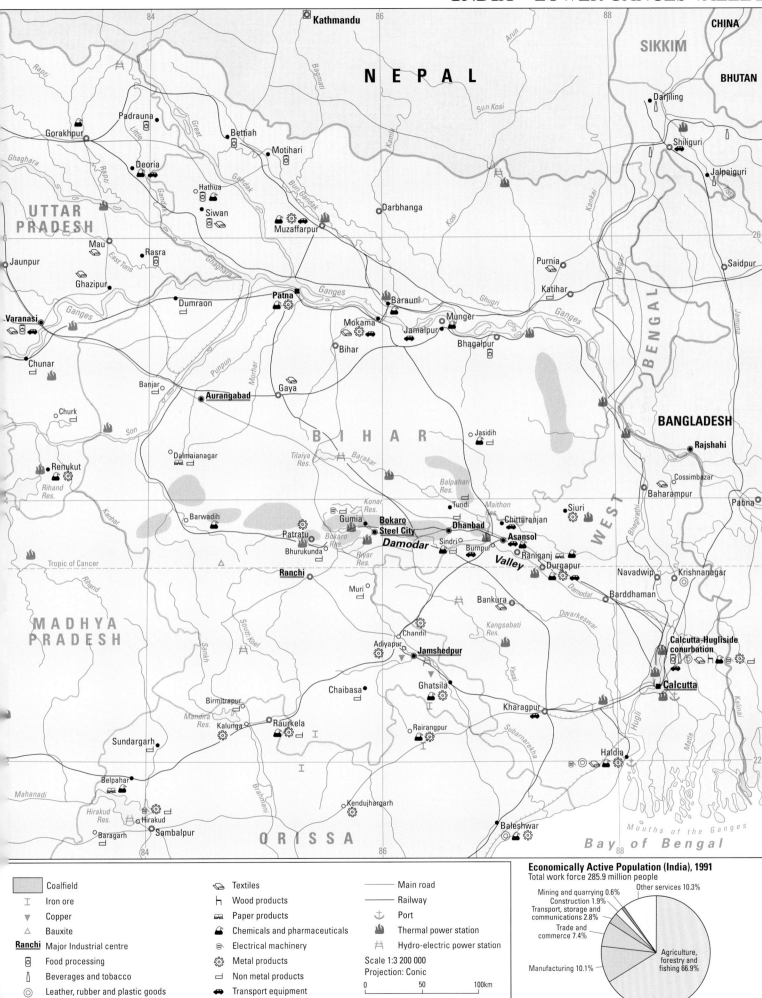

CHINA

SIKKIM

BHUTAN

NEPAL

Kathmandu

UTTAR PRADESH

BIHAR

MADHYA PRADESH

WEST BENGAL

BANGLADESH

ORISSA

Bay of Bengal

Mouths of the Ganges

Tropic of Cancer

Economically Active Population (India), 1991
Total work force 285.9 million people

Mining and quarrying 0.6%
Construction 1.9%
Transport, storage and communications 2.8%
Trade and commerce 7.4%
Other services 10.3%
Manufacturing 10.1%
Agriculture, forestry and fishing 66.9%

▨ Coalfield	◊ Textiles
I Iron ore	⋔ Wood products
▼ Copper	▣ Paper products
△ Bauxite	◭ Chemicals and pharmaceuticals
Ranchi Major Industrial centre	▱ Electrical machinery
◙ Food processing	✿ Metal products
▯ Beverages and tobacco	⊐ Non metal products
◎ Leather, rubber and plastic goods	🚗 Transport equipment

Main road
Railway
⚓ Port
⛰ Thermal power station
⌘ Hydro-electric power station

Scale 1:3 200 000
Projection: Conic

0   50   100km

MIDDLE EAST – PHYSICAL AND POLITICAL

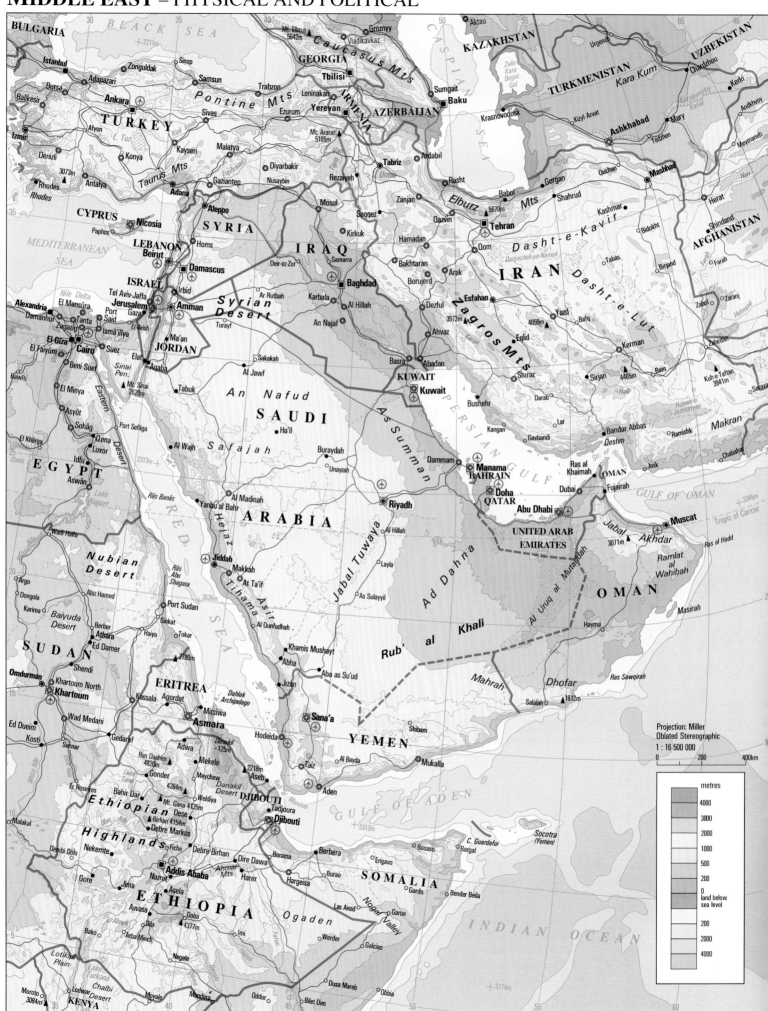

metres	
	4000
	3000
	2000
	1000
	500
	200
	0 land below sea level
	200
	2000
	4000

Projection: Miller
Oblated Stereographic

1 : 16 500 000

0   200   400km

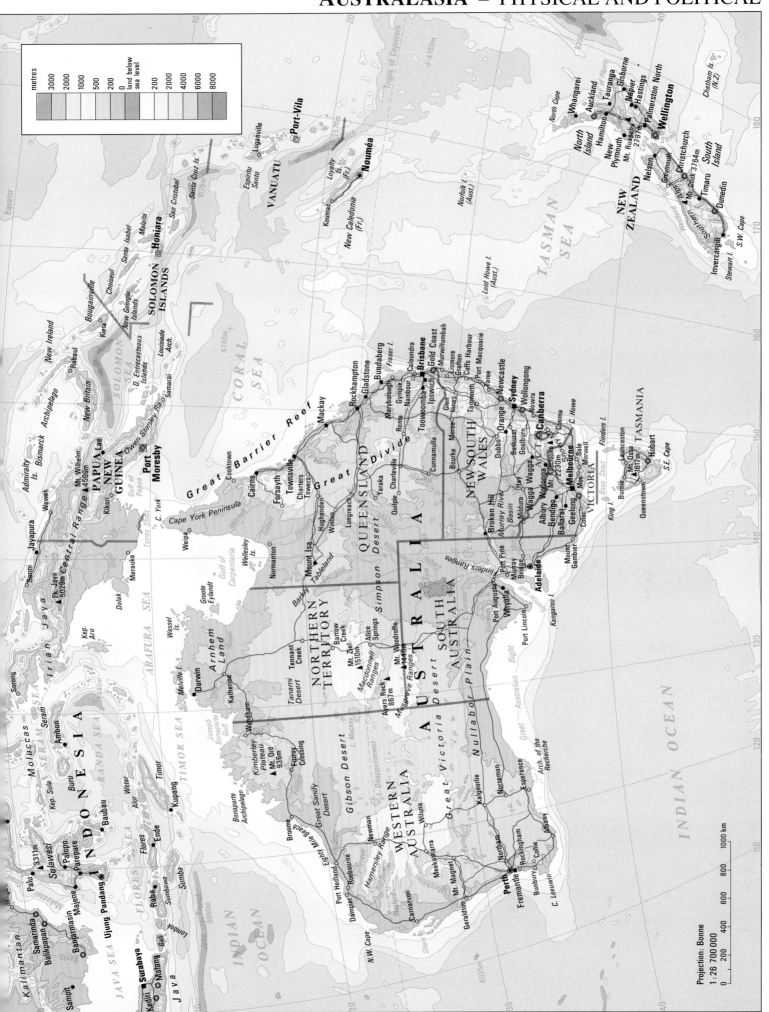

metres						land below sea level						
3000	2000	1000	500	200	0		200	2000	4000	6000	8000	

Equator

INDONESIA

Sampit
Samarinda
Balikpapan
Banjarmasin
Kalimantan
Palu 3311m
Sulawesi
Palopo
Parepare
Majene
Ujung Pandang
Pandang
Baubau
Buru
Ambon
Seram
Kep. Sula
Moluccas
SERAM SEA
BANDA SEA
Sorong
Wewak
Jayapura
Sami
Irian Jaya
Pk. Jaya 5029m
Central Range
Kikori
Lae
PAPUA
NEW
GUINEA
Mt. Wilhelm 4509m
Gulf of Papua
Port Moresby
Owen Stanley Ra.
Merauke
Dolak

Admiralty Is.
Bismarck Archipelago
New Ireland
New Britain
Rabaul
Kavieng
SOLOMON SEA
D. Entrecasteaux Islands
Louisiade Arch.
Samarai

Bougainville
Kieta
New Georgia Islands
Choiseul
Santa Isabel
Malaita
San Cristobal
SOLOMON ISLANDS
Honiara

Santa Cruz Is.

Luganville
Espiritu Santo
VANUATU
Port-Vila

New Hebrides
Koumac
Loyalty Is. (Fr.)
Nouméa
New Caledonia (Fr.)

Tropic of Capricorn

CORAL SEA

Great Barrier Reef

Weipa
C. York
Cape York Peninsula
Gulf of Carpentaria
Wellesley Is.
Groote Eylandt
Wessel Is.
Kep. Aru

TIMOR SEA
Kupang
Timor
Alor
Wetar
Flores
Ende
Sumba
Lombok
Bali
Java
Surabaya
Malang
Kediri
JAVA SEA
Raba
Sumbawa
Makassar Strait

ARAFURA SEA

Melville I.
Darwin
Arnhem Land
Katherine
Wyndham
Joseph Bonaparte Gulf
Bonaparte Archipelago
Broome
Kimberley Plateau
Mt. Ord 936m
Fitzroy Crossing
Great Sandy Desert
Eighty Mile Beach
Port Hedland
Roebourne
Dampier
Hamersley Range
Mt. Magnet
Meekatharra
Wiluna
Newman
Carnarvon
Shark Bay
Geraldton
Northam
WESTERN AUSTRALIA
Gibson Desert
Great Victoria Desert
Kalgoorlie
Coolgardie
Norseman
Nullarbor Plain
Great Australian Bight
Esperance
Albany
Bunbury
Collie
Rockingham
Fremantle
Perth
C. Leeuwin
N.W. Cape
INDIAN OCEAN

NORTHERN TERRITORY
Tennant Creek
Barrow Creek
Tanami Desert
Mt. Zeil 1510m
Alice Springs
Macdonnell Ranges
Ayers Rock 867m
Mt. Woodroffe 1440m
Musgrave Ranges
Simpson Desert
Barkly Tableland
Normanton
Mount Isa
Cloncurry
Georgina

QUEENSLAND
Cooktown
Cairns
Townsville
Charters Towers
Hughenden
Winton
Longreach
Barcaldine
Yaraka
Quilpie
Charleville
Cunnamulla
Great Dividing Range
Rockhampton
Gladstone
Bundaberg
Maryborough
Fraser I.
Gympie
Nambour
Caloundra
Brisbane
Ipswich
Toowoomba
Roma
Gold Coast
Murwillumbah
Lismore
Grafton
Coffs Harbour

SOUTH AUSTRALIA
Woomera
Port Augusta
Whyalla
Port Pirie
Port Lincoln
Kangaroo I.
Murray Bridge
Adelaide
Mount Gambier
Flinders Ranges
Broken Hill
Spencer Gulf

NEW SOUTH WALES
Bourke
Dubbo
Bathurst
Orange
Tamworth
Port Macquarie
Taree
Newcastle
Sydney
Wollongong
Nowra
Goulburn
Canberra
A.C.T.
Cooma
Wagga Wagga
Albury
Wodonga
Hay
Mildura
Murray River
Murrumbidgee Darling
Glen Innes
Meree

VICTORIA
Mt. Kosciusko 2230m
Bendigo
Ballarat
Geelong
Melbourne
Colac
Sale
Morwell
Moe
Bass Strait
King I.
Flinders I.
C. Howe

TASMANIA
Burnie
Launceston
Queenstown
Mt. Ossa 1617m
Hobart
S.E. Cape

NEW ZEALAND
North Cape
Whangarei
Auckland
Hamilton
Tauranga
Bay of Plenty
Gisborne
Napier
Hastings
Palmerston North
New Plymouth
Mt. Ruapehu 2797m
North Island
Wellington
Cook Strait
Nelson
Greymouth
Westland
Christchurch
Mt. Cook 3764m
South Island
Timaru
Dunedin
Invercargill
Southland
Stewart I.
S.W. Cape

Chatham Is. (N.Z.)

TASMAN SEA
Lord Howe I. (Aust.)
Norfolk I. (Aust.)

Tropic of Capricorn

Projection: Bonne
1 : 26 700 000

0   200   400   600   800   1000 km

AUSTRALASIA – CLIMATE

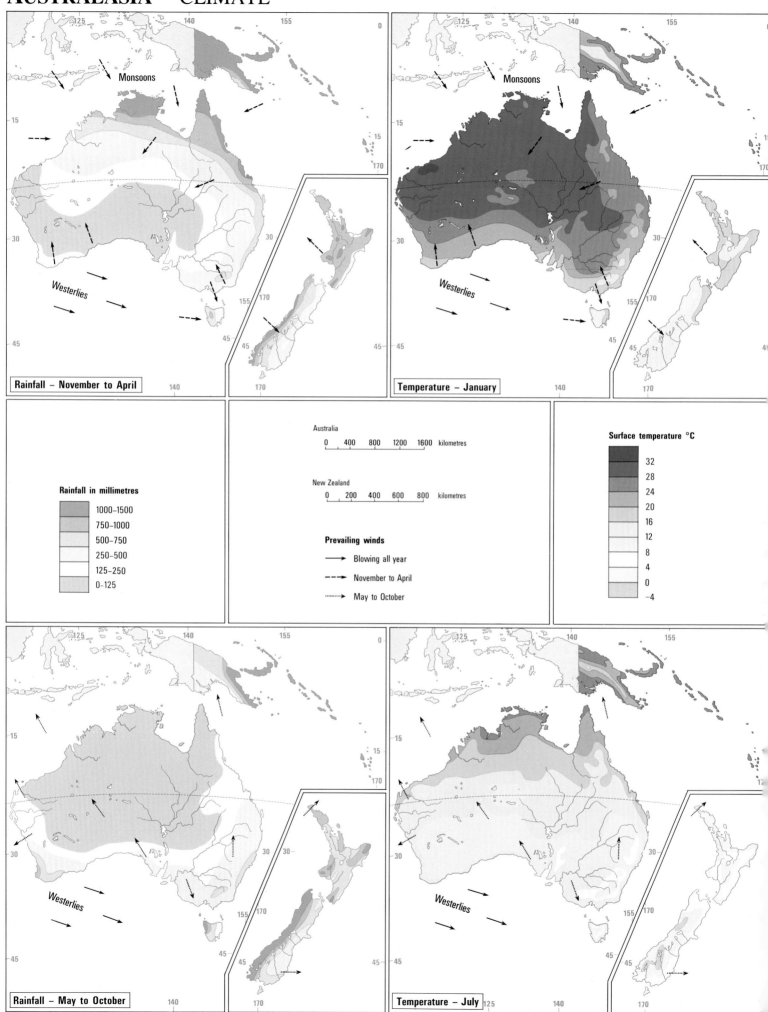

Rainfall – November to April

Monsoons

Westerlies

Temperature – January

Monsoons

Westerlies

Rainfall in millimetres

	1000–1500
	750–1000
	500–750
	250–500
	125–250
	0–125

Australia

0   400   800   1200   1600   kilometres

New Zealand

0   200   400   600   800   kilometres

Prevailing winds

→   Blowing all year

- →   November to April

⋯→   May to October

Surface temperature °C

	32
	28
	24
	20
	16
	12
	8
	4
	0
	-4

Rainfall – May to October

Westerlies

Temperature – July

Westerlies

Land Cover

Land cover maps show a combination of natural vegetation and land use, ie how humans have affected the natural environment with their farming techniques. See also the World Natural Vegetation Map on page 122.

Gibson Desert

Great Artesian Basin

Cultivated land	Grassland
Cultivated land and grassland	Scrub and sparse grassland
Cultivated land and woodland	Swamp and marsh
Forest and woodland	

Australia
0 400 800 1200 1600 km

New Zealand
0 200 400 600 800 km

Agriculture (Human Activity)

Beef cattle	Sheep
Dairying	Sugar cane
Fishing	Timber production
Grain crops	Unproductive

Minerals and Industry

Oil	Nickel	Phosphates	● Major industrial centre
Natural gas	Tungsten	Potash	○ Other industrial centre
Coal	Asbestos	Silver	
Uranium	Copper	Sulphur	
Iron ore	Bauxite	Tin	
Steel	Gold	H.E.P. station	
Manganese	Lead and zinc	Nuclear power station	

Weipa (Bauxite)

Robe River (Iron Ore)

Maryborough

Kalgoorlie

Perth

Whyalla

Newcastle

Sydney

Population Density

Density (persons per sq. km)

Over 100	1–3
25–100	Under 1
3–25	● Cities over 1 million population

Brisbane

Sydney

Melbourne

POLAR REGIONS

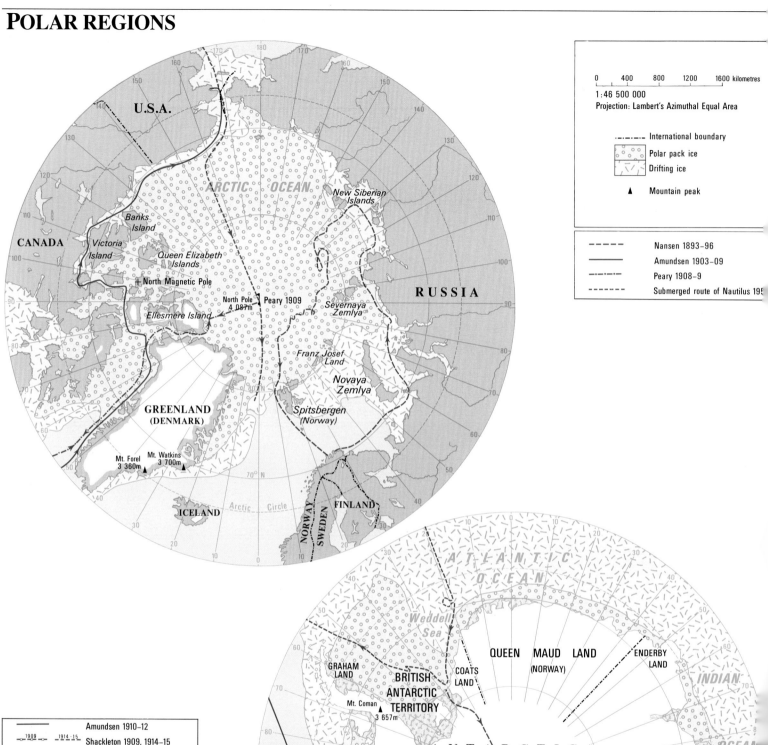

U.S.A.

ARCTIC OCEAN

New Siberian
Islands

Banks
Island

CANADA

Victoria
Island

Queen Elizabeth
Islands

+ North Magnetic Pole

RUSSIA

North Pole
4 087m
Peary 1909

Ellesmere Island

Severnaya
Zemlya

Franz Josef
Land

Novaya
Zemlya

GREENLAND
(DENMARK)

Spitsbergen
(Norway)

Mt. Forel   Mt. Watkins
3 360m   3 700m
▲   ▲

Arctic Circle

ICELAND

NORWAY SWEDEN FINLAND

0 400 800 1200 1600 kilometres	
1 : 46 500 000	
Projection: Lambert's Azimuthal Equal Area	

—·—·— International boundary

Polar pack ice

Drifting ice

▲ Mountain peak

- - - - -	Nansen 1893–96
————	Amundsen 1903–09
—·—·—	Peary 1908–9
- - - - -	Submerged route of Nautilus 195

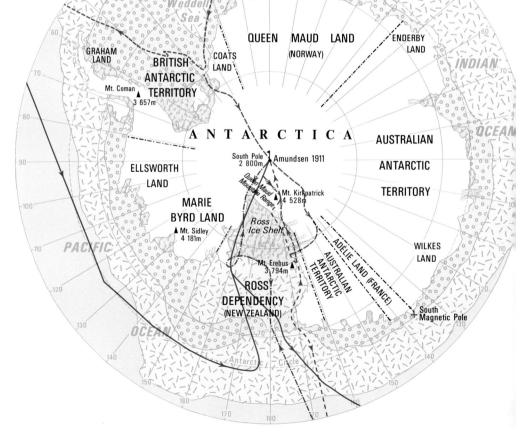

ATLANTIC OCEAN

Weddell
Sea

QUEEN MAUD LAND
(NORWAY)

ENDERBY
LAND

GRAHAM
LAND

BRITISH
ANTARCTIC
TERRITORY

COATS
LAND

INDIAN

Mt. Coman
3 657m

ANTARCTICA

AUSTRALIAN

OCEAN

ELLSWORTH
LAND

South Pole
2 800m   Amundsen 1911

ANTARCTIC

MARIE
BYRD LAND

Queen Maud
Mountain Range

Mt. Kirkpatrick
4 528m

TERRITORY

▲ Mt. Sidley
4 181m

Ross
Ice Shelf

ADÉLIE LAND (FRANCE)
AUSTRALIAN
ANTARCTIC
TERRITORY

WILKES
LAND

PACIFIC

Mt. Erebus
3 794m

ROSS
DEPENDENCY
(NEW ZEALAND)

South
+ Magnetic Pole

OCEAN

Antarctic Circle

————	Amundsen 1910–12
—1909— —1914·15—	Shackleton 1909, 1914–15
- - - - -	Scott 1911–12
—·—·—	Byrd 1928–30
- - - - -	Fuchs 1957–58

0 400 800 1200 1600 kilometres	
1 : 46 500 000	
Projection: Lambert's Azimuthal Equal Area	

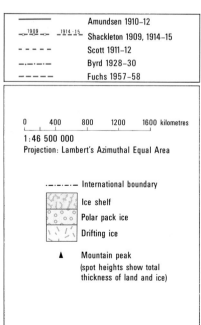

—·—·— International boundary

Ice shelf

Polar pack ice

Drifting ice

▲ Mountain peak
(spot heights show total
thickness of land and ice)

WORLD – TECTONIC PLATES AND SEISMIC ACTIVITY

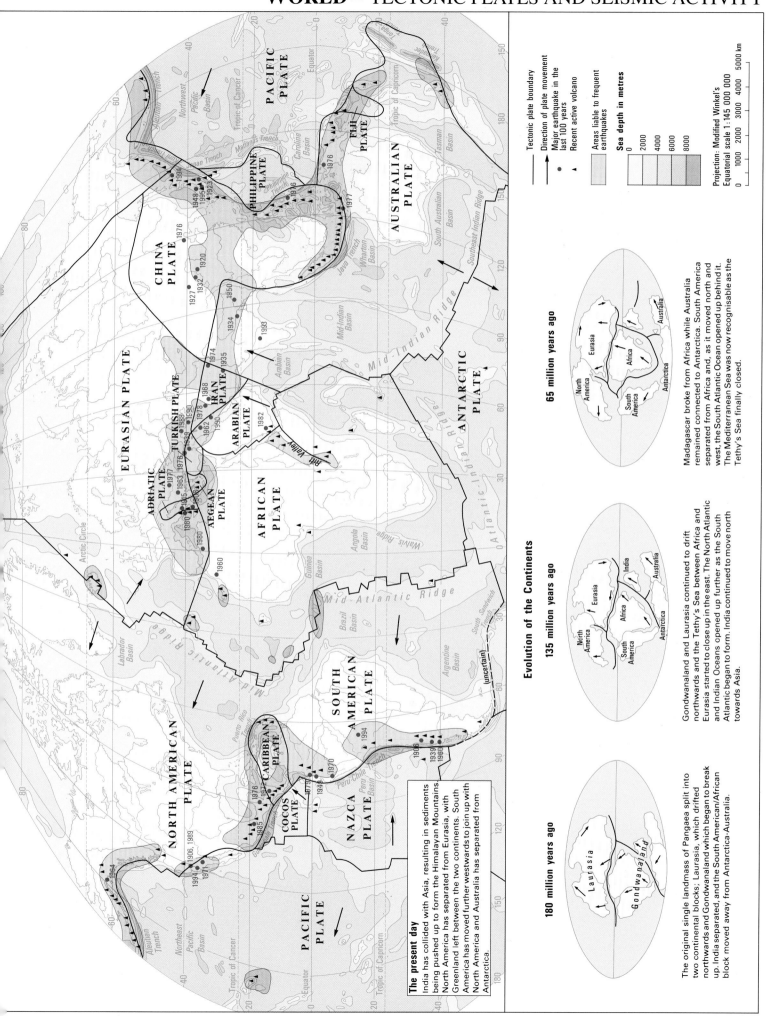

Legend

Tectonic plate boundary

Direction of plate movement

● Major earthquake in the last 100 years

▲ Recent active volcano

Areas liable to frequent earthquakes

Sea depth in metres
0 · 2000 · 4000 · 6000 · 8000

0 1000 2000 3000 4000 5000 km

Projection: Modified Winkel's
Equatorial scale 1:145 000 000

The present day

India has collided with Asia, resulting in sediments being pushed up to form the Himalayan Mountains. North America has separated from Eurasia, with Greenland left between the two continents. South America has moved further westwards to join up with North America and Australia has separated from Antarctica.

Evolution of the Continents

180 million years ago

The original single landmass of Pangaea split into two continental blocks; Laurasia, which drifted northwards and Gondwanaland which began to break up. India separated, and the South American/African block moved away from Antarctica-Australia.

135 million years ago

Gondwanaland and Laurasia continued to drift northwards and the Tethy's Sea between Africa and Eurasia started to close up in the east. The North Atlantic and Indian Oceans opened up further as the South Atlantic began to form. India continued to move north towards Asia.

65 million years ago

Madagascar broke from Africa while Australia remained connected to Antarctica. South America separated from Africa and, as it moved north and west, the South Atlantic Ocean opened up behind it. The Mediterranean Sea was now recognisable as the Tethy's Sea finally closed.

© COPYRIGHT MACMILLAN EDUCATION LTD

111

WORLD – COUNTRIES AND THEIR CAPITALS

Country	Area Sq. Km.	Total Population	GNP Per Capita	Capital	Population of Capital
Australasia					
American Samoa (U.S.)	195	46 800	5 410	Pago Pago	3 075
Australia	7 682 300	16 873 000	17 070	Canberra	310 000
Cook Islands (N.Z.)	237	18 547	N/A	Avarua	N/A
Federated States of Micronesia	700	100 520	1 500	Kolonia	–
Fiji	18 333	764 000	2 010	Suva	141 000
French Polynesia (Fr.)	4 167	199 031	15 270	Papeete	23 496
Guam (U.S.)	549	133 152	5 470	Agaña	N/A
Kiribati	811	72 335	700	Bairiki	25 380
New Caledonia (Fr.)	18 576	187 000	13 400	Nouméa	98 000
New Zealand	268 704	3 392 000	12 060	Wellington	325 000
Palau	508	15 105	N/A	Koror	10 486
Papua New Guinea	462 840	3 874 000	950	Port Moresby	174 000
Solomon Islands	29 785	320 000	710	Honiara	34 000
Tonga	748	90 485	1 350	Nuku'alofa	21 383
Tuvalu	26	8 229	326	Fongafala	2 810
Vanuatu	12 190	147 000	1 220	Port Vila	19 311
Western Samoa	2 831	168 000	940	Apia	33 000
Asia					
Afghanistan	652 090	16 557 000	158	Kabul	1 424 000
Armenia	29 800	3 335 000	780	Yerevan	1 202 000
Azerbaijan	86 600	7 134 000	1670	Baku	1 149 000
Bahrain	676	516 000	7 150	Manama	152 000
Bangladesh	143 999	115 593 000	220	Dhaka	6 105 000
Bhutan	46 500	1 616 000	180	Thimphu	27 000
Brunei	5 766	286 000	17 611	Bandar Seri Begawan	46 000
Burma	678 000	41 675 000	200	Rangoon	2 513 000
Cambodia	181 035	8 246 000	106	Phnom Penh	800 000
China	9 597 000	1 139 080 000	380	Beijing	9 750 000
Georgia	69 700	5 460 000	850	Tbilisi	1 279 000
Hong Kong (U.K.)	1 067	5 851 000	15 380	Victoria	1 251 000
India	3 166 829	827 057 000	310	New Delhi	8 375 000
Indonesia	1 919 400	179 300 000	670	Jakarta	7 886 000
Iran	1 648 000	54 607 000	2 190	Tehran	6 476 000
Iraq	434 924	18 920 000	3654	Baghdad	4 649 000
Israel[5]	20 770[1]	4 600 000	13 230	Jerusalem	495 000[2]
Japan	377 765	123 460 000	28 220	Tokyo	11 936 000
Jordan	97 740[3]	4 009 000	1 120	Amman	1 160 000
Kazakhstan	2 717 300	16 742 000	1 680	Alma-Ata	1 147 000
Korea, North	122 098	21 773 000	943	Pyongyang	2 639 000
Korea, South	99 022	42 793 000	6 790	Seoul	10 628 000
Kuwait	17 818	1 600 000	16 160	Kuwait	189 000
Kyrgyzstan	198 500	4 395 000	810	Bishkek	625 000
Laos	236 800	4 139 000	250	Vientiane	377 000
Lebanon	10 452	2 701 000	1 550	Beirut	1 500 000
Macau (Port.)	19	395 304	13 500	–	–
Malaysia	329 747	17 891 000	2 790	Kuala Lumpur	938 000
Maldives	298	215 000	500	Malé	55 000
Mongolia	1 565 000	2 180 000	473	Ulan Bator	575 000
Nepal	147 181	19 143 000	170	Kathmandu	235 000
Oman	272	1 502 000	6 490	Muscat	250 000
Pakistan	796 095	112 050 000	410	Islamabad	204 000
Philippines	300 000	62 413 000	770	Manila	7 832 000
Qatar	11 437	368 000	16 240	Doha	217 000
Russia	17 075 000	148 292 000	2 680	Moscow	8 801 000
Saudi Arabia	2 200 000	14 134 000	7 940	Riyadh	2 000 000
Singapore	620	2 700 000	15 750	Singapore	3 003 000
Sri Lanka	65 609	17 217 000	540	Colombo	1 863 000
Syria	185 180	1 2 530 000	1 170	Damascus	1 378 000
Taiwan	36 179	20 100 000	10 202	T'ai-pei	2 718 000
Tajikistan	143 100	5 303 000	480	Dushanbe	582 000
Thailand	514 000	57 196 000	1 840	Bangkok	5 876 000
Turkmenistan	488 100	3 668 000	1 270	Ashkhabad	407 000
United Arab Emirates	92 100	1 589 000	22 220	Abu Dhabi	537 000
Uzbekistan	447 400	20 515 000	860	Tashkent	2 094 000
Vietnam	329 566	66 593 000	109	Hanoi	2 571 000
Yemen	482 682	11 282 000	520	Sana'a	427 000

Country	Area Sq. Km.	Total Population	GNP Per Capita	Capital	Population of Capital
Africa					
Algeria	2 381 741	24 960 000	2 020	Algiers	1 722 000
Angola	1 246 700	10 020 000	620	Luanda	1 544 000
Benin	112 622	4 830 000	410	Porto Novo	208 000
Botswana	582 000	1 304 000	2 790	Gaborone	138 000
Burkina Faso	274 122	8 996 000	290	Ouagadougou	442 000
Burundi	27 834	5 472 000	210	Bujumbura	241 000
Cameroon	465 054	11 833 000	820	Yaoundé	750 000
Cape Verde	4 033	341 491	850	Praia	57 748
Central African Republic	622 436	3 039 000	410	Bangui	597 000
Chad	1 284 000	5 678 000	220	N'Djaména	688 000
Comoros	1 862	460 000	510	Moroni	22 000
Congo	342 000	2 271 000	1 030	Brazzaville	938 000
Côte d'Ivoire	322 463	11 997 000	670	Yamoussoukro	120 000
Djibouti	23 000	409 000	1 236	Djibouti	290 000
Egypt	1 002 000	53 153 000	630	Cairo	6 663 000
Equatorial Guinea	28 051	352 000	330	Malabo	37 000
Eritrea	93 679	2 614 699	N/A	Asmara	358 000
Ethiopia	1 157 603	39 570 253	110	Addis Ababa	1 913 000
Gabon	267 667	1 172 000	4 450	Libreville	830 000
Gambia, The	10 689	861 000	390	Banjul	150 000
Ghana	238 305	15 028 000	450	Accra	1 420 000
Guinea	245 857	5 755 000	510	Conakry	763 000
Guinea-Bissau	36 125	964 000	210	Bissau	125 000
Kenya	582 600	24 031 000	330	Nairobi	1 429 000
Lesotho	30 355	1 774 000	590	Maseru	109 000
Liberia	112 600	2 575 000	450	Monrovia	425 000
Libya	1 759 549	4 545 000	5 310	Tripoli	980 000
Madagascar	587 041	12 004 000	230	Antananarivo	802 000
Malaŵi	118 484	8 754 000	210	Lilongwe	234 000
Mali	1 240 142	8 156 000	300	Bamako	646 000
Mauritania	1 030 700	2 024 000	530	Nouakchott	393 000
Mauritius	2 040	1 082 000	2 700	Port Louis	143 000
Morocco	458 730	25 061 000	1 040	Rabat	893 000
Mozambique	799 380	15 656 000	60	Maputo	1 070 000
Namibia	824 269	1 500 000	1 610	Windhoek	115 000
Niger	1 186 408	7 731 000	300	Niamey	398 000
Nigeria	923 773	86 000 000	320	Abuja	378 671
Réunion (Fr.)	2 512	597 828	7 015	Saint-Denis	121 950
Rwanda	26 338	7 237 000	250	Kigali	233 000
São Tomé and Príncipe	1 001	117 504	370	São Tomé	35 000
Senegal	196 192	7 327 000	780	Dakar	1 382 000
Seychelles	444	69 000	5 480	Victoria	24 000
Sierra Leone	73 326	4 151 000	170	Freetown	470 000
Somalia	637 657	7 497 000	150	Mogadishu	1 000 000
South Africa	1 221 037	31 586 000	2 670	Cape Town	1 912 000
				Pretoria	823 000
Sudan	2 505 813	25 203 000	400	Khartoum	561 000
Swaziland	17 400	788 000	1 080	Mbabane	38 000
Tanzania	945 200	25 635 000	110	Dodoma	204 000
Togo	56 785	3 531 000	400	Lomé	500 000
Tunisia	164 150	8 180 000	1 740	Tunis	1 395 000
Uganda	236 000	18 794 000	170	Kampala	773 000
Western Sahara (SADR)	252 120	178 000	1 040	El Aaiún	97 000
Zaïre	2 344 885	35 568 000	220	Kinshasa	2 796 000
Zambia	752 614	8 452 000	290	Lusaka	921 000
Zimbabwe	390 308	9 709 000	570	Harare	681 000

Notes
1. Area of Israel agreed in 1949, excluding areas taken under Israeli control since 1949.
2. Including East Jerusalem, annexed in 1949.
3. Including West Bank, currently occupied by Israel.
4. Includes the Republics of Montenegro and Serbia.
5. Including the Gaza Strip and Jericho now controlled by the Palestinians.

Population figures are the latest census figures or the latest official estimate where available.
N/A Information not available.

Europe

Country	Area Sq. Km.	Total Population	GNP Per Capita	Capital	Population of Capital
Albania	28 748	3 245 000	820	Tiranë	243 000
Andorra	465	47 000	21 151	Andorra la Vella	20 000
Austria	83 855	7 583 000	22 110	Vienna	1 540 000
Belarus	207 600	10 260 000	2 910	Minsk	1 613 000
Belgium	30 519	9 845 000	20 830	Brussels	1 331 000
Bosnia & Herzegovina	51 129	4 347 000	N/A	Sarajevo	526 000
Bulgaria	110 912	9 010 000	1 330	Sofia	1 141 000
Croatia	56 538	4 770 000	5 205	Zagreb	931 000
Cyprus	9 251	701 000	9 820	Nicosia	169 000
Czech Republic	78 864	10 364 599	2 440	Prague	1 216 076
Denmark	43 075	5 143 000	25 930	Copenhagen	1 337 000
Estonia	45 100	1 583 000	2 750	Tallinn	499 000
Finland	338 145	4 975 000	22 980	Helsinki	498 000
France	543 965	56 138 000	22 300	Paris	9 319 000
Germany	357 039	78 479 000	21 046	Berlin	3 446 000
Greece	131 957	10 047 000	7 180	Athens	3 097 000
Hungary	93 032	10 652 000	3 010	Budapest	2 016 000
Iceland	103 000	253 000	23 670	Reykjavik	143 000
Ireland, Rep.of	89 894	3 500 000	12 100	Dublin	1 024 000
Italy	301 268	57 061 000	20 510	Rome	2 791 000
Latvia	63 700	2 684 000	1 930	Riga	917 000
Liechtenstein	160	28 000	N/A	Vaduz	5 000
Lithuania	65 200	3 737 000	1 310	Vilnius	593 000
Luxembourg	2 586	373 000	35 260	Luxembourg	76 000
Macedonia, Former Yugoslav Republic of	25 713	2 024 964	N/A	Skopje	563 301
Malta	246	353 000	7 300	Valletta	102 000
Moldova	33 700	4 365 000	1 260	Kishinev	676 000
Monaco	2	30 000	N/A		
Netherlands	33 963	14 951 000	18 840	Amsterdam	1 091 000
Norway	323 878	4 212 000	25 800	Oslo	683 000
Poland	312 683	38 423 000	1 960	Warsaw	1 655 000
Portugal	92 072	10 285 000	7 450	Lisbon	678 000
Romania	237 500	23 160 000	1 090	Bucharest	2 217 000
San Marino	61	23 000	8 356	San Marino	4 000
Slovakia	49 035	5 310 154	1 920	Bratislava	441 000
Slovenia	20 251	1 968 000	6 330	Ljubljana	323 000
Spain	504 750	39 187 000	14 020	Madrid	3 121 000
Sweden	449 964	8 444 000	26 780	Stockholm	1 503 000
Switzerland	41 293	6 609 000	36 230	Bern	299 000
Turkey (Europe and Asia)	779 452	58 637 000	1 950	Ankara	3 022 000
Ukraine	603 700	51 892 000	1 670	Kiev	2 616 000
United Kingdom	243 362	57 237 000	17 760	London	6 378 000
Vatican City	0.44	830	N/A	–	–
Yugoslavia⁴	102 173	10 406 742	900	Belgrade	1 137 915

North America

Country	Area Sq. Km.	Total Population	GNP Per Capita	Capital	Population of Capital
Canada	9 215 430	2 521 000	20 320	Ottawa	921 000
Greenland (Denmark)	2 175 600	56 000	8 780	Godthåb	12 000
USA (including Alaska & Hawaii)	9 363 000	249 224 000	23 120	Washington D.C.	3 924 000

Caribbean & Central America

Country	Area Sq. Km.	Total Population	GNP Per Capita	Capital	Population of Capital
Anguilla (U.K.)	96	8 960	N/A	The Valley	595
Antigua and Barbuda	442	65 962	4 770	St John's	30 000
Aruba	193	70 415	N/A	Oranjestad	N/A
Bahamas	13 939	259 000	11 720	Nassau	172 196
Barbados	430	259 300	6 630	Bridgetown	7 516
Belize	22 965	209 000	2 050	Belmopan	3 927
Bermuda (U.K.)	53	59 549	N/A	Hamilton	1 100
British Virgin Islands (U.K.)	153	17 383	N/A	Road Town	2 500
Cayman Islands (U.K.)	260	27 200	N/A	George Town	12 921
Costa Rica	51 100	3 064 000	2 000	San José	297 000
Cuba	110 860	10 822 000	1 739	Havana	2 096 000
Dominica	750	71 183	2 520	Roseau	20 755
Dominican Rep.	48 422	7 313 000	1 040	Santo Domingo	2 200 000
El Salvador	21 393	5 262 000	1 170	San Salvador	497 644
Grenada	345	94 806	2 310	St George's	4 439
Guadeloupe (Fr.)	1 780	387 034	6 073	Basse-Terre	14 003
Guatemala	108 889	10 030 000	980	Guatemala City	1 133 000
Haiti	27 750	6 764 000	380	Port-au-Prince	738 342
Honduras	112 088	5 105 000	590	Tegucigalpa	608 000
Jamaica	10 991	2 374 193	1 340	Kingston	588 000
Martinique (Fr.)	1 100	359 579	7 705	Fort-de-France	101 540
Mexico	1 958 201	89 538 000	3 470	Mexico City	8 237 000
Montserrat (U.K.)	102	11 900	N/A	Plymouth	3 500
Netherlands Antilles (Neths.)	800	189 600	7 395	Willemstad	125 000
Nicaragua	148 000	4 130 000	410	Managua	608 000
Panama	78 046	2 515 000	2 440	Panama City	625 000
Puerto Rico	8 959	3 621 000	6 610	San Juan	434 849
St Christopher and Nevis	267	41 800	3 990	Basseterre	16 400
St Lucia	616	138 151	2 900	Castries	51 994
St Vincent and the Grenadines	389	107 598	1 990	Kingstown	15 670
Trinidad & Tobago	5 128	1 170 000	3 940	Port of Spain	52 000
Turks and Caicos Islands (U.K.)	430	14 000	N/A	Cockburn Town	2 500
United States Virgin Islands (U.S.)	355	101 809	8 717	Charlotte Amalie	11 842

South America

Country	Area Sq. Km.	Total Population	GNP Per Capita	Capital	Population of Capital
Argentina	2 778 815	32 322 000	2 780	Buenos Aires	11 256 000
Bolivia	1 098 581	7 314 000	680	La Paz	1 126 000
Brazil	8 511 965	150 368 000	2 770	Brasília	1 598 000
Chile	757 626	13 173 000	2 730	Santiago	5 343 000
Colombia	1 141 748	32 978 000	1 290	Bogotá	4 921 000
Ecuador	270 670	10 587 000	1 070	Quito	1 508 000
Falkland Islands (U.K.)	12 173	2 125	N/A	Stanley	1 329
French Guiana (Fr.)	83 533	98 000	2 800	Cayenne	42 000
Guyana	214 969	739 553	268	Georgetown	72 049
Paraguay	406 752	4 277 000	1 340	Asunción	729 000
Peru	1 285 216	22 330 000	950	Lima	6 415 000
Suriname	163 820	405 000	3 700	Paramaribo	200 000
Uruguay	186 296	3 094 000	3 340	Montevideo	1 248 000
Venezuela	912 050	18 735 000	2 900	Caracas	3 247 000

WORLD – POLITICAL

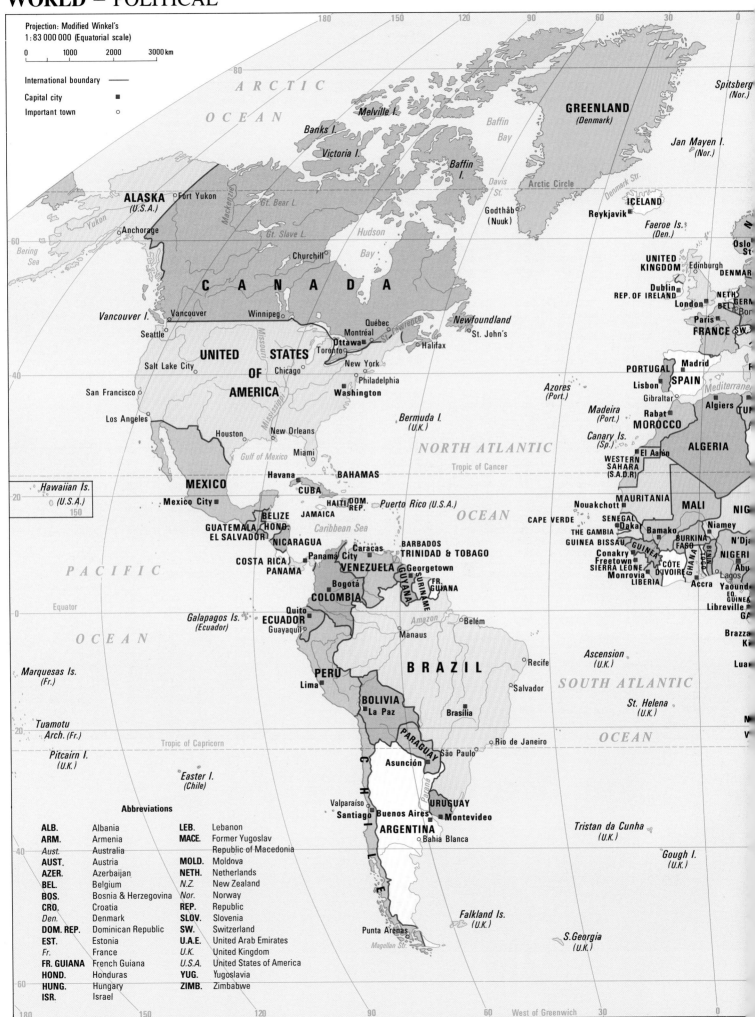

Projection: Modified Winkel's
1:83 000 000 (Equatorial scale)

0   1000   2000   3000 km

International boundary ——
Capital city ■
Important town ○

Abbreviations

ALB.	Albania	**LEB.**	Lebanon
ARM.	Armenia	**MACE.**	Former Yugoslav
Aust.	Australia		Republic of Macedonia
AUST.	Austria	**MOLD.**	Moldova
AZER.	Azerbaijan	**NETH.**	Netherlands
BEL.	Belgium	*N.Z.*	New Zealand
BOS.	Bosnia & Herzegovina	*Nor.*	Norway
CRO.	Croatia	**REP.**	Republic
Den.	Denmark	**SLOV.**	Slovenia
DOM. REP.	Dominican Republic	**SW.**	Switzerland
EST.	Estonia	**U.A.E.**	United Arab Emirates
Fr.	France	*U.K.*	United Kingdom
FR. GUIANA	French Guiana	*U.S.A.*	United States of America
HOND.	Honduras	**YUG.**	Yugoslavia
HUNG.	Hungary	**ZIMB.**	Zimbabwe
ISR.	Israel		

ARCTIC OCEAN

Barents Sea

Severnaya Zemlya

New Siberian Is.

80

Novaya Zemlya

Murmansk

Arkhangelsk

Verkhoyansk

Arctic Circle

Bering Str.

Helsinki
Tallinn
Riga
LATVIA
Vilnius
Minsk
BELARUS

St. Petersburg

RUSSIA

Okhotsk

60

Bering Sea

Kamchatka

Moscow

Perm

Yekaterinburg

Ob

Novosibirsk

Irkutsk L. Baikal

Sakhalin

Aleutian Is.

Kiev
UKRAINE
MOLD.

Rostov

Omsk

Ob

Yenisey

Lena

Amur

Kuril Is.

Vladivostok

KAZAKHSTAN

L. Balkhash

Ulan Bator

MONGOLIA

Harbin

Shenyang

NORTH
Pyongyang
KOREA

40

BULGARIA
Istanbul
Ankara
TURKEY

Black Sea

GEORGIA
Tbilisi
ARM. AZER.

Caspian Sea

Volga

Aral

UZBEKISTAN
Tashkent
TURKMENISTAN
Ashkhabad
TAJIKISTAN

Alma Ata

Bishkek
KYRGYZSTAN

Dushanbe

CHINA

Beijing

Huang He

Seoul
SOUTH

Tokyo
Osaka

JAPAN

PACIFIC

CYPRUS
LEB.
ISR.

SYRIA Baghdad
Damascus
JORDAN IRAQ
KUWAIT

Tehran

AFGHANISTAN
Kabul

Islamabad

Lahore

TIBET

Chongqing

Nanjing

Wuhan

Shanghai

T'ai-pei
TAIWAN

Tropic of Cancer

Cairo

EGYPT

IRAN

Basra

PAKISTAN

New
Delhi

NEPAL
BHUTAN
Ganges

OCEAN

Nile

SAUDI
Riyadh
ARABIA

QATAR

U.A.E.

Muscat

Karachi

BANGLA-
DESH

BURMA

Hanoi

Hong Kong
(U.K.)

Wake I.
(U.S.A.)

20

Makkah

Red Sea

OMAN

Arabian Sea

INDIA

Bombay

Calcutta

Bay of
Bengal

Rangoon

LAOS

Hainan

China Sea

ERITREA
Asmara
DJIBOUTI
Djibouti

YEMEN
Sana'a

Socotra
(Yemen)

Lakshadweep
(India)

Madras

Andaman and Nicobar
Is. (India)

THAILAND
Bangkok

VIETNAM

CAMBODIA

Manila

Quezon City

PHILIPPINES

Mariana Is.
(U.S.A.)

Marshall Is.
(U.S.A.)

Khartoum

SUDAN

ETHIOPIA

Addis Ababa

SOMALIA

Colombo

SRI LANKA

MALDIVES

Ho Chi
Minh City

Caroline Is.
(U.S.A.)

UGANDA
Kampala
KENYA

Mogadishu

Nairobi

SEYCHELLES

PENINSULAR
MALAYSIA
Kuala Lumpur

SINGAPORE

Sarawak

BRUNEI

SABAH

MALAYSIA

Kalimantan

Equator

0

RWANDA
BURUNDI
ZAIRE

TANZANIA
Dodoma

Dar es Salaam

INDIAN OCEAN

Sumatra

Sulawesi

Irian Jaya

PAPUA
NEW
GUINEA

SOLOMON IS.

MALAWI

COMOROS

Cocos Is.
(Aust.)

Christmas I.
(Aust.)

Jakarta

Java

INDONESIA

Timor

Port Moresby

ZAMBIA
Lusaka
MOZAMBIQUE
Lilongwe

Antananarivo

Harare

MAURITIUS

Darwin

Coral
Sea

VANUATU

ZIMB.
BOTSWANA

MADAGASCAR

Réunion
(Fr.)

Tropic of Capricorn

New Caledonia
(Fr.)

20

S. Africa
Johannesburg

Maputo

SWAZILAND

LESOTHO

Durban

Cape Town

AUSTRALIA

Alice Springs

Perth

Fremantle

Brisbane

Norfolk I.
(Aust.)

Sydney

Adelaide

Murray

Darling

Canberra

Auckland

Melbourne

NEW
ZEALAND

Wellington
Christchurch

40

Tasmania

Hobart

Kerguelen I.
(Fr.)

Antipodes
(N.Z.)

60

East of Greenwich 60 90 120 150 180

60 90 120 150 180 150

WORLD – PHYSICAL

ARCTIC OCEAN

Ellesmere Island

Queen Elizabeth Islands

Greenland

BEAUFORT SEA

Banks I.

Baffin Bay

Victoria Island

Baffin Island

Denmark Strait

Iceland

NORWEGIAN SEA

Brooks Range

Arctic Circle

Davis Strait

C. Farewell

British Isles

NORTH SEA

Bear Lake

Alaska Range

Mt. McKinley
6194 m

Mackenzie Mts.

Gulf of Alaska

Bering Strait

Alaska Pen.

Gt. Slave Lake

Churchill

Nelson

Hudson Bay

Laurentian Plateau

Newfoundland

Bay of Biscay

Mt. Blanc
4807 m

Pyrenees

Mt. Robson
3954 m

L. Winnipeg

Saskatchewan

Superior

NORTH

Rocky Mountains

NORTH AMERICA

Cascade Ra.

L. Michigan

L. Huron

St. Lawrence

Appalachian Mts.

C. Sable

North East Atlantic Basin

Azores

Atlas Mts.

Mt. Toubkal
4167 m

Great Basin

Mt. Elbert
4399 m

Ohio

ATLANTIC

Mid Atlantic Ridge

Sierra Nevada

Mt. Whitney
4418 m

Bermuda

North American Basin

OCEAN

Canary Is.

Sahara

AFRICA

Tropic of Cancer

Hawaiian Is.

Sierra Madre

Mississippi

Gulf of Mexico

4023m

6483m

Canary Basin

Cape Verde Is.

C. Vert

C. San Lucas

Bahama Is.

Milwaukee Depth 9200m

Citaltepetl
5700 m

Greater Antilles

Cape Verde Basin

6390m

Fouta Djalon

Guatemala

6889m

CARIBBEAN SEA

Lesser Antilles

Hog

5110m

PACIFIC

G. of Panama

Llanos

Orinoco

Guiana Highlands

Galapagos Is.

Gulf of Guinea

Equator

Chimborazo
6267 m

Amazon

OCEAN

Selvas

C. São Roque

Ascension

Madeira

Andes

SOUTH

Brazil Basin

Atlantic Ridge

Angola Basin

East Pacific Ridge

Peru Basin

Mato Grosso

Brazilian Highlands

AMERICA

St. Helena

Paraná

Tropic of Capricorn

Easter I.

Peru Chile Trench

Atacama Desert

Andes

8055m

SOUTH

Aconcagua
6980m

Pampas

Atlantic Ridge

Argentine Basin

ATLANTIC

Tristan da Cunha

8245m

Patagonia

OCEAN

Falkland Is.

South Georgia

Pacific Antarctic Basin

Tierra del Fuego

C. Horn

Magellan Strait

SCOTIA SEA

South Sandwich Is.

8265m

South Shetland Is.

South Georgia

Antarctic Pen.

metres

6000	
5000	
4000	
3000	
2000	
1000	
500	
200	
0	land below sea level
2000	
4000	
6000	
8000	

Projection : Modified Winkel's
1 : 83 000 000 (Equatorial Scale)

0   1000   2000   3000 km

World - Geographical Stati	
Continents	
Asia	43 60
Africa	30 33
North America	25 34
South America	17 61
Europe	10 49
Australasia	8 92

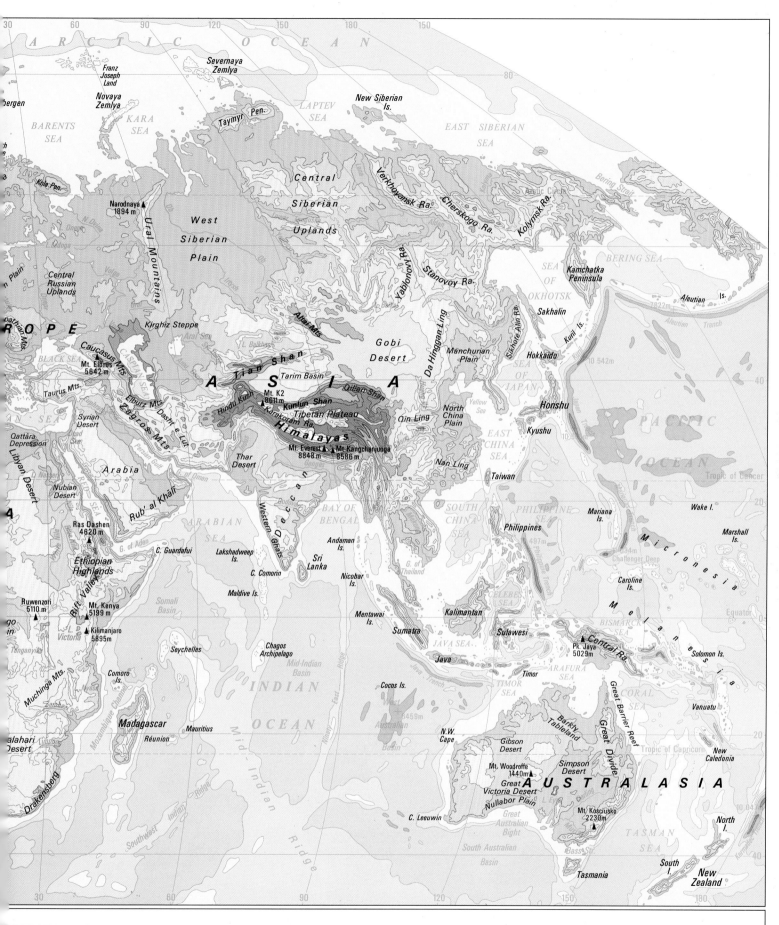

...and Seas		Highest Mountains		Deepest Sea Trenches		Longest Rivers		Largest Inland Seas and Lakes	
...cean	165 384 000 km²	Mt. Everest, Nepal/China	8 848 m	Marianas Trench, Pac. Oc.	11 034 m	Nile, Africa	6 695 km	Caspian Sea, Asia	372 000 km²
...Ocean	82 217 000 km²	Mt. K2. Pakistan/China	8 611 m	Tonga Trench, Pac. Oc.	10 882 m	Amazon, South America	6 516 km	Lake Superior, U.S.A./Canada	82 400 km²
...cean	73 481 000 km²	Mt. Kangchenjunga, Nepal/China	8 586 m	Japan Trench, Pac. Oc.	10 595 m	Mississippi-Missouri, N. America	6 019 km	Lake Victoria, East Africa	67 900 km²
...cean	14 056 000 km²	Mt. Makalu, Nepal/China	8 482 m	Kuril Trench, Pac. Oc.	10 542 m	Chang Jiang, Asia	5 470 km	Aral Sea, Asia	66 500 km²
...nean Sea	2 505 000 km²	Mt. Dhaulagiri, Nepal	8 222 m	Philippine Trench, Pac. Oc.	10 497 m	Ob-Irtysh, Asia	5 410 km	Lake Huron, U.S.A./Canada	59 600 km²
...hina Sea	2 318 000 km²	Mt. Nanga Parbat, Pakistan	8 126 m	Kermadec Trench, Pac. Oc.	10 047 m	Huang He, Asia	4 840 km	Lake Michigan, U.S.A.	58 020 km²

WORLD – CLIMATE

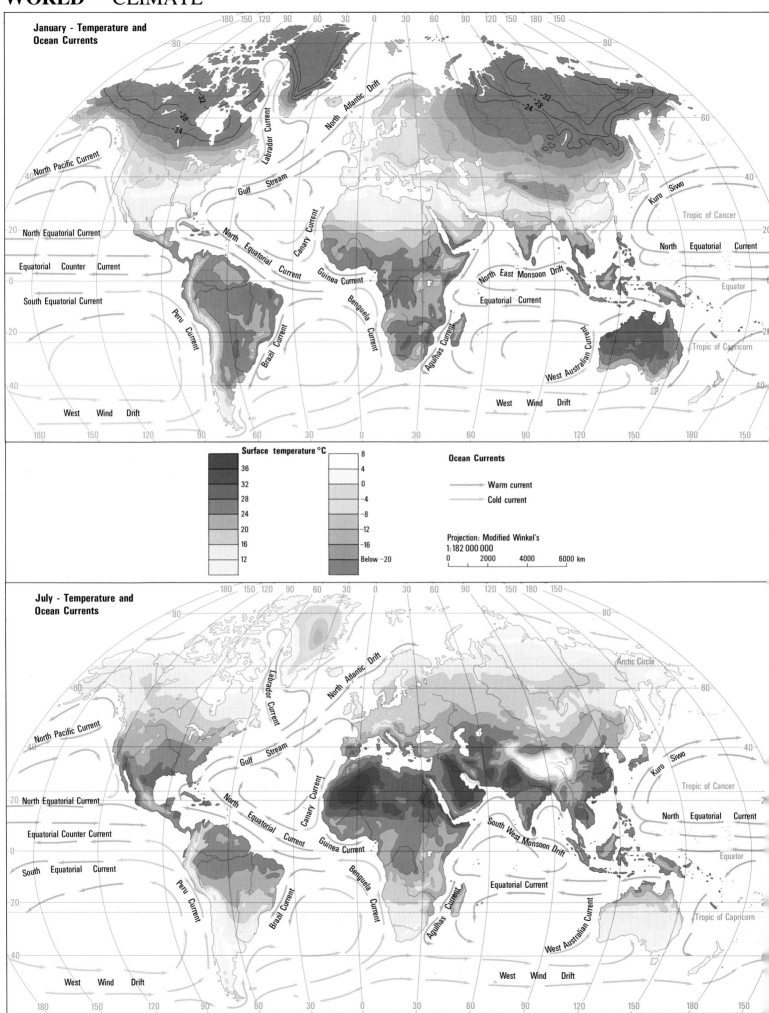

January - Temperature and Ocean Currents

July - Temperature and Ocean Currents

Surface temperature °C

36	8
32	4
28	0
24	-4
20	-8
16	-12
12	-16
	Below -20

Ocean Currents

→ Warm current
→ Cold current

Projection: Modified Winkel's
1:182 000 000

0   2000   4000   6000 km

Precipitation and Winds

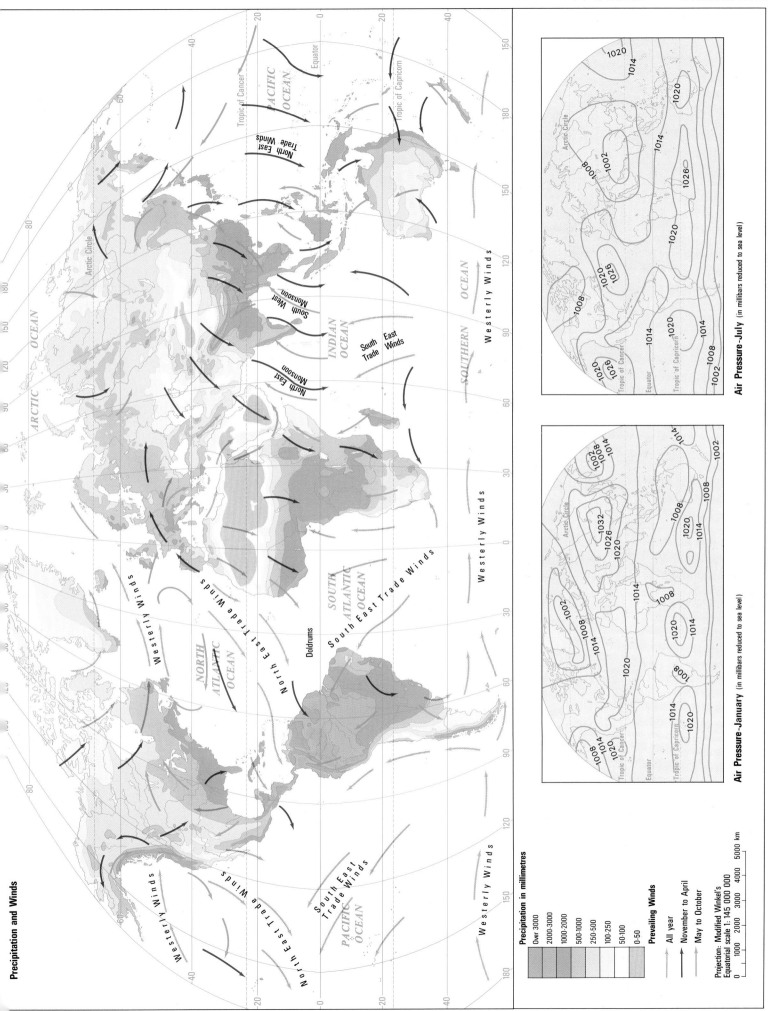

Air Pressure - July (in millibars reduced to sea level)

Air Pressure - January (in millibars reduced to sea level)

Precipitation in millimetres

- Over 3000
- 2000-3000
- 1000-2000
- 500-1000
- 250-500
- 100-250
- 50-100
- 0-50

Prevailing Winds

- All year
- November to April
- May to October

Projection: Modified Winkel's
Equatorial scale 1: 145 000 000

0 1000 2000 3000 4000 5000 km

WORLD – CLIMATIC REGIONS

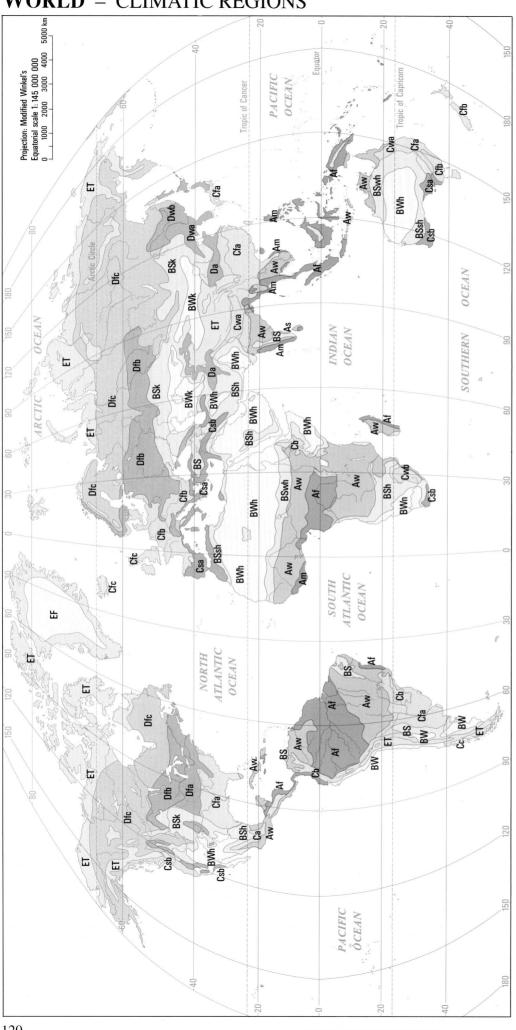

Projection: Modified Winkel's
Equatorial scale 1:145 000 000

0 1000 2000 3000 4000 5000 km

Köppen's Climatic Classification

The above map shows the world divided into major climatic regions according to the Köppen system of classification. In this system each region has been defined according to fixed values of temperature and precipitation. The classification is characterised by a shorthand code of letters, each of which designates a major climatic group. The table on the left gives a brief definition of these regions. The five main groups (A, B, C, D and E) have then been subdivided — the 2nd order subdivision relating to the seasonal characteristics of precipitation, and the 3rd order to temperature.

As with all systems of classification, only the broadest climatic types can be recognised. In general, many of the values used by Köppen to establish the climatic boundaries coincide fairly closely with the limits of the main vegetation types. It is for this reason, and because of its relative simplicity that the Köppen system is widely used and accepted, especially for teaching purposes.

3rd order

a	Hot summer. Warmest month above 22°C.
b	Warm summer. Warmest month below 22°C. 4–12 months above 10°C.
c	Cool summer. Warmest month below 22°C. 1–3 months above 10°C.
d	Severe winter. Coldest month below -38°C.
h	Hot. All months above 18°C.
k	Cold winter. Yearly mean temperature below 18°C. Warmest month above 18°C.
n	Frequent fog.

2nd order

f	Every month has at least 60 mm rainfall.
m	Monsoon climate. Short dry season. Heavy rainfall during the rest of the year.
s	Dry season in summer.
w	Dry season in winter.

Definition – 1st order

A	Rainy climate with no defined winter. Mean temperature of coldest month above 18°C.
B	Limits of regions defined by rainfall and temperature formulae.
C	Mean temperature of the coldest month in the range 18°C to -3°C. Warmest month in no case below 10°C.
D	Mean temperature of the coldest month below -3°C. Warmest month in no case below 10°C.
E	Mean temperature of every month below 10°C.

Climatic Regions

A Tropical Rain Climates	Rain forest	
	Savanna	
B Arid Climates	Steppe	BS
	Desert	BW
C Temperate Rain Climates	Mediterranean	
	Humid subtropical	
	Maritime west coast	
D Cold Snow Climates	Continental warm summer	
	Continental cool summer	
	Subarctic	
E Polar	Tundra	ET
	Ice cap	EF

120

© COPYRIGHT MACMILLAN EDUCATION LTD

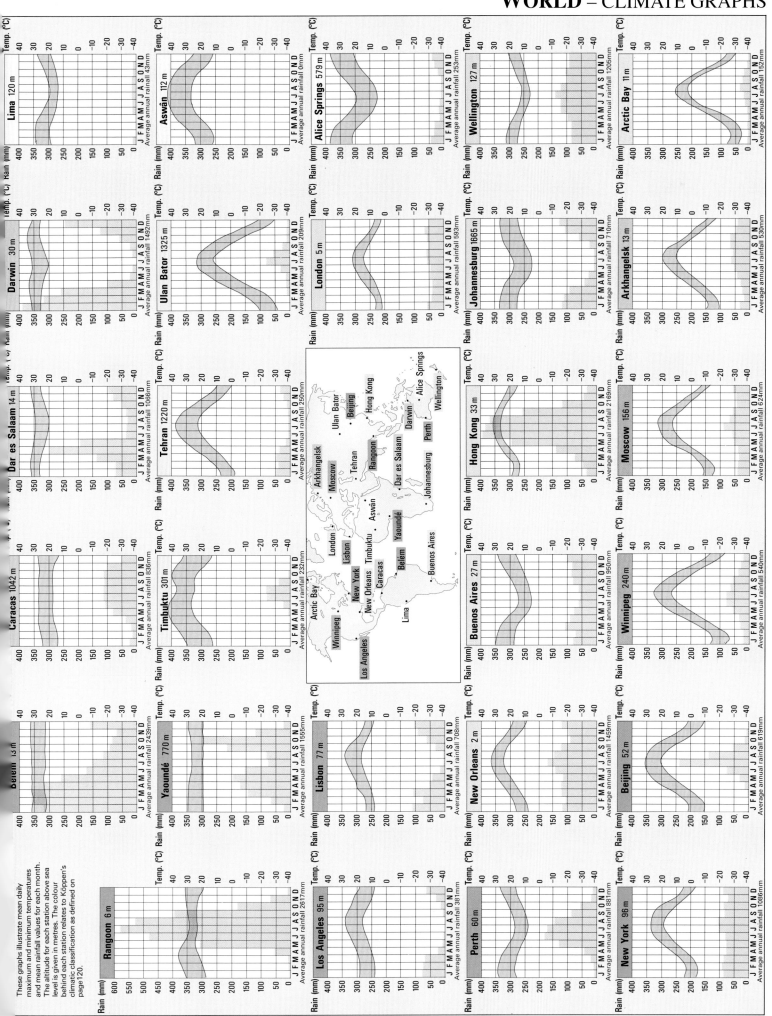

These graphs illustrate mean daily maximum and minimum temperatures and mean rainfall values for each month. The altitude for each station above sea level is given in metres. The colour behind each station relates to Köppen's climatic classification as defined on page120.

WORLD – NATURAL VEGETATION

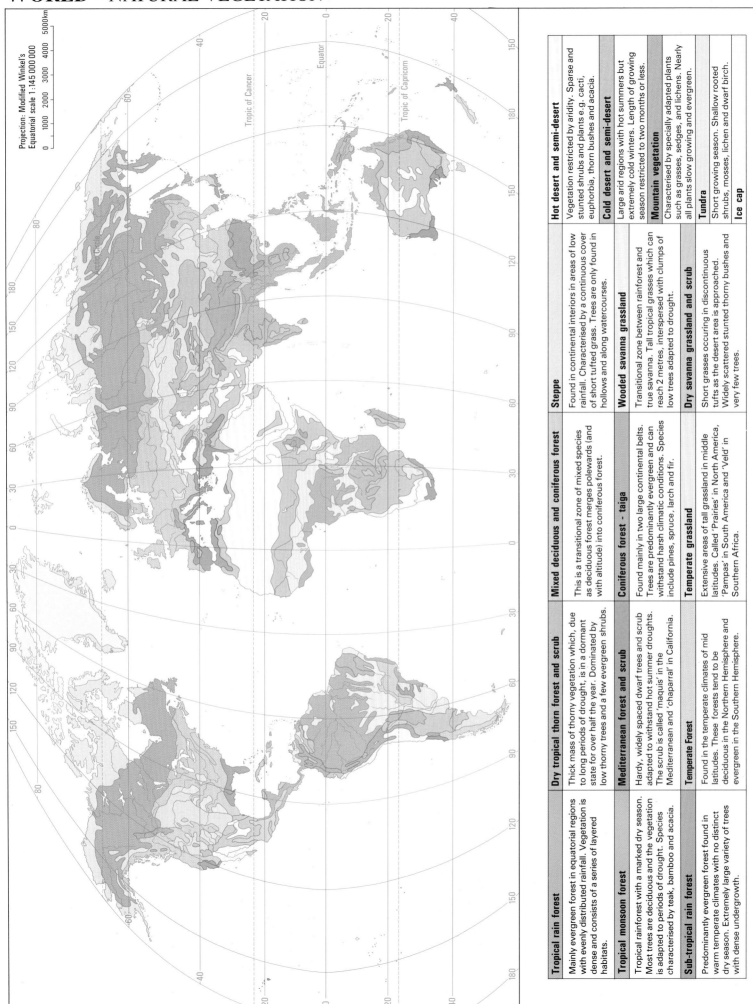

Projection: Modified Winkel's
Equatorial scale 1:145 000 000

0   1000   2000   3000   4000   5000km

Tropical rain forest	Dry tropical thorn forest and scrub	Mixed deciduous and coniferous forest	Hot desert and semi-desert
Mainly evergreen forest in equatorial regions with evenly distributed rainfall. Vegetation is dense and consists of a series of layered habitats.	Thick mass of thorny vegetation which, due to long periods of drought, is in a dormant state for over half the year. Dominated by low thorny trees and a few evergreen shrubs.	This is a transitional zone of mixed species as deciduous forest merges polewards (and with altitude) into coniferous forest.	Vegetation restricted by aridity. Sparse and stunted shrubs and plants e.g. cacti, euphorbia, thorn bushes and acacia.

Tropical monsoon forest	Mediterranean forest and scrub	Coniferous forest - taiga	Cold desert and semi-desert
Tropical rainforest with a marked dry season. Most trees are deciduous and the vegetation is adapted to periods of drought. Species characterised by teak, bamboo and acacia.	Hardy, widely spaced dwarf trees and scrub adapted to withstand hot summer droughts. The scrub is called 'maquis' in the Mediterranean and 'chaparral' in California.	Found mainly in two large continental belts. Trees are predominantly evergreen and can withstand harsh climatic conditions. Species include pines, spruce, larch and fir.	Large arid regions with hot summers but extremely cold winters. Length of growing season restricted to two months or less.

Sub-tropical rain forest	Temperate Forest	Temperate grassland	Mountain vegetation
Predominantly evergreen forest found in warm temperate climates with no distinct dry season. Extremely large variety of trees with dense undergrowth.	Found in the temperate climates of mid latitudes. These forests tend to be deciduous in the Northern Hemisphere and evergreen in the Southern Hemisphere.	Extensive areas of tall grassland in middle latitudes. Called 'Prairies' in North America, 'Pampas' in South America and 'Veld' in Southern Africa.	Characterised by specially adapted plants such as grasses, sedges, and lichens. Nearly all plants slow growing and evergreen.

		Steppe	Dry savanna grassland and scrub	Tundra
		Found in continental interiors in areas of low rainfall. Characterised by a continuous cover of short tufted grass. Trees are only found in hollows and along watercourses.	Short grasses occuring in discontinuous tufts as the desert area is approached. Widely scattered stunted thorny bushes and very few trees.	Short growing season. Shallow rooted shrubs, mosses, lichen and dwarf birch.

	Wooded savanna grassland	Ice cap
	Transitional zone between rainforest and true savanna. Tall tropical grasses which can reach 2 metres, interspersed with clumps of low trees adapted to drought.	

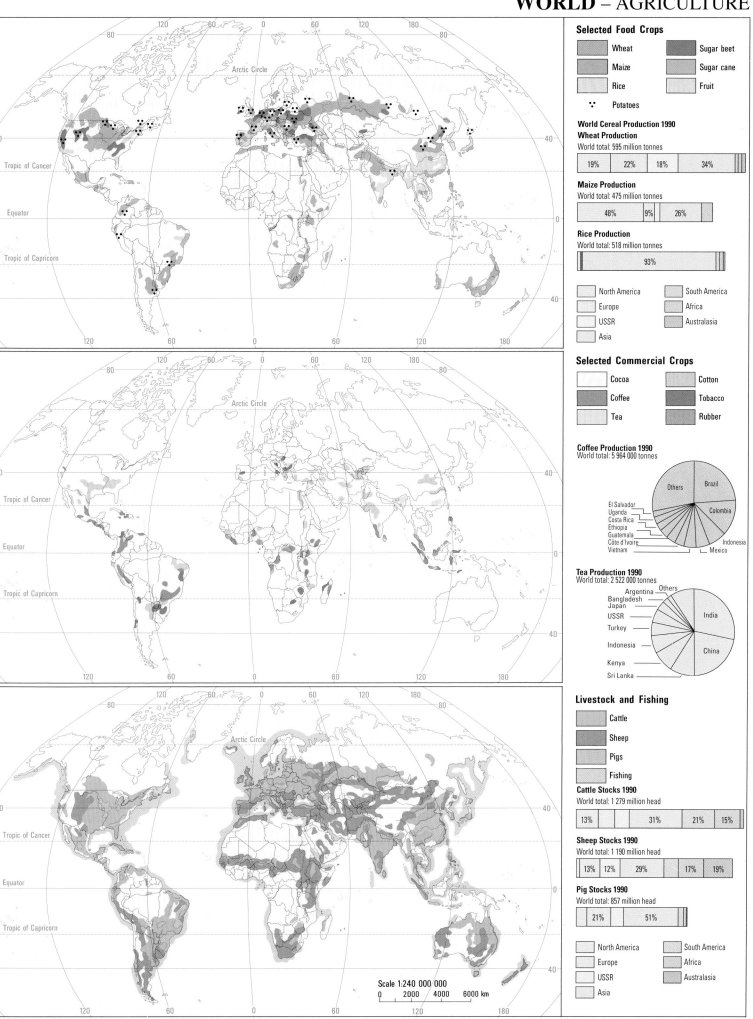

Selected Food Crops

- Wheat
- Maize
- Rice
- Sugar beet
- Sugar cane
- Fruit
- ∴ Potatoes

World Cereal Production 1990

Wheat Production
World total: 595 million tonnes

19%	22%	18%	34%

Maize Production
World total: 475 million tonnes

48%	9%	26%

Rice Production
World total: 518 million tonnes

93%

- North America
- Europe
- USSR
- Asia
- South America
- Africa
- Australasia

Selected Commercial Crops

- Cocoa
- Coffee
- Tea
- Cotton
- Tobacco
- Rubber

Coffee Production 1990
World total: 5 964 000 tonnes

Others, Brazil, Colombia, Indonesia, Mexico, Vietnam, Côte d'Ivoire, Guatemala, Ethiopia, Costa Rica, Uganda, El Salvador

Tea Production 1990
World total: 2 522 000 tonnes

Argentina, Others, Bangladesh, Japan, USSR, Turkey, Indonesia, Kenya, Sri Lanka, India, China

Livestock and Fishing

- Cattle
- Sheep
- Pigs
- Fishing

Cattle Stocks 1990
World total: 1 279 million head

13%		31%	21%	15%

Sheep Stocks 1990
World total: 1 190 million head

13%	12%	29%	17%	19%

Pig Stocks 1990
World total: 857 million head

21%	51%

- North America
- Europe
- USSR
- Asia
- South America
- Africa
- Australasia

Scale 1:240 000 000

0   2000   4000   6000 km

WORLD – MINERALS

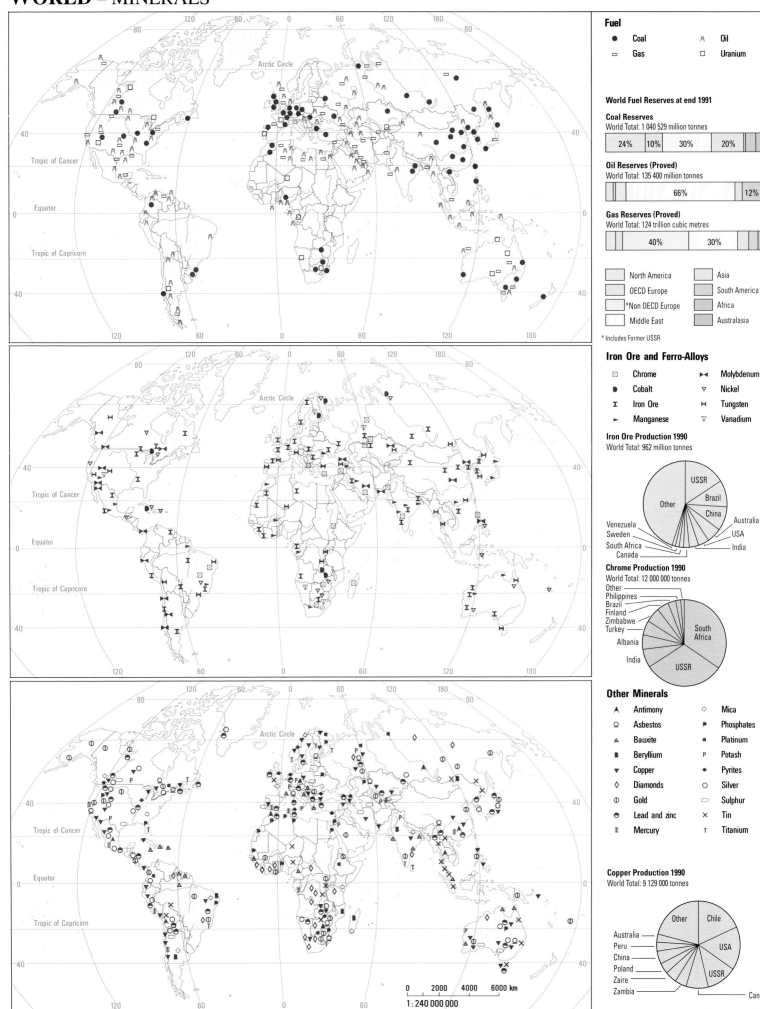

Fuel

- ● Coal
- ⊟ Gas
- ⋀ Oil
- ☐ Uranium

World Fuel Reserves at end 1991

Coal Reserves
World Total: 1 040 529 million tonnes

24%	10%	30%	20%	

Oil Reserves (Proved)
World Total: 135 400 million tonnes

	66%	12%

Gas Reserves (Proved)
World Total: 124 trillion cubic metres

	40%	30%	

- North America
- OECD Europe
- *Non OECD Europe
- Middle East
- Asia
- South America
- Africa
- Australasia

* Includes Former USSR

Iron Ore and Ferro-Alloys

- ⊠ Chrome
- ◗ Cobalt
- I Iron Ore
- ► Manganese
- ◄ Molybdenum
- ▽ Nickel
- Ⱶ Tungsten
- ▽ Vanadium

Iron Ore Production 1990
World Total: 962 million tonnes

Pie chart segments: USSR, Brazil, China, Australia, USA, India, Canada, South Africa, Sweden, Venezuela, Other

Chrome Production 1990
World Total: 12 000 000 tonnes

Pie chart segments: Other, Philippines, Brazil, Finland, Zimbabwe, Turkey, Albania, India, USSR, South Africa

Other Minerals

- ⋀ Antimony
- ⵔ Asbestos
- △ Bauxite
- ▣ Beryllium
- ▼ Copper
- ◇ Diamonds
- ⏀ Gold
- ⊖ Lead and zinc
- ⧪ Mercury
- ✦ Mica
- ◀ Phosphates
- ◀ Platinum
- P Potash
- ◆ Pyrites
- ○ Silver
- ⊖ Sulphur
- ✕ Tin
- T Titanium

Copper Production 1990
World Total: 9 129 000 tonnes

Pie chart segments: Other, Chile, USA, USSR, Canada, Zambia, Zaire, Poland, China, Peru, Australia

0   2000   4000   6000 km
1 : 240 000 000

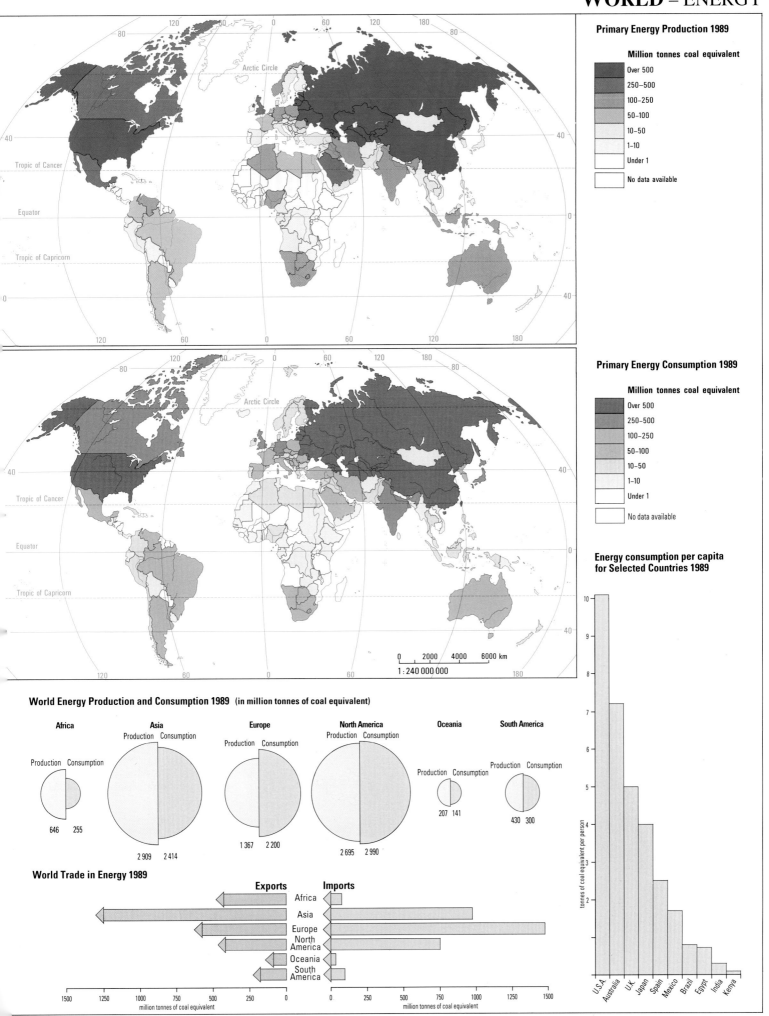

Primary Energy Production 1989

Million tonnes coal equivalent

- Over 500
- 250–500
- 100–250
- 50–100
- 10–50
- 1–10
- Under 1
- No data available

Primary Energy Consumption 1989

Million tonnes coal equivalent

- Over 500
- 250–500
- 100–250
- 50–100
- 10–50
- 1–10
- Under 1
- No data available

Energy consumption per capita for Selected Countries 1989

0   2000   4000   6000 km

1 : 240 000 000

World Energy Production and Consumption 1989 (in million tonnes of coal equivalent)

Africa
Production Consumption
646   255

Asia
Production Consumption
2 909   2 414

Europe
Production Consumption
1 367   2 200

North America
Production Consumption
2 695   2 990

Oceania
Production Consumption
207   141

South America
Production Consumption
430   300

World Trade in Energy 1989

Exports   Imports

Africa
Asia
Europe
North America
Oceania
South America

1500 1250 1000 750 500 250 0
million tonnes of coal equivalent

0 250 500 750 1000 1250 1500
million tonnes of coal equivalent

tonnes of coal equivalent per person

U.S.A. · Australia · U.K. · Japan · Spain · Mexico · Brazil · Egypt · India · Kenya

WORLD – ECONOMIC DEVELOPMENT

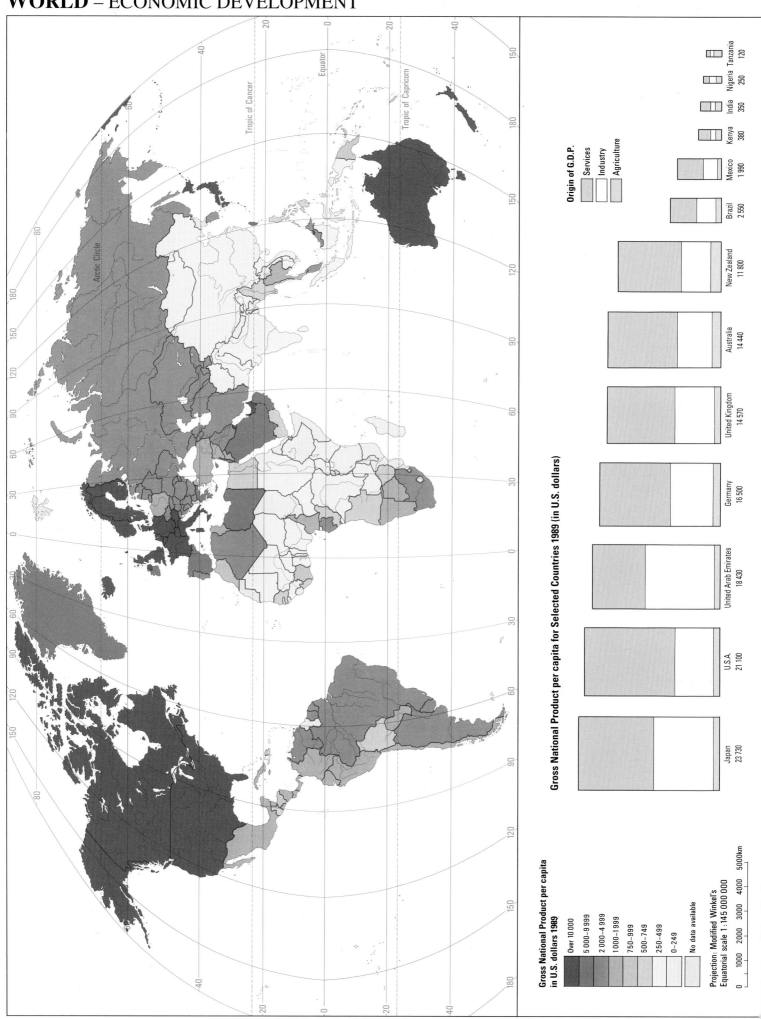

Gross National Product per capita in U.S. dollars 1989

- Over 10 000
- 5 000–9 999
- 2 000–4 999
- 1 000–1 999
- 750–999
- 500–749
- 250–499
- 0–249
- No data available

Projection: Modified Winkel's
Equatorial scale 1:145 000 000

0 1000 2000 3000 4000 5000km

Gross National Product per capita for Selected Countries 1989 (in U.S. dollars)

Origin of G.D.P.
- Services
- Industry
- Agriculture

Japan	23 730
U.S.A.	21 100
United Arab Emirates	18 430
Germany	16 500
United Kingdom	14 570
Australia	14 440
New Zealand	11 800
Brazil	2 550
Mexico	1 990
Kenya	380
India	350
Nigeria	250
Tanzania	120

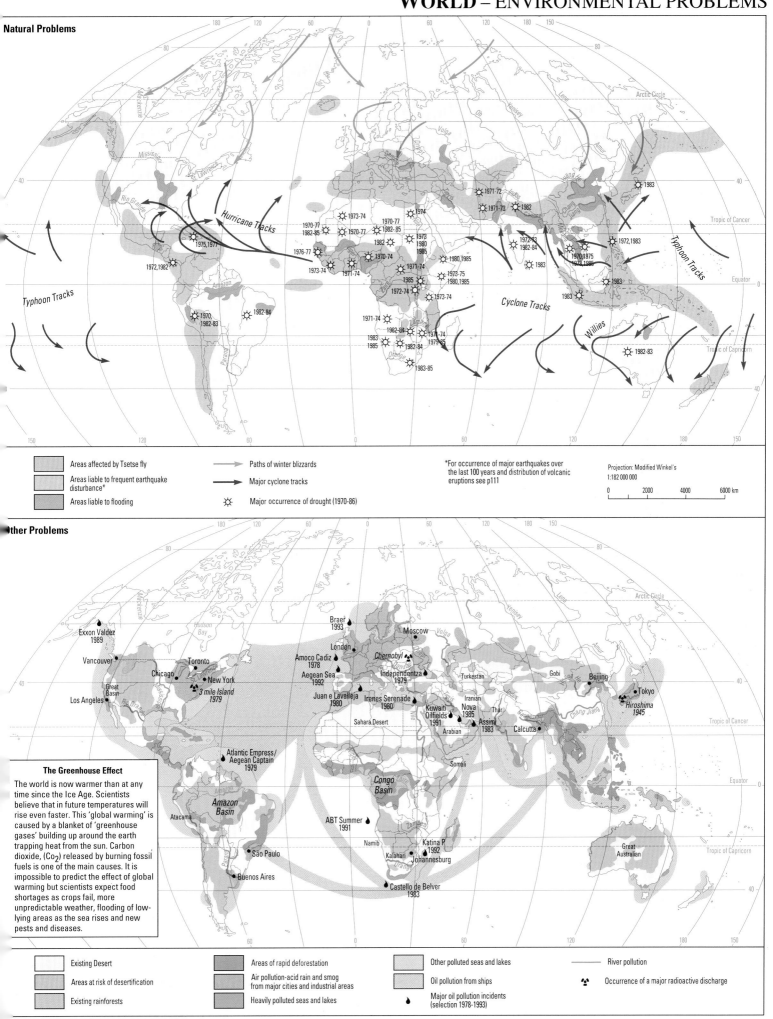

Natural Problems

Mackenzie · Mississippi · Rio Grande · St. Lawrence · Amazon · Paraná · Danube · Volga · Tigris · Nile · Congo · Zambezi · Orange · Ob · Yenisey · Lena · Amur · Hwang He · Chang Jiang · Indus · Ganges

Arctic Circle

Tropic of Cancer

Equator

Tropic of Capricorn

Hurricane Tracks

Typhoon Tracks

Typhoon Tracks

Cyclone Tracks

Willies

Drought years (☼ markers):
1975,1977 · 1972,1982 · 1976-77 · 1973-74 · 1973-74 · 1970-77 1982-85 · 1970-77 · 1970-77 1982-85 · 1973-74 · 1974 · 1982 · 1970-74 · 1971-74 · 1973 1980 1985 · 1985 · 1972-74 · 1980,1985 · 1973-75 1980,1985 · 1973-74 · 1971-72 · 1971-73 · 1982 · 1972-73 1982-84 · 1983 · 1970,1975 1978,1985 · 1972,1983 · 1983 · 1983 · 1983 · 1983 · 1971-74 · 1982-84 · 1971-74 1979-85 · 1983 1985 · 1982-84 · 1983-85 · 1970, 1982-83 · 1982-84 · 1982-83

Projection: Modified Winkel's
1:182 000 000

0   2000   4000   6000 km

	Legend (Natural Problems)
(stipple)	Areas affected by Tsetse fly
(light grey)	Areas liable to frequent earthquake disturbance*
(dark grey)	Areas liable to flooding
→	Paths of winter blizzards
→	Major cyclone tracks
☼	Major occurrence of drought (1970-86)

*For occurrence of major earthquakes over the last 100 years and distribution of volcanic eruptions see p111

Other Problems

The Greenhouse Effect

The world is now warmer than at any time since the Ice Age. Scientists believe that in future temperatures will rise even faster. This 'global warming' is caused by a blanket of 'greenhouse gases' building up around the earth trapping heat from the sun. Carbon dioxide, (CO_2) released by burning fossil fuels is one of the main causes. It is impossible to predict the effect of global warming but scientists expect food shortages as crops fail, more unpredictable weather, flooding of low-lying areas as the sea rises and new pests and diseases.

Locations/incidents:
Exxon Valdez 1989 · Vancouver · Los Angeles · Great Basin · Chicago · Toronto · New York · 3 mile Island 1979 · Atlantic Empress/ Aegean Captain 1979 · Amazon Basin · Atacama · São Paulo · Buenos Aires · Braer 1993 · Moscow · London · Amoco Cadiz 1978 · Aegean Sea 1992 · Chernobyl · Independentza 1979 · Juan e Lavalleja 1980 · Irenes Serenade 1980 · Kuwaiti Oilfields 1991 · Sahara Desert · Congo Basin · ABT Summer 1991 · Namib · Kalahari · Katina P 1992 · Johannesburg · Orange · Castello de Belver 1983 · Nova 1985 · Assimi 1983 · Arabian · Iranian · Turkestan · Thar · Calcutta · Somali · Gobi · Beijing · Tokyo · Hiroshima 1945 · Great Australian

	Legend (Other Problems)
(white)	Existing Desert
(stipple)	Areas at risk of desertification
(grey)	Existing rainforests
(dark grey)	Areas of rapid deforestation
(grey)	Air pollution-acid rain and smog from major cities and industrial areas
(dark grey)	Heavily polluted seas and lakes
(light grey)	Other polluted seas and lakes
(grey)	Oil pollution from ships
◆	Major oil pollution incidents (selection 1978-1993)
—	River pollution
☢	Occurrence of a major radioactive discharge

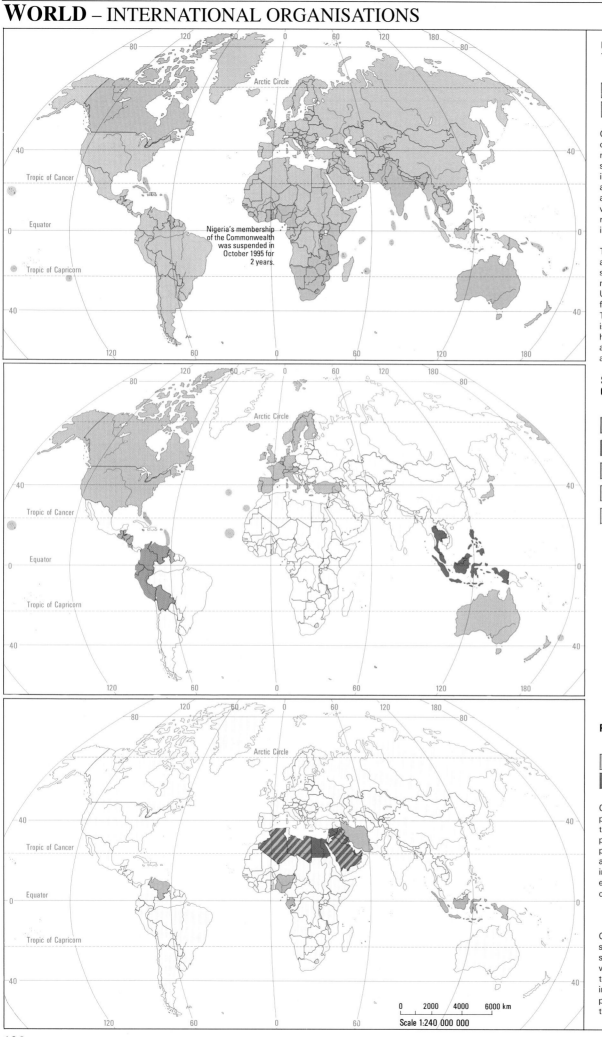

Nigeria's membership of the Commonwealth was suspended in October 1995 for 2 years.

United Nations and The Commonwealth

- United Nations (UN)
- The Commonwealth and United Nations

On 24 October 1945 the UN organisation was established to maintain international peace and security, and to develop co-operation in solving economic, social, cultural and humanitarian problems. The main advisory body is the General Assembly whilst the Security Council bears the responsibility for maintaining international peace.

The Commonwealth is a voluntary association of sovereign independent states, founded in 1949. There are now 53 members comprising the United Kingdom and most of its former colonies and dependencies. The Secretariat, established in 1965, is the central co-ordinating body and has several divisions responsible for areas such as education, technology and health.

Selected Regional Economic Organisations

- Andean Group
- Association of South East Asian Nations (ASEAN)
- Central American Common Market (CACM)
- Caribbean Community and Common Market (CARICOM) see p.14
- Organisation for Economic Co-operation and Development (OECD)

Petroleum Exporting Organisations

- Organisation of the Petroleum Exporting Countries (OPEC)
- Organisation of Arab Petroleum Exporting Countries (OAPEC)

OPEC was established in 1960 to link petroleum exporting countries. It aims to unify and co-ordinate members' petroleum policies and to stabilise prices in international oil markets. It also attempts to establish a steady income for OPEC countries and to ensure a regular supply of oil to consumer nations.

OAPEC was set up in 1968 to safeguard the interests of member states and to establish co-operation within the petroleum industry. It aims to co-ordinate several aspects of the industry including attempts to link petroleum research institutes within the Arab States.

0   2000   4000   6000 km

Scale 1:240 000 000

WORLD – INTERNATIONAL ORGANISATIONS

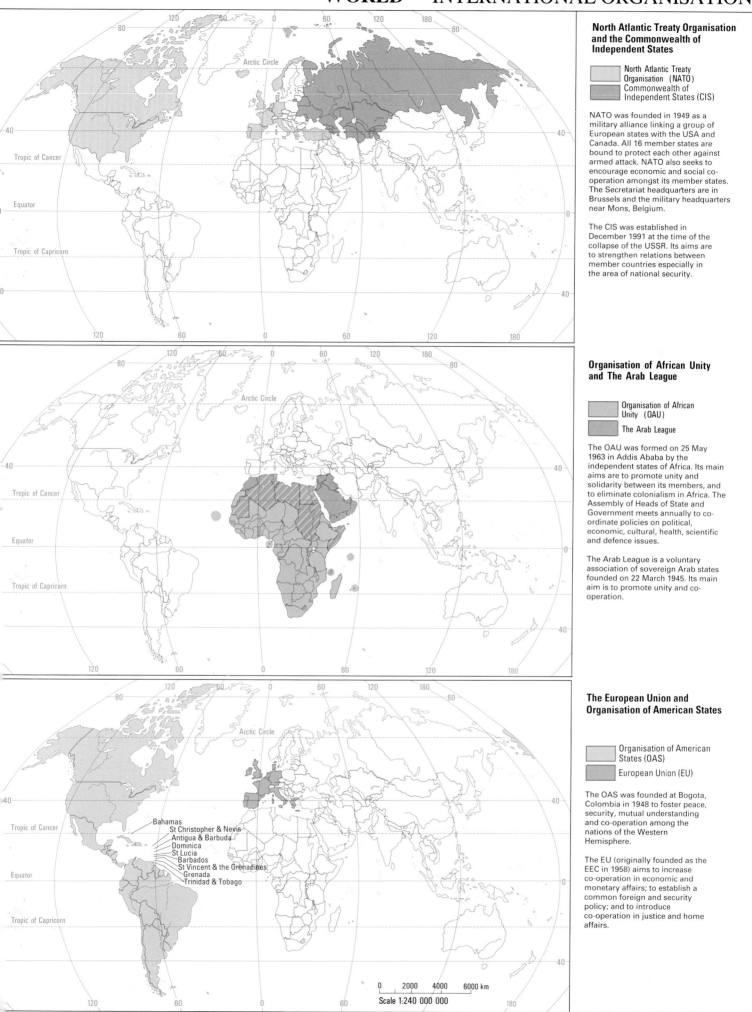

North Atlantic Treaty Organisation and the Commonwealth of Independent States

North Atlantic Treaty Organisation (NATO)

Commonwealth of Independent States (CIS)

NATO was founded in 1949 as a military alliance linking a group of European states with the USA and Canada. All 16 member states are bound to protect each other against armed attack. NATO also seeks to encourage economic and social co-operation amongst its member states. The Secretariat headquarters are in Brussels and the military headquarters near Mons, Belgium.

The CIS was established in December 1991 at the time of the collapse of the USSR. Its aims are to strengthen relations between member countries especially in the area of national security.

Organisation of African Unity and The Arab League

Organisation of African Unity (OAU)

The Arab League

The OAU was formed on 25 May 1963 in Addis Ababa by the independent states of Africa. Its main aims are to promote unity and solidarity between its members, and to eliminate colonialism in Africa. The Assembly of Heads of State and Government meets annually to co-ordinate policies on political, economic, cultural, health, scientific and defence issues.

The Arab League is a voluntary association of sovereign Arab states founded on 22 March 1945. Its main aim is to promote unity and co-operation.

The European Union and Organisation of American States

Organisation of American States (OAS)

European Union (EU)

The OAS was founded at Bogota, Colombia in 1948 to foster peace, security, mutual understanding and co-operation among the nations of the Western Hemisphere.

The EU (originally founded as the EEC in 1958) aims to increase co-operation in economic and monetary affairs; to establish a common foreign and security policy; and to introduce co-operation in justice and home affairs.

Bahamas
St Christopher & Nevis
Antigua & Barbuda
Dominica
St Lucia
Barbados
St Vincent & the Grenadines
Grenada
Trinidad & Tobago

Scale 1:240 000 000

0 2000 4000 6000 km

© COPYRIGHT MACMILLAN EDUCATION LTD

129

WORLD – POPULATION

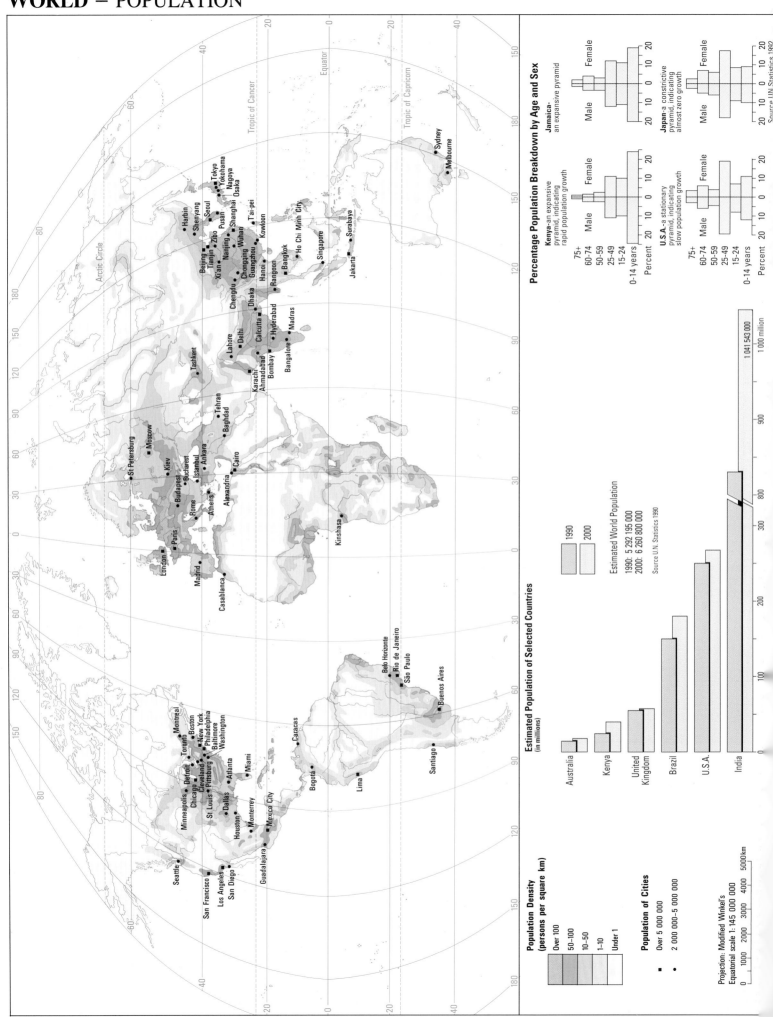

Percentage Population Breakdown by Age and Sex

Jamaica-an expansive pyramid

Male   Female

Japan-a constrictive pyramid, indicating almost zero growth

Male   Female

Source UN Statistics 1992

Kenya-an expansive pyramid, indicating rapid population growth

75+
60-74
50-59
25-49
15-24
0-14 years

Male   Female

Percent

U.S.A.-a stationary pyramid, indicating slow population growth

75+
60-74
50-59
25-49
15-24
0-14 years

Male   Female

Percent

Estimated Population of Selected Countries
(in millions)

1990
2000

Australia
Kenya
United Kingdom
Brazil
U.S.A.
India

Estimated World Population

1990: 5 292 195 000
2000: 6 260 800 000

Source U.N. Statistics 1990

**Population Density
(persons per square km)**

Over 100
50-100
10-50
1-10
Under 1

Population of Cities

■ Over 5 000 000
● 2 000 000-5 000 000

Projection: Modified Winkel's
Equatorial scale 1:145 000 000

0 1000 2000 3000 4000 5000km

INDEX

Abbreviations

Arch.	Archipelago	I(s).	Island(s)
B.	Bay	L.	Lake
C.	Cape	Mass.	Massachusetts
Cent.	Central	Mt(s).	Mountain(s)
Chan.	Channel	N.	North
E.	East	Pen.	Peninsula
G.	Gulf	Pass.	Passage
		Pk.	Peak

Pt.	Point	Sd.	Sound
R.	River	St.	Saint
Ra.	Range	Ste.	Sainte
Res.	Reservoir	UAE	United Arab Emirates
Rep.	Republic	UK	United Kingdom
S.	South	USA	United States of America
SADR	Sahrawi Arab Democratic Republic	W.	West

INDEX

132

INDEX

INDEX

INDEX

Place	Lat.	Long.	Page
rogresso Lagoon, L., *Belize*	18 15N	88 23W	47
rome, *Burma*	18 50N	95 05E	104
rospect, *Grenada*	12 13N	61 40W	39
rospect, Pt., *Jamaica*	17 51N	76 21W	25
routes, *Barbados*	13 09N	59 34W	40
rovidence, *Barbados*	13 04N	59 31W	40
rovidence, *USA*	41 41N	71 15W	57
rovidenciales, Is., *Turks and Caicos Is.*	21 47N	72 15W	27
rudhoe Bay, *Alaska, USA*	70 00N	148 00W	50
ucallpa, *Peru*	8 20S	74 20W	67
uebla, *Mexico*	19 00N	98 10W	49
ueblo, *USA*	38 20N	104 40W	57
uerca, Pt., *Puerto Rico*	18 14N	65 33W	30
uerto Arroyo, *Puerto Rico*	17 56N	66 05W	30
uerto Ayacucho, *Venezuela*	5 40N	67 35W	15
uerto Barrios, *Guatemala*	16 20N	88 55W	49
uerto Cabello, *Venezuela*	10 30N	68 10W	15
uerto Cabezas, *Nicaragua*	13 50N	83 20W	14
uerto Carreño, *Colombia*	6 50N	67 30W	49
uerto Cortés, *Honduras*	16 20N	87 50W	49
uerto Maldonado, *Peru*	12 45S	69 00W	67
uerto Montt, *Chile*	41 28S	73 00W	61
uerto Padre, *Cuba*	21 10N	76 35W	22
uerto Rico, *W. Indies*	18 15N	66 15W	30
uerto Yabucoa, *Puerto Rico*	18 03N	65 48W	30
mp, B., *St. Christopher*	17 21N	62 51W	32
ne, *India*	18 20N	74 00E	104
no, *Peru*	16 05S	70 02W	67
nta Arenas, *Chile*	53 00S	71 00W	61
nta Gorda, *Belize*	16 07N	88 50W	47
nta La Cruz, *Venezuela*	10 15N	64 30W	15
ntarenas, *Costa Rica*	10 20N	85 00W	49
nto Fijo, *Venezuela*	11 40N	70 10W	15
rus, R., *Brazil*	5 30S	63 30W	68
san, *S. Korea*	35 04N	129 05E	102
tumayo, R., *Colombia/Peru*	1 30S	74 30W	67
ongyang, *N. Korea*	39 04N	125 40E	95
renees, Mts., *France/Spain*	42 40N	0 30E	76
ndahar, *Afghanistan*	31 32N	65 30E	94
tar, *Asia*	25 30N	51 00E	106
ttâra Depression, *Egypt*	29 40N	27 30E	77
na, *Egypt*	26 08N	32 42E	106
ian Shan, Mts., *China*	39 00N	100 00E	101
gdao, *China*	36 25N	121 00E	101
ghai Hu, L., *China*	37 00N	98 30E	101
ling, Mts., *China*	34 30N	110 00E	101
ihar, *China*	47 35N	124 00E	101
m, *Iran*	34 40N	51 00E	106
arantine, Pt., *Grenada*	12 01N	61 46W	39
arter, The, *Anguilla*	18 11N	63 03W	34
artier d'Orleans, *St. Martin*	18 04N	63 01W	45
artier de Grand' Case, *St. Martin*	18 06N	63 04W	45
ébec, *Canada*	46 50N	71 19W	57
ebradillas, *Puerto Rico*	18 29N	66 56W	30
een Charlotte, Is., *Canada*	53 10N	132 00W	50
een Charlotte, Sd., *Canada*	52 00N	130 00W	57
een Elizabeth, Is., *Canada*	75 00N	95 00W	50
een Maud, Ra., *Antarctica*	88 00S	160 00W	110
een Maud Land, *Antarctica*	75 00S	15 00E	110
eensland, *Australia*	24 00S	145 00E	107
eenstown, *Australia*	42 07S	145 33E	107
eenstown, *S. Africa*	31 45S	27 00E	89
elimane, *Mozambique*	17 52S	36 52E	89
rétaro, *Mexico*	20 30N	100 20W	49
tta, *Pakistan*	30 15N	66 55E	104
zon City, *Philippines*	14 30N	121 10E	95
ck Step, *Jamaica*	18 15N	77 42W	24
pie, *Australia*	26 35S	144 10E	107
to, *Ecuador*	0 12S	78 35W	61
a, *Indonesia*	8 27S	118 45E	107
at, *Morocco*	34 00N	6 59W	76
aul, *apua New Guinea*	4 07S	152 06E	107
bit, I., *Barbuda*	17 41N	61 49W	33
e, C., *Newfoundland, anada*	47 00N	54 00W	60
e Course, *Jamaica*	17 50N	77 17W	24
ged, Pt., *Barbados*	13 09N	59 25W	40
ged Island Range, *he Bahamas*	22 22N	75 45W	28
ad, R., *Sudan*	12 45N	35 30E	106
ier, Mt., *USA*	46 50N	121 50W	57
y, L., *Canada*	48 30N	92 30W	60
ur, *India*	21 00N	81 40E	104
a, *Nicaragua*	12 00N	84 00W	14
ble, *Jamaica*	17 58N	76 37W	25
bund, *St. Martin*	18 04N	63 04W	45
panalgas, *Trinidad*	10 40N	60 55W	42
ville ou Chancel, I., *artinique*	14 40N	60 52W	35

Place	Lat.	Long.	Page
Rancagua, *Chile*	34 10S	70 45W	61
Rancho Dolores, *Belize*	17 35N	88 37W	47
Ranchuelo, *Cuba*	22 15N	80 10W	22
Rangoon, *Burma*	16 50N	96 10E	104
Rangpur, *Bangladesh*	25 40N	89 20E	104
Rann of Kutch, *India*	23 30N	70 00E	104
Ras Abu Shagara, *Sudan*	21 00N	37 30E	106
Râs Banâs, *Egypt*	24 00N	36 00E	106
Rasht, *Iran*	37 20N	49 40E	106
Rat, I., *St. Lucia*	14 01N	60 58W	37
Raúl Leoni, L., *Venezuela*	7 40N	63 00W	15
Raurkela, *India*	22 10N	84 40E	104
Rawalpindi, *Pakistan*	33 38N	73 08E	104
Ray, C., *Newfoundland, Canada*	47 50N	59 30W	60
Reading, *Jamaica*	18 26N	77 57W	24
Recherche, Arch. of the, *Australia*	35 00S	123 00E	107
Recife, *Brazil*	8 00S	35 00W	68
Red, R., *USA*	31 50N	94 30W	57
Red Bays, *The Bahamas*	25 07N	78 07W	28
Red Cliff, *Nevis*	17 06N	62 32W	32
Red Deer, *Canada*	53 00N	114 00W	57
Red Hills, Mts., *Jamaica*	18 05N	76 51W	25
Red Sea, *Africa/Asia*	20 30N	38 00E	106
Redhead, *Trinidad*	10 50N	60 55W	42
Redoute, *Martinique*	14 36N	61 02W	35
Reform, *Trinidad*	10 15N	61 20W	42
Regensburg, *Germany*	48 50N	12 10E	75
Reggio, *Italy*	38 07N	15 38E	76
Regina, *Canada*	50 30N	104 35W	57
Rehoboth, *Namibia*	23 15S	17 05E	89
Reindeer, L., *Canada*	57 30N	104 00W	50
Rendezvous, *Barbados*	13 04N	59 34W	40
Rendezvous, *Montserrat*	16 47N	62 11W	34
Rendezvous, B., *Anguilla*	18 10N	63 07W	34
Rendezvous, B., *Montserrat*	16 47N	62 11W	34
Rendezvous Bluff, *Montserrat*	16 46N	62 11W	34
Rennes, *France*	48 07N	1 41W	76
Reno, *USA*	39 40N	119 50W	57
Requin, Pt., *Grenada*	12 01N	61 38W	39
Resistencia, *Argentina*	27 28S	59 00W	61
Rest, *Jamaica*	17 53N	77 21W	24
Reuss, R., *Switzerland*	47 20N	8 18E	79
Revillagigedo, Is., *Cent.America*	18 50N	111 20W	49
Reykjavik, *Iceland*	64 06N	21 59W	69
Rheinwaldhorn, Mt., *Switzerland*	46 28N	9 04E	79
Rhine, R., *Germany*	50 20N	7 15E	75
Rhodes, I., *Greece*	36 00N	28 00E	76
Rhône, R., *France*	44 30N	4 30E	76
Ribeirão Prêto, *Brazil*	21 09S	47 48W	68
Rices, *Barbados*	13 05N	59 27W	40
Richardson Peak, Mt., *Belize*	16 37N	88 46W	47
Richland Park, *St. Vincent*	13 11N	61 10W	38
Richmond, *Jamaica*	18 14N	76 54W	25
Richmond, *USA*	37 33N	77 27W	57
Richmond, R., *St. Vincent*	13 17N	61 13W	38
Richmond Peak, Mt., *St. Vincent*	13 17N	61 11W	38
Riding, Pt., *Grand Bahama I.*	26 47N	78 08W	28
Riga, *Latvia*	56 53N	24 08E	69
Rijeka, *Croatia*	45 20N	14 21E	76
Rimouski, *Canada*	48 30N	68 50W	57
Rincon, *Bonaire*	12 05N	68 30W	45
Rincón, B., *Puerto Rico*	17 56N	66 20W	30
Ringelspitz, Mt., *Switzerland*	46 51N	9 17E	79
Rio Branco, *Brazil*	9 59S	67 49W	68
Rio Bueno, *Jamaica*	18 28N	77 27W	24
Rio Claro, *Trinidad*	10 15N	61 10W	42
Rio de Janeiro, *Brazil*	23 00S	43 12W	68
Río de la Plata, *S. America*	35 00S	57 00W	61
Río Gallegos, *Argentina*	51 35S	69 15W	61
Rio Grande, *Brazil*	32 03S	52 08W	68
Rio Grande, *Puerto Rico*	18 23N	65 50W	30
Rio Grande, R., *USA/Mexico*	29 47N	101 15W	57
Rio Nuevo, R., *Jamaica*	18 23N	77 02W	24
Rio Piedras, *Puerto Rico*	18 24N	66 02W	30
Riohacha, *Colombia*	11 30N	72 40W	14
Riva, *Italy*	45 52N	10 51E	79
Rivas, *Nicaragua*	11 25N	85 45W	14
River, B., *Barbados*	13 19N	59 35W	40
Riversdale, *Belize*	16 44N	88 18W	47
Rivière Pilote, *Martinique*	14 28N	60 54W	35
Rivière Salée, *Martinique*	14 30N	60 58W	35
Riyadh, *Saudi Arabia*	24 44N	46 43E	106
Road Bay, *Anguilla*	18 12N	63 07W	34
Roadtown, *British Virgin Islands*	18 28N	64 38W	31
Roaring Creek, *Belize*	17 17N	88 47W	47
Roaring Creek, R., *Belize*	17 10N	88 51W	47
Roberts, Mt., *Trinidad*	10 45N	61 05W	42
Robertsport, *Liberia*	6 40N	11 15W	91
Robinsons, *Barbados*	13 07N	59 26W	40
Robson, Mt., *Canada*	53 10N	119 10W	57
Roche's Bluff, *Montserrat*	16 43N	62 09W	34
Rochester, *USA*	43 30N	76 55W	60
Rock Hall, *Barbados*	13 11N	59 36W	40
Rock Hall, *Barbados*	13 17N	59 36W	40
Rock Hall, *Jamaica*	18 04N	76 53W	25
Rock River, *Jamaica*	18 04N	77 13W	24
Rock Sound, *The Bahamas*	24 54N	76 08W	28
Rockhampton, *Australia*	23 22S	150 32E	107
Rockingham, *Australia*	32 17S	115 43E	107
Rockly, B., *Tobago*	11 05N	60 45W	43
Rockstone, *Guyana*	5 55N	58 30W	46

Place	Lat.	Long.	Page
Rocky, Mts., *N. America*	45 00N	113 00W	57
Rocky, Pt, *Belize*	18 25N	88 10W	47
Rocky, Pt., *Jamaica*	17 49N	77 08W	24
Roebourne, *Australia*	20 48S	117 10E	107
Roger, *Dominica*	15 20N	61 23W	36
Rojo, C., *Puerto Rico*	17 55N	67 15W	30
Rolleville, *The Bahamas*	23 40N	75 58W	28
Roma, *Australia*	26 30S	148 50E	107
Romania, *Europe*	46 00N	25 30E	77
Romano, I., *Cuba*	22 15N	78 00W	22
Rome, *Italy*	41 55N	12 28E	76
Ronde, Pt., *Dominica*	15 32N	61 29W	36
Roper, R., *Australia*	14 30S	135 00E	107
Roraima, Mt., *Guyana*	5 15N	60 30W	46
Roraima, Mt., *Venezuela*	5 10N	60 40W	61
Rosalie, *Dominica*	15 22N	61 15W	36
Rosalie, B., *Dominica*	15 21N	61 15W	36
Rosalie, Pt., *Dominica*	15 22N	61 15W	36
Rosario, *Argentina*	33 00S	60 50W	61
Rose, Mt., *Grenada*	12 11N	61 37W	39
Rose, Pt., *Martinique*	14 38N	60 52W	35
Rose Hall, *Guyana*	6 10N	57 20W	46
Rose Hill, *Barbados*	13 16N	59 37W	40
Rose Hill, *Grenada*	12 12N	61 37W	39
Roseau, *Dominica*	15 17N	61 23W	36
Roseau, R., *Dominica*	15 18N	61 22W	36
Roseau, R., *St. Lucia*	13 57N	61 00W	37
Rosehall, *St. Vincent*	13 16N	61 14W	38
Rosignal, *Guyana*	6 15N	57 30W	46
Rosita, *Belize*	17 55N	88 56W	47
Ross Dependency, *Antarctica*	75 00S	175 00W	110
Ross Ice Shelf, *Antarctica*	84 00S	170 00W	110
Rostock, *Germany*	54 04N	12 09E	75
Rostov, *Russia*	47 14N	39 15E	77
Roswell, *USA*	33 20N	104 30W	57
Rotterdam, *Netherlands*	51 57N	4 30E	75
Rouche, I., *St. Lucia*	13 57N	60 52W	37
Rouen, *Barbados*	13 06N	59 35W	40
Rouen, *France*	49 27N	1 04E	76
Rouge, B., *St. Martin*	18 04N	63 06W	45
Round Hill, Mt., *Jamaica*	17 51N	77 23W	24
Routhiers, *Guadeloupe*	16 02N	61 36W	35
Roxborough, *Tobago*	11 15N	60 35W	43
Ruapehu, Mt., *New Zealand*	39 18S	175 36E	107
Rub al Khali, *Saudi Arabia*	19 00N	50 00E	106
Rum Cay, I., *The Bahamas*	23 40N	74 52W	28
Runaway Bay, *Jamaica*	18 27N	77 21W	24
Rundu, *Namibia*	18 00S	19 45E	89
Runde, R., *Zimbabwe*	21 20S	32 00E	89
Rupert, R., *Canada*	52 00N	78 30W	60
Rupununi, R., *Guyana*	3 10N	59 25W	46
Ruse, *Bulgaria*	43 48N	25 59E	77
Russia, *Europe/Asia*	57 00N	95 00E	94
Rustenburg, *S. Africa*	25 30S	27 30E	89
Ruth Howard, *Grenada*	12 00N	61 45W	39
Rutland, R., *St. Vincent*	13 12N	61 15W	38
Rwanda, *Africa*	2 00S	30 00E	81
Ryazan, *Russia*	54 40N	39 40E	69
Rybinsk, Res., *Russia*	58 30N	38 00E	69
Ryuku, Is., *Japan*	26 00N	127 00E	102

S

Place	Lat.	Long.	Page
S. Ambrosio, I., *Chile*	26 00S	80 00W	61
S. Felix, I., *Chile*	26 00S	80 00W	61
Saane, R., *Switzerland*	46 50N	7 08E	79
Saanen, *Switzerland*	46 29N	7 15E	79
Saas-Fee, *Switzerland*	46 20N	7 52E	79
Saba, *W.Indies*	17 38N	63 15W	45
Sabana de la Mar, *Dominican Republic*	19 00N	69 20W	29
Sabana Grande de Boya, *Dominican Republic*	18 50N	69 45W	29
Sabana Grande de Palenque, *Dominican Republic*	18 15N	70 10W	29
Sabanalarga, *Colombia*	10 25N	74 50W	14
Sabaneta, *Dominican Republic*	19 30N	71 20W	29
Sabinal, I., *Cuba*	21 35N	77 15W	22
Sable, C., *Canada*	43 29N	65 38W	57
Sable, C., *USA*	25 00N	81 30W	57
Sabradinho, Dam, *Brazil*	10 00S	40 00W	68
Sacramento, *USA*	38 39N	121 30W	57
Sacramento, R., *USA*	40 00N	122 30W	57
Sadhoowa, *Trinidad*	10 05N	61 25W	42
Saddlers, *St. Christopher*	17 24N	62 47W	32
Safajah, *Saudi Arabia*	26 30N	39 30E	106
Sagua de Tánamo, *Cuba*	20 35N	75 15W	22
Sagua la Grande, *Cuba*	22 50N	80 05W	22
Saguenay, R., *Canada*	48 00N	70 30W	60
Saharan Atlas, Mts., *Morocco*	34 00N	1 45E	76
Saharanpur, *India*	30 00N	77 20E	104
St. Andrew, Mt., *St. Vincent*	13 11N	61 12W	38
St-Anne, *Guadeloupe*	16 12N	61 22W	35
Ste-Anne, *Martinique*	14 26N	60 52W	35
St. Ann's Bay, *Jamaica*	18 26N	77 12W	24
St. Barthélemy, *W. Indies*	17 50N	62 50W	45
St. Catherine, Mt., *Grenada*	12 09N	61 40W	39
St. Christoffelburg, Mt., *Curaçao*	12 30N	69 10W	45
St. Christopher (St. Kitts), *W. Indies*	17 20N	62 45W	32
St. Claude, *Guadeloupe*	16 00N	61 40W	35
St. Cloud, *USA*	56 00N	94 30W	57
St. Croix, I., *US Virgin Islands*	17 45N	64 45W	31
St. Croix, R., *USA*	46 30N	91 45W	60

Place	Lat.	Long.	Page
St. Croix Roadstead, *St. Lucia*	14 04N	60 58W	37
St. Davids, *Barbados*	13 05N	59 33W	40
St. David's, I., *Bermuda*	32 22N	64 38W	28
St. David's, Pt., *Grenada*	12 00N	61 40W	39
St. Etienne, *France*	45 27N	4 22E	76
St. Eustatius, *W. Indies*	17 30N	62 58W	45
St-François, *Guadeloupe*	16 14N	61 16W	35
St. Gallen, *Switzerland*	47 28N	9 21E	79
St. George, *Bermuda*	32 23N	64 40W	28
St. George's, *Grenada*	12 03N	61 45W	39
St. George's, I., *Bermuda*	32 23N	64 43W	28
St. George's Hill, *Montserrat*	16 44N	62 11W	34
St. Georges Plains, *Jamaica*	18 15N	78 07W	24
St. Giles, I., *Tobago*	11 20N	60 30W	43
St. Gotthard Tunnel, *Switzerland*	46 33N	8 33E	79
St. Jago Plains, *Jamaica*	17 56N	76 58W	25
St. Jean, L., *Canada*	48 10N	71 40W	60
St. Jean, Pt., *Dominica*	15 14N	61 15W	36
St. John, *Canada*	45 20N	66 08W	57
St. John, I., *US Virgin Islands*	18 27N	64 45W	31
St. John's, *Antigua*	17 07N	61 50W	33
St. John's, *Canada*	47 35N	52 40W	50
St. John's, *Montserrat*	16 46N	62 10W	34
St. Johns, R., *Grenada*	12 03N	61 44W	39
St. John's Harbour, *Antigua*	17 08N	61 52W	33
St. Johnstone, *Antigua*	17 07N	61 49W	33
St. Joris, B., *Curaçao*	12 08N	68 50W	45
St. Joseph, *Dominica*	15 24N	61 25W	36
St. Joseph, *Martinique*	14 40N	61 00W	35
St. Joseph, *Trinidad*	10 15N	59 55W	42
St. Joseph, *Trinidad*	10 35N	61 20W	42
St. Joseph, L., *Canada*	51 30N	91 00W	60
St. Kitts-Nevis, *W. Indies*	17 25N	62 45W	61
St. Lawrence, *Barbados*	13 04N	59 34W	40
St. Lawrence, G. of, *Canada*	48 00N	62 30W	57
St. Lawrence, R., *N. America*	48 00N	68 00W	57
St. Louis, *Marie Galante*	15 55N	61 20W	35
St. Louis, *Senegal*	16 08N	16 27W	91
St. Louis, *USA*	38 41N	90 07W	57
St. Louis, R., *Marie Galante*	15 55N	61 20W	35
St. Louis du Nord, *Haiti*	19 50N	72 40W	29
St. Louis du Sud, *Haiti*	18 15N	73 30W	29
Ste-Luce, *Martinique*	14 28N	60 54W	35
St. Lucia, *W. Indies*	13 55N	61 00W	37
St. Lucia, C., *S. Africa*	28 20S	33 00E	89
St. Lucia, Chan., *St. Lucia*	14 07N	60 56W	37
St. Lukes, *Antigua*	17 04N	61 49W	33
St. Maarten, *W. Indies*	18 01N	63 03W	45
St. Marc, *Haiti*	19 05N	72 35W	29
St. Margaret, *Trinidad*	10 20N	61 25W	42
St. Margarets Bay, *Jamaica*	18 12N	76 31W	25
Ste-Marguerite, *Guadeloupe*	16 22N	61 24W	35
Ste-Maria, *Guadeloupe*	16 06N	61 32W	35
St. Maria, B., *Curaçao*	12 16N	69 03W	45
St. Marie, *Martinique*	14 46N	61 00W	35
St. Marie, L., *Curaçao*	12 18N	69 04W	45
St. Mark, B., *Grenada*	12 12N	61 42W	39
St. Martin, *W. Indies*	18 05N	63 03W	45
St. Martins, *Barbados*	13 05N	59 28W	40
St. Mary's, *Trinidad*	10 10N	61 30W	42
St. Mary's, *Trinidad*	10 25N	61 25W	42
St. Michel de l'Attalaye, *Haiti*	19 20N	72 20W	29
St. Michiel, *Curaçao*	12 11N	68 55W	45
St. Moritz, *Switzerland*	46 30N	9 50E	79
St. Nicolas, *Aruba*	12 05N	70 00W	45
St. Patricks, *Barbados*	13 05N	59 30W	40
St. Patrick's, *Montserrat*	16 42N	62 11W	34
St. Paul, *USA*	44 54N	93 05W	57
St. Paul, R., *Liberia*	7 00N	10 00W	91
St. Paul's, *St. Christopher*	17 24N	62 50W	32
St. Peter's, *Montserrat*	16 45N	62 11W	34
St. Peter's, *St. Christopher*	17 19N	62 43W	32
St. Petersburg, *Russia*	59 50N	30 25E	69
St. Petersburg, *USA*	27 45N	82 40W	57
St. Philips, *Antigua*	17 02N	61 43W	33
St. Pierre, *Martinique*	14 46N	61 10W	35
Ste-Rose, *Guadeloupe*	16 20N	61 42W	35
St. Sauveur, *Guadeloupe*	16 00N	61 34W	35
St. Thomas, I., *US Virgin Islands*	18 27N	64 57W	31
St. Urbain, *St. Lucia*	13 45N	60 56W	37
St. Vincent, *W. Indies*	13 10N	61 10W	61
St. Vincent and The Grenadines, *W. Indies*	13 15N	61 10W	38
St. Willibrordus, *Curaçao*	12 18N	69 05W	45
Sajama, Mt., *Bolivia*	18 09S	68 52W	61
Sakai, *Japan*	34 30N	135 30E	102
Sakakah, *Saudi Arabia*	29 55N	40 45E	106
Sakhalin, I., *Russia*	52 00N	143 00E	95
Sal, I., *Cape Verde*	15 09N	24 55W	91
Salado, R., *Argentina*	30 00S	61 30W	61
Salado, R., *Argentina*	36 00S	66 50W	61
Salado, R., *Cuba*	20 40N	76 30W	22
Salamanca, *Spain*	41 05N	5 45W	76
Salcedo, *Dominican Republic*	19 20N	70 20W	29
Saldanha, *S. Africa*	33 00S	17 56E	89
Sale, *Australia*	38 03S	147 02E	107
Salée, R., *Guadeloupe*	16 16N	61 32W	35
Salekhard, *Russia*	66 33N	66 35E	94
Salem, *India*	11 40N	78 10E	104

Place	Lat.	Long.	Page
ongkhla, *Thailand*	7 12N	100 35E	94
orobon, *Bonaire*	12 05N	68 30W	45
orocaba, *Brazil*	23 30S	47 32W	68
orong, *Indonesia*	0 55S	131 20E	107
oto, *Curaçao*	12 20N	69 10W	45
oubise, *Grenada*	12 06N	61 37W	39
oufrière, *Dominica*	15 13N	61 22W	36
oufrière, *St. Lucia*	13 51N	61 03W	37
oufrière, B., *Dominica*	15 13N	61 22W	36
oufrière, B., *St. Lucia*	13 51N	61 04W	37
oufrière, Mt., *St. Vincent*	13 20N	61 11W	38
oufrière Hills, *Montserrat*	16 43N	62 10W	34
outh, Pt., *Barbados*	13 02N	59 31W	40
outh Africa, Rep. of, *Africa*	30 00S	27 30E	89
outh Australia, *Australia*	29 00S	133 00E	107
outh Caicos, I., *Turks and Caicos Is.*	21 32N	71 30W	27
uth China Sea, *Asia*	12 00N	115 00E	94/5
uth East Cape, *Australia*	42 07S	145 33E	107
uth Friars, B., *St. Christopher*	17 15N	62 41W	32
uth Georgia, I., *S. Atlantic Ocean*	54 40S	36 00W	61
uth Hill, *Anguilla*	18 11N	63 05W	34
uth Island, *New Zealand*	45 00S	170 00E	107
uth Korea, *Asia*	37 00N	128 00E	101
uth Negril, Pt., *Jamaica*	18 15N	78 22W	24
uth Olivees, R., *St. Christopher*	17 18N	62 44W	32
uth Pole, *Antarctica*	90 00S	0 00	110
uth Rivers, *St. Vincent*	13 14N	61 08W	38
uth Sandwich Is., *S. Atlantic Ocean*	55 00S	28 00W	61
uth Shetland Is., *S. Atlantic Ocean*	62 00S	55 00W	108
uth Sound, *British Virgin Islands*	18 29N	64 23W	31
uth Town, *Cayman Is.*	19 38N	80 06W	27
uth Union, *St. Vincent*	13 12N	61 08W	38
uth West, Pt., *Jamaica*	18 12N	78 15W	24
uth West Cape, *New Zealand*	47 17S	167 29E	107
uthampton, *UK*	51 00N	1 25W	80
uthampton, I., *Canada*	65 00N	84 00W	50
uthern Alps, *New Zealand*	43 35S	170 10E	107
uthern Bush, B. *Turks and Caicos Is.*	21 40N	71 36W	27
uthern Indian, L., *Canada*	58 00N	99 00W	57
uthern Long Cay, I., *Belize*	17 06N	88 03W	47
uthfield, *Jamaica*	17 52N	77 40W	24
vetskaya Gavan, *Russia*	48 57N	140 16E	95
vcotts, *Antigua*	17 03N	61 49W	33
in, *Europe*	40 00N	4 00E	76
ldings, *Jamaica*	18 09N	77 27W	24
nish, Pt., *Barbuda*	17 33N	61 44W	33
nish, Pt., *Bermuda*	32 17N	64 49W	28
nish, Pt., *Montserrat*	16 44N	62 09W	34
nish Town, *British Virgin Islands*	18 28N	64 26W	31
nish Town, *Jamaica*	17 59N	76 58W	25
nish Water, B., *Curaçao*	12 04N	68 52W	45
nish Wells, *The Bahamas*	25 30N	76 45W	28
ightstown, *Barbados*	13 14N	59 38W	40
yside, *Tobago*	11 15N	60 30W	43
zia, *Italy*	44 07N	9 48E	76
sbergen, I., *Arctic Ocean*	78 00N	15 00E	94
, *Croatia*	43 40N	16 20E	77
kane, *USA*	47 45N	117 25W	57
t Bay, *Cayman Is.*	19 43N	79 43W	27
ng Garden, *Guyana*	7 00N	58 30W	46
ng Hall, *Barbados*	13 18N	59 36W	40
ng Village, *St. Vincent*	13 15N	61 14W	38
ngfield, Illinois, *USA*	39 50N	89 50W	57
ngfield, Mass. *USA*	42 30N	72 00W	60
ngfield, Missouri, *USA*	37 15N	93 30W	57
Tree, *Jamaica*	17 59N	77 33W	24
anka, *Asia*	6 50N	81 00E	104
agar, *India*	34 12N	74 50E	104
ford Creek, *The Bahamas*	24 42N	77 55W	28
e Bank, *Turks and Caicos Is.*	21 35N	71 31W	27
iel Cay, I., *The Bahamas*	24 10N	76 28W	28
ley, *Falkland Islands, UK*	51 45S	57 56W	61
ovoy, Ra., *Russia*	57 30N	129 00E	94
leton, *St. Christopher*	17 19N	62 44W	32
ve Gulf, B., *Jamaica*	17 54N	77 50W	24
anger, *Norway*	58 57N	5 40E	75
a Maris, *The Bahamas*	23 32N	75 15W	28
enbosch, *S. Africa*	33 56S	18 51E	89
ney, Mt., *Barbados*	13 16N	59 35W	40
art, I., *New Zealand*	46 58S	167 54E	107
art Town, *Jamaica*	18 23N	77 27W	24
kholm, *Sweden*	59 19N	18 03E	75
kton, *USA*	38 00N	121 15W	57

Place	Lat.	Long.	Page
Stoney Ground, *Anguilla*	18 12N	63 02W	34
Stony Hill, *Jamaica*	18 06N	76 47W	25
Strasbourg, *France*	48 37N	7 42E	80
Streatham, *Montserrat*	16 44N	62 10W	34
Stroude Land, *Barbados*	13 07N	59 27W	40
Stubbs, *St. Vincent*	13 09N	61 09W	38
Stubbs, B., *St. Vincent*	13 08N	61 09W	38
Stutterheim, *S. Africa*	32 30S	27 30E	89
Stuttgart, *Germany*	48 47N	9 10E	75
Sucia, B., *Puerto Rico*	17 55N	67 10W	30
Sucre, *Bolivia*	19 00S	65 15W	61
Sudan, *Africa*	14 50N	28 00E	81
Sudbury, *Canada*	46 30N	81 00W	57
Suez, *Egypt*	29 58N	32 31E	106
Suez Canal, *Egypt*	30 00N	32 29E	106
Suffisant Dorp, *Curaçao*	12 12N	68 57W	45
Sugar, B., *Montserrat*	16 43N	62 11W	34
Sugar Loaf, *Grenada*	12 13N	61 36W	39
Suizhou, *China*	31 30N	114 20E	101
Sukkur, *Pakistan*	27 42N	68 54E	104
Sulawesi, I., *Indonesia*	2 00S	120 00E	95
Sullana, *Peru*	4 55S	81 00W	67
Sulu Sea, *Indonesia*	8 07N	120 00E	95
Sumatra, I., *Indonesia*	0 45S	103 10E	94
Sumba, I., *Indonesia*	10 00S	119 30E	95
Sumbawa, I., *Indonesia*	8 10S	118 30E	95
Sumbe, *Angola*	11 20S	14 00E	89
Sundsvall, *Sweden*	62 23N	17 25E	69
Sunyani, *Ghana*	7 22N	2 18W	91
Superior, *USA*	47 00N	93 00W	57
Superior, L., *N. America*	47 30N	87 30W	57
Surabaya, *Indonesia*	7 25S	112 40E	94
Surat, *India*	21 00N	73 00E	104
Surgut, *Russia*	61 13N	73 20E	94
Suriname, *S. America*	4 00N	56 00W	61
Sursee, *Switzerland*	47 10N	8 05E	79
Surt, *Libya*	31 10N	16 35E	77
Sverdrup, Is., *Canada*	79 00N	100 00W	50
Swakopmund, *Namibia*	22 37S	14 30E	89
Swasey Branch, R., *Belize*	16 37N	88 32W	47
Swaziland, *Africa*	26 30S	31 30E	89
Sweden, *Europe*	62 00N	15 00E	69
Sweeting Cay, I., *Grand Bahama I.*	26 35N	77 55W	28
Swetes, *Antigua*	17 03N	61 47W	33
Switzerland, *Europe*	46 30N	8 30E	79
Sydney, *Australia*	33 53S	151 10E	107
Sydney, *Canada*	46 00N	60 10W	57
Syr Darya, R., *Kazakhstan*	44 00N	66 00E	94
Syracuse, *USA*	42 50N	76 00W	57
Syria, *Asia*	35 30N	38 00E	106
Syrian Desert, *Middle East*	32 30N	39 00E	106
Szczecin, *Poland*	53 27N	14 27E	75
Szeged, *Hungary*	46 16N	20 10E	77

T

Place	Lat.	Long.	Page
T'ai-pei, *Taiwan*	25 02N	121 30E	101
T'aichung, *Taiwan*	24 15N	120 45E	101
Tabac, Mt., *St. Lucia*	13 52N	61 02W	37
Tabaquite, *Trinidad*	10 20N	61 15W	42
Tabernacle, *St. Christopher*	17 23N	62 46W	32
Tableland, *Trinidad*	10 15N	61 15W	42
Tabriz, *Iran*	38 07N	46 20E	106
Tabuk, *Saudi Arabia*	28 20N	36 45E	106
Tacarigua, *Trinidad*	10 35N	61 20W	42
Tacarigua, R., *Trinidad*	10 40N	61 20W	42
Tacna, *Peru*	18 40S	70 30W	67
Tacuarembó, *Uruguay*	31 42S	56 00W	61
Tadjoura, *Djibouti*	11 49N	42 56E	106
Taegu, *S. Korea*	35 40N	125 30E	101
Tafelberg, Mt., *Curaçao*	12 04N	68 51W	45
Taganrog, *Russia*	47 12N	38 50E	77
Tagus, R., *Portugal*	39 30N	8 30W	76
Tahoua, *Niger*	14 50N	5 25E	91
Taitao, Pen., *Chile*	46 30S	75 00W	61
Taiwan, *Asia*	23 30N	121 00E	101
Taiyuan, *China*	38 00N	112 30E	101
Taiz, *Yemen*	14 10N	43 50E	106
Tajikistan, *Asia*	38 00N	72 00E	94
Tajumulco, Volcán, Mt., *Guatemala*	15 05N	92 00W	14
Takamatsu, *Japan*	34 20N	134 15E	102
Talara, *Peru*	4 20S	81 30W	67
Talca, *Chile*	35 28S	71 40W	61
Talcahuano, *Chile*	36 40S	73 10W	61
Tallahassee, *USA*	30 40N	84 10W	57
Tallinn, *Estonia*,	59 22N	24 48E	69
Talparo, *Trinidad*	10 30N	61 15W	42
Tamale, *Ghana*	9 22N	0 50W	91
Tambacounda, *Senegal*	13 45N	13 40W	91
Tamesna, *Mali*	18 30N	3 30E	91
Tamgak, Mt., *Niger*	19 05N	8 45E	91
Tampa, *USA*	27 57N	82 30W	57
Tampere, *Finland*	61 30N	23 50E	69
Tampico, *Mexico*	22 19N	97 50W	49
Tamworth, *Australia*	31 00S	150 58E	107
Tana, L., *Ethiopia*	12 00N	37 30E	106
Tanami Desert, *Australia*	19 00S	131 00E	107
Tangshan, *China*	39 40N	118 10E	101
Tanjungkarang, *Indonesia*	5 20S	105 20E	94
Tanout, *Niger*	15 00N	9 05E	91
Tanta, *Egypt*	31 15N	31 45E	106
Tanzania, *Africa*	6 40S	34 00E	89
Taolanaro, *Madagascar*	25 00S	46 45E	89
Tapachula, *Mexico*	15 00N	93 00W	49
Tapajós, R., *Brazil*	6 00S	57 00W	68
Taparo, Pt., *Trinidad*	10 00N	61 35W	42
Taranto, *Italy*	40 25N	17 10E	77
Tarapoto, *Peru*	6 45S	76 30W	67
Taree, *Australia*	31 58S	152 34E	107
Tarim Basin, *China*	40 00N	83 00E	101

Place	Lat.	Long.	Page
Tarkwa, *Ghana*	5 15N	2 00W	91
Tashkent, *Uzbekistan*	41 30N	69 00E	94
Tasman Sea, *Australasia*	36 00S	165 00E	107
Tasmania, *Australia*	42 00S	146 30E	107
Tatra, Mt., *Czech Republic*	49 20N	20 00E	69
Taunggyi, *Burma*	20 50N	97 15E	104
Taupo, L., *New Zealand*	38 00S	175 00E	107
Tauranga, *New Zealand*	37 35S	176 11E	107
Taurus, Mts., *Turkey*	37 00N	34 00E	76
Taylor's Pasture, *Nevis*	17 07N	62 34W	32
Taymyr, Pen., *Russia*	76 00N	98 00E	94
Tbilisi, *Georgia*	41 50N	44 50E	106
Tegucigalpa, *Honduras*	14 10N	87 00W	49
Tehran, *Iran*	35 43N	51 29E	106
Tekeze, R., *Ethiopia*	14 00N	37 30E	106
Tel Aviv-Jaffa, *Israel*	32 04N	34 04E	77
Telegraph, Mt., *Jamaica*	18 09N	76 46W	25
Telescope, Pt., *Grenada*	12 07N	61 36W	39
Telposiz, Mt., *Russia*	63 35N	59 00E	69
Tema, *Ghana*	5 40N	0 00	91
Temash, R., *Belize*	16 02N	89 10W	47
Tempé, *Grenada*	12 03N	61 44W	39
Temuco, *Chile*	38 45S	72 40W	61
Ténéré, *Niger*	18 00N	11 15E	91
Tennant Creek, *Australia*	19 34S	134 08E	107
Tennessee, R., *USA*	35 00N	85 00W	57
Tenryu, R., *Japan*	35 40N	137 50E	102
Tépic, *Mexico*	22 30N	105 00W	49
Terek, R., *Russia*	44 00N	45 00E	69
Teresina, *Brazil*	5 02S	42 45W	68
Terni, *Italy*	42 30N	12 40E	76
Ternopol, *Ukraine*	49 40N	25 25E	77
Terre Haute, *USA*	39 30N	87 30W	57
Tessalit, *Mali*	20 11N	1 02E	91
Tete, *Mozambique*	16 15S	33 45E	89
Tête Morne, *Dominica*	15 14N	61 20W	36
Texarkana, *USA*	33 40N	93 50W	57
Thabana Ntlenyana, Mt., *S. Africa*	29 00S	29 15E	89
Thailand, G. of, *S. China Sea*	12 50N	104 00E	94
Thames, R., *UK*	51 20N	0 40W	80
Thar (Great Indian Desert), *India*	27 40N	72 00E	104
Thebaide, *Grenada*	12 03N	61 40W	39
Thelon, R., *Canada*	65 00N	105 00W	50
Thessaloniki, *Greece*	40 38N	23 00E	77
Thibaud, *Dominica*	15 36N	61 24W	36
Thicket, *Barbados*	13 09N	59 27W	40
Thiès, *Senegal*	14 49N	16 52W	91
Thimphu, *Bhutan*	27 31N	89 45E	104
Thomas, R., *Jamaica*	18 07N	77 20W	24
Thompson, *Canada*	57 00N	97 00W	57
Thomson, R., *Australia*	25 00S	141 30E	107
Thorpes, *Barbados*	13 09N	59 37W	40
Three Houses, *Barbados*	13 08N	59 27W	40
Three Points, C., *Ghana*	4 42N	2 06W	91
Thule, *Greenland*	76 00N	69 00W	50
Thun, *Switzerland*	46 45N	7 35E	79
Thunder Bay, *Canada*	49 00N	89 50W	57
Thuner See, L., *Switzerland*	46 45N	7 38E	79
Thur, R., *Switzerland*	47 40N	8 50E	79
Thusis, *Switzerland*	46 43N	9 30E	79
Ti Rocher, *St. Lucia*	13 49N	60 55W	37
Ti Rocher, *St. Lucia*	13 59N	60 58W	37
Tian Shan, Mts., *Asia*	41 30N	80 00E	101
Tianjin, *China*	39 00N	117 25E	101
Tibet, *China*	32 00N	85 00E	101
Ticino, R., *Switzerland*	46 23N	8 50E	79
Tierra del Fuego, I., *S. America*	54 00S	69 00W	61
Tigre, R., *Peru*	2 30S	75 30W	67
Tigris, R., *Asia*	34 00N	43 10E	106
Tihama, *Saudi Arabia*	20 00N	41 00E	106
Tijuana, *Mexico*	32 00N	116 00W	49
Tillabéri, *Niger*	14 30N	1 30E	91
Timaru, *New Zealand*	44 23S	171 14E	107
Timbuktu, *Mali*	16 50N	3 00W	91
Timehri, *Guyana*	6 30N	58 15W	46
Timmins, *Canada*	48 45N	81 30W	57
Timor, I., *Indonesia*	9 30S	126 00E	95
Timor Sea, *Asia*	11 00S	127 00E	107
Tintamarre, I., *St. Martin*	18 07N	62 59W	45
Tiranë, *Albania*	41 19N	19 45E	77
Tirano, *Italy*	46 14N	10 07E	79
Tiruchchirappalli, *India*	10 45N	78 50E	104
Titicaca, L., *Bolivia*	15 30S	69 30W	61
Titlis, Mt., *Switzerland*	46 46N	8 28E	79
Titograd, *Yugoslavia*	42 30N	19 10E	77
Tivoli, *Grenada*	12 10N	61 37W	39
Tizimin, *Mexico*	21 10N	88 00W	14
Toa Alta, *Puerto Rico*	18 23N	66 15W	30
Toa Baja, *Puerto Rico*	18 27N	66 15W	30
Toamasina, *Madagascar*	18 15S	49 00E	89
Tobago, *W. Indies*	11 15N	60 40W	43
Tobolsk, *Russia*	58 15N	68 12E	94
Tocantins, R., *Brazil*	4 00S	49 30W	68
Toco, *Trinidad*	10 50N	60 55W	42
Tocuyo, R., *Venezuela*	10 40N	69 00W	15
Todd's Road, *Trinidad*	10 25N	61 20W	42
Todi, Mt., *Switzerland*	46 48N	8 55E	79
Togliatti, *Russia*	53 45N	48 30E	69
Togo, *Africa*	8 00N	1 35E	91
Toiny, Pt., *St. Barthélemy*	17 50N	62 50W	45
Tokar, *Sudan*	18 30N	37 45E	106
Tokara, Is., *Japan*	29 35N	129 45E	102
Tokushima, *Japan*	33 55N	134 35E	102
Tokyo, *Japan*	35 48N	139 48E	102
Toledo, *USA*	41 50N	84 30W	57
Toliara, *Madagascar*	23 29S	43 30E	89
Tomakomai, *Japan*	42 40N	141 40E	102
Tombua, *Angola*	15 45S	12 00E	89
Tomsk, *Russia*	56 30N	85 05E	94
Tongchuan, *China*	35 00N	108 10E	101
Tongliao, *China*	43 30N	122 30E	101

Place	Lat.	Long.	Page
Tongue of the Ocean, *The Bahamas*	24 20N	77 30W	28
Toowoomba, *Australia*	27 32S	151 56E	107
Top Rock, *Barbados*	13 03N	59 33W	40
Topeka, *USA*	38 50N	95 40W	57
Torne, R., *Sweden*	68 00N	21 00E	69
Toronto, *Canada*	43 47N	79 27W	57
Torrens, L., *Australia*	31 00S	137 50E	107
Torreón, *Mexico*	25 33N	103 25W	49
Torres, Str., *Australia*	10 22S	142 02E	107
Tortola, I., *British Virgin Islands*	18 29N	64 37W	31
Tortue, I., *Haiti*	20 00N	72 40W	29
Torun, *Poland*	52 50N	18 40E	75
Toss, R., *Switzerland*	47 25N	8 52E	79
Totness, *Suriname*	6 10N	56 40W	15
Tottori, *Japan*	35 30N	134 20E	102
Toulaman, R., *Dominica*	15 32N	61 20W	36
Toulon, *France*	43 10N	5 55E	76
Toulouse, *France*	43 37N	1 28E	76
Toungoo, *Burma*	19 00N	96 20E	104
Tourama, R., *St. Vincent*	13 19N	61 08W	38
Tours, *France*	47 22N	0 40E	76
Towakaima, *Guyana*	7 15N	60 00W	46
Townsville, *Australia*	19 15S	146 45E	107
Toyama, B., *Japan*	37 00N	137 15E	102
Toyohashi, *Japan*	34 50N	137 25E	102
Toyota, *Japan*	35 05N	137 10E	102
Trabzon, *Turkey*	41 00N	39 20E	77
Trafalgar, *Dominica*	15 19N	61 21W	36
Trant's, B., *Montserrat*	16 45N	62 09W	34
Treasure Beach, *Jamaica*	17 53N	77 44W	24
Trials, *Montserrat*	16 43N	62 11W	34
Trieste, *Italy*	45 39N	13 45E	76
Trincomalee, *Sri Lanka*	8 30N	81 00E	104
Trinidad, *Bolivia*	14 46S	64 50W	61
Trinidad, *W. Indies*	10 30N	61 15W	42
Trinite, *Martinique*	14 46N	61 02W	35
Trinity Hills, *Trinidad*	10 05N	61 05W	42
Trinity Ville, *Jamaica*	17 57N	76 32W	25
Tripoli, *Lebanon*	32 49N	13 07E	77
Tripoli, *Libya*	32 54N	13 10E	76
Tristan da Cunha, I., *Atlantic Ocean*	37 06S	12 20W	106
Trivandrum, *India*	8 31N	77 00E	104
Trois-Rivières, *Canada*	46 30N	72 30W	57
Trois-Rivières, *Guadeloupe*	15 58N	61 38W	35
Troja, *Jamaica*	18 12N	76 56W	25
Tromsø, *Norway*	69 40N	19 00E	69
Trondheim, *Norway*	63 25N	10 25E	69
Troumaka, *St. Vincent*	13 16N	61 15W	38
Troumaka, B., *St. Vincent*	13 16N	61 16W	38
Troumassée, R., *St. Lucia*	13 50N	60 57W	37
Troyes, *France*	48 19N	4 03E	76
Trujillo, *Honduras*	15 59N	86 00W	14
Trujillo, *Peru*	8 00S	79 00W	67
Trujillo, *Venezuela*	9 25N	70 30W	15
Trujillo Alto, *Puerto Rico*	18 22N	66 00W	30
Truro, *Canada*	45 00N	64 00W	57
Tselinograd, *Kazakhstan*	51 10N	71 28E	94
Tshabong, *Botswana*	26 10S	21 45E	89
Tshane, *Botswana*	24 00S	22 10E	89
Tsimlyansk, Res., *Russia*	48 00N	43 00E	77
Tsiroanomandidy, *Madagascar*	18 45S	46 00E	89
Tsu, *Japan*	34 45N	136 30E	102
Tsugaru, Str., *Japan*	41 30N	140 30E	102
Tsumeb, *Namibia*	19 09S	17 44E	89
Tsuruoka, *Japan*	38 40N	139 45E	102
Tubruq, *Libya*	32 07N	23 55E	77
Tucker's Town, *Bermuda*	32 19N	64 41W	28
Tucson, *USA*	32 14N	110 59W	57
Tuitt's, *Montserrat*	16 44N	62 09W	34
Tuitt's Ghaut, *Montserrat*	16 44N	62 10W	34
Tula, *Russia*	54 13N	37 32E	69
Tulsa, *USA*	36 07N	95 58W	57
Tumaco, *Colombia*	1 40N	78 55W	14
Tumatumari, *Guyana*	5 15N	59 00W	46
Tumbes, *Peru*	3 30S	80 45W	67
Tumereng, *Guyana*	6 00N	60 00W	46
Tunapuna, *Trinidad*	10 35N	61 20W	42
Tungabhadra, R., *India*	16 00N	77 00E	104
Tunis, *Tunisia*	37 00N	10 11E	76
Tunisia, *Africa*	34 00N	9 00E	76
Tunja, *Colombia*	6 40N	73 10W	14
Turayf, *Saudi Arabia*	31 30N	38 20E	106
Turfan Depression, *China*	43 00N	92 00E	101
Turin, *Italy*	45 03N	7 40E	76
Turkey, *Europe/Asia*	39 30N	34 00E	77
Turkmenistan, *Asia*	40 00N	58 00E	94
Turks, Is, *W. Indies*	21 20N	71 10W	27
Turks Island Pass., *Turks and Caicos Is.*	21 20N	71 25W	27
Turku, *Finland*	60 27N	22 14E	69
Turneffe, Is., *Belize*	17 25N	87 45W	47
Turquino, Mt., *Cuba*	20 00N	76 50W	22
Tuticorin, *India*	8 40N	78 10E	104
Tuxtla Gutiérras, *Mexico*	17 00N	94 00W	49
Tuz, L., *Turkey*	38 45N	33 30E	77
Twin Falls, *USA*	43 15N	114 50W	57
Tyrrhenian Sea, *Europe*	40 00N	12 30E	75
Tzaneen, *S. Africa*	23 45S	30 15E	89

U

Place	Lat.	Long.	Page
Ube, *Japan*	33 50N	131 15E	102
Uberaba, *Brazil*	17 47S	48 57W	68
Uberlândia, *Brazil*	17 30S	48 20W	68
Ucayali, R., *Peru*	6 00S	74 00W	67
Uchiura, B., *Japan*	42 25N	140 40E	102
Udaipur, *India*	24 50N	74 55E	104
Uelen, *Russia*	66 30N	170 00W	50
Ufa, *Russia*	54 45N	55 55E	69
Uganda, *Africa*	2 00N	32 00E	81

INDEX